C000179319

REPORTS OF THE RESEARCH COMMITTEE

OF THE SOCIETY OF ANTIQUARIES OF LONDON, NO. 54

The Changing Face of Dalmatia

The Changing Face of Dalmatia

Archaeological and Ecological Studies in a Mediterranean Landscape

John Chapman,
Robert Shiel and
Šime Batović

LEICESTER UNIVERSITY PRESS

in association with
THE SOCIETY OF ANTIQUARIES OF LONDON

Leicester University Press
A Cassell Imprint
Wellington House, 125 Strand, London WC2R 0BB
127 West 24th Street, New York, NY 10011

The Society of Antiquaries of London
Burlington House
Piccadilly
London W1V 0HS

British Library Cataloguing-in-Publication Data
A catalogue record for this book is available from the British Library.
ISBN 0 7185 1148 2

Library of Congress Cataloging-in-Publication Data
Chapman, John, 1951–
The changing face of Dalmatia: archeological studies in a Mediterranean landscape/John Chapman, Robert Sheil, and Šime Batović.
p. cm.—(Reports of the Research Committee of the Society of Antiquaries of London : no. 54.)
Includes bibliographical references and index.
ISBN 0–7185–0048–2
1. Dalmatia (Croatia)—Antiquities. 2. Excavations (Archeology)–Croatia—Dalmatia. I. Shields, Rob, 1961– . II. Batović, Šime.
III. Title. IV Series.
DR1623.C48 · 1996
937'.3—dc20 95–51207
CIP

Front cover illustration: The multi-period monument of Sveti Nikola, near Nin, where the west end of an early medieval Byzantine church, built on top of a presumably Bronze Age barrow, has been fortified in the Ottoman period. Painting by an unknown Zadar water colourist

Typeset by Ben Cracknell Studios

Printed and bound in Great Britain by Redwood Books, Trowbridge, Wilts

Contents

List of Figures

List of Tables

Preface

The writing of this book about Dalmatia is separated by an almost unbridgeable gulf from the visits to the East Adriatic region in which the fieldwork and excavations were accomplished. At the beginning of the first season, in 1982, no-one could have imagined that a civil war between Serbia and Croatia would break out within a decade, soon to escalate through its extension into Bosnia into the largest European conflict since World War Two. The impression of Zadar – that invigorating regional capital of North Dalmatia – shared by all the British and American members of the team was of a tourist centre full of delightful architecture, art galleries and restaurants. The shelling of the city by the Serbian Army, or JNA, was shocking and distressing. News followed that many of the hilltop monuments investigated by the project had been taken over as military strongholds by the JNA; the damage caused to these sites by the excavation of army trenches cannot be underestimated. And the massacre by the Army of an unknown number of Croats in the hamlet of Nadin, where the project worked for three seasons, can only be the cause of the deepest regret.

Since the spring and summer of 1992, few tourists have visited Zadar. Even fewer archaeologists have visited the hill-forts and enclosures of the Ravni Kotari. The proximity of our study region to the Krajina, that Serb-dominated part of West Croatia, meant that local vendettas and blood-feuds continued in the rural areas. It is unlikely that foreign research teams will return to the area for some time. In a real sense, therefore, this book represents a watershed – the first and the last Anglo-Yugoslav fieldwork project to have been organized since the Second World War. The study region is now part of a new country, which won international recognition on 15 January 1992 – Croatia.

This book is written by individuals who loved the former Yugoslavia and still love the new countries which have emerged from the break-up of the federal state. The book is dedicated to all peace-loving inhabitants of South-East Europe.

This book represents an abbreviated version of the full project report. The full version is available on floppy disks from the University of Newcastle Department of Archaeology. Part I contains: Introduction, Theory and Method, the Archaeological Field Survey, Analysis of Settlement Data, the Analytical Survey, the Work Study and a Summary of the Fieldwork Results. Part II contains the Excavation Reports on Tinj-Podlivade, Buković-Lastvine, Mataci-Jazvinački Brijeg, Čauševica, Polača-Dražice and Nadin-Gradina, the Ethnographic Study of the Zadar Lowlands, the Velebit Mountains and the Iž pottery industry, Historical Studies, Explanatory Models and Conclusions.

All those colleagues who have contributed in full to Parts I and II of the project report have kindly made available their results in abbreviated form for this volume: Dr Wendy Bracewell (Venetian and Ottoman history), Richard Carlton, Dr Duje Cerina (geology), Dr Simon Ellis (town planning of Nadin), Dr Huw Evans (early medieval Croatia), Stašo Forenbaher, Dr Karen Griffiths (Roman pottery), Dr Eberhard Grüger (pollen), Dr John Hayes (Roman fine wares), Drs Jacqui Huntley and Sandra Nye (carbonized plant remains) and Dr Charles Schwartz (faunal remains) Ronnie Tylecote and Pavle Vranjicán. We are grateful to these authors for their skilled research.

Acknowledgements

We acknowledge with thanks the financial support for the Neothermal Dalmatia Project provided by: The British Academy, the Society of Antiquaries of London, National Geographic Society and the University of Newcastle upon Tyne. It is a pleasure to acknowledge the encouragement and support for the project of Professors John Evans, Colin Renfrew, Peter Fowler, Rosemary Cramp, the late Martin Harrison, James Griffin, Greg Johnson, Bernard Wailes, Henry Wright and the late Ronnie Tylecote. We are also grateful to colleagues who commented on previous drafts of the book: Professor Anthony Harding, Dr John Bintliff, Mr Andrew Fleming and two anonymous reviewers. We are immensely grateful to Sandra Rowntree and Margaret Finch for their line-drawings and to the Audio Visual Centre of the University of Newcastle upon Tyne for black and white photographs. We acknowledge the skills of the Groningen and the Zagreb radiocarbon laboratories for processing project samples. Thanks are also due to Dr Trevor Cox for his help with mathematical equations; to Dr Dave Surtees for statistical advice; to Richard Tufnell and Jacky Simkins for help with drystone walling; to Dr Slobodan Čače for many discussions and for permitting consultation of his unpublished Ph.D. thesis; to Ms Ljiljana Klarin for her help at Nin; to Dr Duje Cerina for geological advice; and to Dr Judith Turner for her help with Project botanical research. I am grateful to members of the Newcastle Department of Archaeology for assistance in the interpretation of many data.

We are also most grateful to the General Secretary of the Society of Antiquaries, Dai Morgan Evans, for his patient support and to the Society's editors, Janet Clayton and Liz Nichols, for their creative encouragement. It is a pleasure to acknowledge the help of the entire staff of The Arheološki Muzej Zadar and the Narodni Muzej (Etnografski Odjel) Zadar, and especially the Director of the AMZ, Professor R. Jurić, without whom this project could never have been brought to fruition.

There are countless people in the city of Zadar and in the communities on the Plain of Zadar, who showed Project members many kindnesses, large and small. We are especially grateful to 'Moma', whose friendliness helped all team members who stayed in her flat, and to 'Anonymus', for his local informant skills. We are also deeply touched by all those farmers who fed and watered us while we were in the field. A special tribute should be paid to those living in the Nadin hamlet.

Our final debt of gratitude is to all those students from Newcastle and Zadar who fieldwalked and excavated, mapped soil, washed pottery and operated flotation buckets, repaired 'Pretty Polly' more times than seemed possible, collected mussels from the submerged reef at Novigrad, drank litres of black coffee and gallons of red wine and who contributed in so many other ways to making the Project such a happy time.

1 Setting the scene

The flavour of Dalmatia

If there are popular images of that part of the east Adriatic zone known as Dalmatia, they would certainly include blazing summer heat, rich dark blue seas, dazzlingly white rocks plunging abruptly into the water or rising from the coast to insurmountable heights, and Dalmatians themselves, those ever-present counterpoints to the harsh, unyielding environment (fig. 1), those welcome figures in the landscape.

Beyond this consensus view lie differing perceptions, as variegated as the hues of Dalmatian autumn vegetation (fig. 2). Contrasts depend on whether one is tourist or traveller, soldier or diplomat. Dubrovnik, Split or Zadar can be coloured labels on a luggage trunk, a stronghold to capture or the key to a labyrinth of historical tracks, crisscrossing the rock-hewn monuments of the coastal region, even returning to the vaguer depths of prehistory.

The time-depth of the Mediterranean lands (fig. 3) is so clear that it almost evades attention. Even a simple evening meal conceals traces of a past that cannot

1. Pag and the Ražanac ridge

easily be dislocated from its present, whether it is the habit of sitting at tables, drinking wine from glass vessels, or sharing domesticated olives and sheep meat flavoured with Mediterranean herbs, accompanied by local salad plants. The 'klapas' – traditional unaccompanied male voice songs – come from a different world, as do the 'folk' costumes worn by older people in the market. The dyes are ground from natural plants, the material is pure linen or wool and the broad horizontal loom on which they are woven was once part of a dowry. These material traces of a vivid past-into-present play descant to the language, the heart of any

2. The Velebit Mountains, from Pridraga cairnfield

3. Map of the Mediterranean, with regional divisions

culture, itself betokening a long past, with vocabulary and grammar distinguishing citizenry from peasantry, Croat from Serb, Italian influence from Bosnian, Catholic from Orthodox, Eastern from Western European. It is impossible to understand Dalmatia without a feeling for the historical nuances of the language and its regional dialect 'dalmatinjski'.

The French structuralist Roland Barthes has long since (1972) made the case for the utter fascination of the 'usual', the 'obvious', wherein often the most significant cultural differentiation between 'Dalmatian' and 'other' are played out. But this is to beg several questions: who are the 'Dalmatians'? when did they assume this name? who lived in Dalmatia before the Dalmatians? etc. If the material traces of a past-into-present are today under serious threat of destruction, the search for links back into a Dalmatian past becomes pressing. This volume is one attempt to make this connection between Dalmatian past and present, through the use of primarily if not wholly archaeological evidence.

Project aims and problem orientation

After a reconnaissance visit to the east Adriatic coast in 1980 (fig. 4), one of us (JCC) became convinced that a study of the later prehistoric regional settlement patterns was overdue, necessary and possible. In conjunction with Professor Šime Batović of Zadar University, a programme of fieldwork was designed to look into Mesolithic, Neolithic and Bronze Age remains in north Dalmatia. But colleagues in Britain soon convinced me that the best returns on field survey came from multi-period studies, including the historic periods. Thus survey interests expanded to cover the Mesolithic to medieval. However, in the first field season, it became unthinkable to conduct research in Dalmatia without relating the archaeology to the living ethnography which framed our work. We soon added a soils component to the team (RSS), and the combination of soil and ethnographic data yielded land

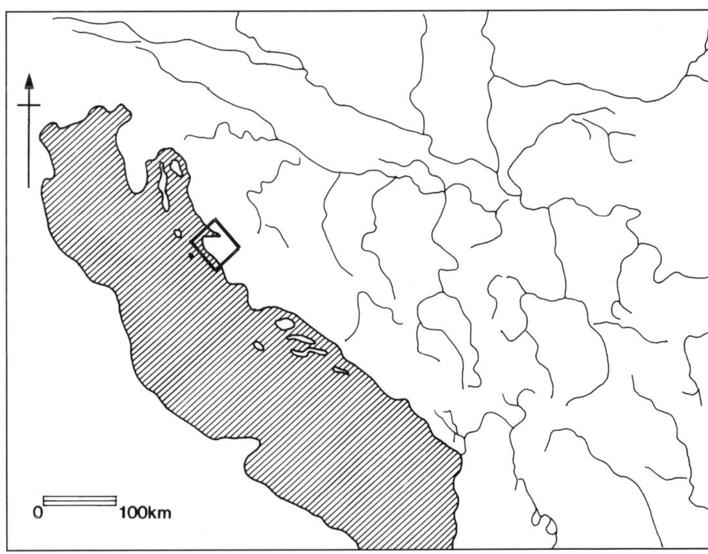

4. Location map of the Study Region in Croatia

use models for modern communities. This left a gap in our regional coverage from the medieval to the modern period, and we recruited a historian to the project, Dr Wendy Bracewell from London/SSEES.

When the first field remains of Palaeolithic flints were recovered, we had to confess that the project theme had changed from a regional later prehistory into a broader regional study covering the last 50,000 years (or longer!). Since the main focus of our interest was the last 8,000 years, or 'Neothermal' period (a climatic term meaning the 'new warm period', or Holocene), the title of the project became the 'NEOTHERMAL DALMATIA PROJECT' (henceforth 'NDP').

The general aims of NDP were to identify and explain changes in the environment, settlement pattern and social structure of human communities in north Dalmatia over the last 8,000 years. But since north Dalmatia was rarely in the vanguard of prehistoric or historic change, an additional aim was to explain the persistence of tradition and the maintenance of established patterns of behaviour (van der Leeuw and Torrence 1989). The interplay between tradition and change implied significant social relationships both within the study region and with surrounding areas; regional sequence could not be divorced from inter-regional transformations.

It is however clear that the general aim of seeking to define regional continuity and change over millennia could easily become a recipe for the inductive accumulation of massive data sets, to be processed by computer analysis yet divorced from any significant theoretical questions. One way out of this impasse was to define a series of problems of inter-regional importance towards which data collection would be focused (though never exclusively) in the study region.

Within the ambit of the last eight millennia, there are certain changes in the social landscape which stand out as particularly significant both for Dalmatia and for the Mediterranean Basin as a whole. Three such changes can be defined:

1. The origins of food production.
2. The relationship between agricultural intensification, the growth of social hierarchies and environmental change.
3. The development of political centralization at the time of the expansion of the Roman Empire.

The question of the origins of food production has been central to European prehistoric studies for the last two decades (Higgs and Jarman 1969; Reed 1977; Jarman, Bailey and Jarman 1981; Zvelebil 1986; Clutton-Brock 1987). As the theoretical framework for the problem has shifted from the global (Cohen 1977) to the regional (Zvelebil 1986; Chapman and Müller 1990), so regional sequences of settlement change and subsistence development have begun to play a more significant explanatory role. The origins of farming represent an immense set of changes, in social action as much as in the re-orientation of approaches to the natural landscape. The beginnings of a place-centred world-view, with all its implications, can be glimpsed in this period of change.

In the established farming period, there is widespread evidence in the Mediterranean for strategies of agricultural intensification (Renfrew 1972; Gilman 1981; Tosi 1981; Lewthwaite 1986). The origins of such strategies and the definition of degrees of intensification are especially important in semi-arid zones such as the Mediterranean, areas characterized not only by a shortage of fertile arable land but also by fragility of sub-optimal land, where overuse can inflict lasting damage. In many cases, agricultural intensification took the form of the construction of fixed markers and boundaries across the landscape, linking social groups to their places of residence even more firmly.

In the first millennium Cal. BC, the Mediterranean basin became the scene of intense competition between core-states for resources, land and manpower (Collis 1984; Nash 1987; Dietler 1989). While the balance of power between core-states was often critical in regional cultural development, the resource potential of different regions and the development of successful local economies were also important factors in the sequence of cultural change. The imposition of an imperial network of political and commercial directives in the Roman period led to an expansion in the quantity of social surplus and the concentration of much of that surplus in urban forms and local administrative centres. This centralization ushered in a new phase of ideological developments in the landscape, matched by the creation of yet new arenas of social power.

Information pertinent to these problems forms the core of NDP data, especially the field survey data and palaeoenvironmental evidence. It proved difficult to relate field data to the historical account and hard to integrate Palaeolithic data with any other class of information.

Each of these three problems is embedded in a history of its own – the past research traditions of Dalmatian and other 'extra-regional' archaeologists. It is now time to survey the research frameworks for the study of prehistoric and historic archaeology in Dalmatia.

Previous research in Dalmatia

There has been an exponential rise in the quantity of archaeological data in the republics of the former Yugoslavia since the late nineteenth century. This trend is paralleled by an increase in the number of archaeological institutions, and hence archaeologists, over the same time period (table 1). These changes are found in field survey, excavation and the frameworks within which change is explained.

Table 1 Foundation of archaeological institutions in Yugoslavia

	B/H	Cro	Mac	Mon	Ser	Slo	Total
1820–99	1	9	0	0	6	3	19
1900–14	0	2	0	1	1	1	5
1918–39	1	3	1	1	4	3	13
1946–70	12	15	9	9	34	15	94
Total	14	29	10	11	45	22	131

Source: Novak 1971

B/H Bosnia and Hercegovina Mac Macedonia Ser Serbia
Cro Croatia Mon Montenegro Slo Slovenia

In field survey, early archaeologists were guided by three principles: the basic unit of operations is the 'site'; the site can be defined operationally as a high density of finds in a restricted area; and surface finds date the 'site', with excavations providing chronological refinement. These principles remained important until recently. In the inter-war years, the Italian occupation of Dalmatia prevented planned surveys which had begun in other parts of Yugoslavia. After the Second World War, there were widespread opportunities for large-scale survey programmes in all republics of the new socialist state. However, the theoretical basis of survey remained essentially the same until the impact of 'New Archaeology' – with its problem-orientation and statistical methods – in the 1980s. In that decade, Western European influences in Dalmatian research led to NDP and the Hvar survey (Chapman *et al.* 1988). A recent development is the use of Geographical Information Systems to interpret field survey data on Hvar (Gaffney and Stančić 1991).

Because of the visibility and wealth of their monumental remains, the classical and medieval periods were the main focus of excavation well into the twentieth century. By comparison, most prehistoric excavations have remained small-scale and partial, with seven exceptions (table 2). Trial excavations are known from 30–40 Mesolithic and Neolithic sites (Batović 1966; Malez 1979), 30 cairnfields (Batović 1983), 60 hill-forts (Batović 1977) and some 50 other Bronze/Iron Age sites (Batović 1983, 1987). Classical excavations have targeted urban sites such as Salona, Split and Zadar, with a strong bias against rural settlements. Similarly, early medieval excavations show a bias in favour of Christian churches and cemeteries and against pagan sites and settlements. The results of these excavations provide a chronology for the study region (table 3).

Advances in scientific and environmental archaeology have led to several research projects in Dalmatia, such as the Göttingen Botany School's vegetational reconstructions (Beug 1961, 1977; Brande 1973) and van Straaten's studies of sea-level change (1965, 1970). But these studies have remained unrelated to archaeological data, as has important soils research (e.g. Marić 1964). This lack of

Table 2 Rate of discovery of Neolithic sites in Dalmatia

Period	No. of new Neolithic settlements	Mean no. of sites per annum
1876–99	45	1.9
1900–14	30	2.0
1919–39	39	1.9
1946–66	50	2.5
1967–80	30	2.1

Source: Batović 1966

Table 3 Chronological sequence for Dalmatia

Period	Absolute date (calibrated C14)	Cultural groups
Middle Palaeolithic	80,000–40,000	
Late Palaeolithic	40,000–9,000	
Mesolithic	9,000–5,000	
Early Neolithic	6,000–5,000	Impressed Ware
Middle Neolithic	5,500–(4,500)	Danilo
Late Neolithic	(4,500)–3,500	Smilčič IV, Hvar
Eneolithic	3,500–2,400	Nakovane, Cetina
Earlier Bronze Age	2,400–1,800	Cetina
Later Bronze Age	1,400–900	proto-Liburnian
Earlier Iron Age	900–400	Early Liburnian
Later Iron Age	400–150 BC	Late Liburnian
Roman	150 BC–AD 500	
Early medieval	500–1000	Byzantines, Ostrogoths, Avars, Croats
Croatian	1000–1409	
Venetian	1409–1797	
Modern	1797–present	

integration, added to the paucity of C14 dates and palaeoeconomic data (Chapman 1981), led to the conclusion that Dalmatia was a region where the full potential of the archaeological and environmental record had scarcely been realized.

Most of Dalmatian archaeological thinking has been, and still is, conducted within an invasionist/diffusionist paradigm peopled by archaeological cultures. It is perhaps inconceivable for those living in an area subjugated by at least twelve invading groups in the last two millennia, and riven by a civil war in the 1990s, to accept the existence of an alternative model. Yet we cannot assume that the past is merely an imitation of the present. With L. P. Hartley (quoted in Lowenthal 1985), we recognize that: 'the past is a foreign country: they do things differently there'.

The invasionist/diffusionist paradigm dominates all periods under study in Dalmatia, whether it be the movement of people from the Near East, Anatolia and Greece to initiate farming and the Neolithic, the incursion of Indo-European warrior nomads at the start of the Bronze Age, the mounted military élites bringing iron to Dalmatia at the inception of the Iron Age, the large-scale ethnic colonization of rich Dalmatian farmland by Italians in the Roman period, or the plethora of invasions in the so-called 'Migration Period' of the early medieval.

Just as the 'site' forms the basic unit of study in field survey, so the 'culture' forms the building-block of archaeological interpretation (fig. 5). Kossinna's (1896) notion of repeated associations of similar material remains in a limited region (Childe 1925) has been refined by the addition of ethnic designators to each culture (cf. Kossinna 1911). One other higher-level entity is common in archaeological interpretation – the 'culture-area' (Ehrich 1956; Sterud 1975). Fixed geographical regions within which cultural traditions can be followed in unbroken succession, the culture-area is opposed to the invasion, providing the region with any conceptual stability it may require.

It may quickly be appreciated that the conceptual tools within which the prehistory and history of Dalmatia have been constructed are in need of urgent attention, if not immediate replacement. What alternatives exist to cultures, culture-areas, invasions and diffusion for Dalmatian archaeology?

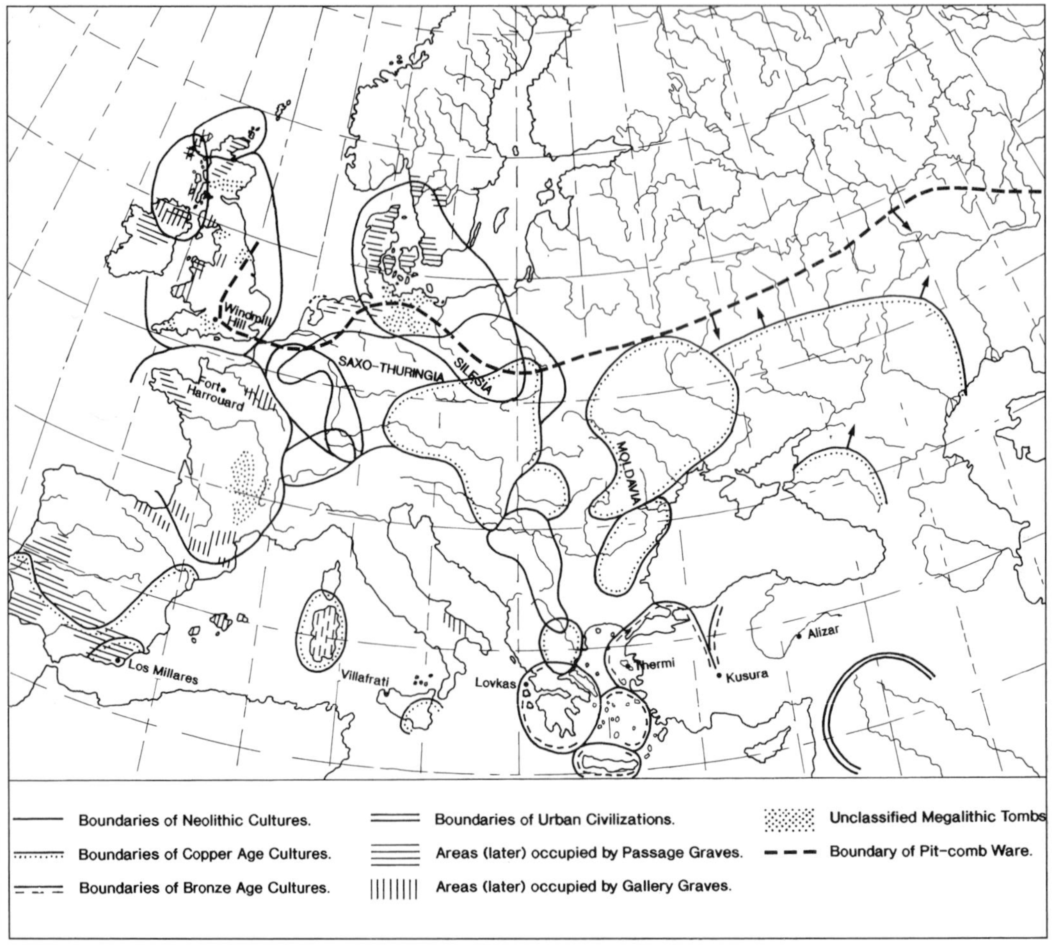

5. An example of prehistoric 'cultures'. *Source:* Childe 1925

Towards a new theoretical framework

Four aspects of archaeology have been found to converge on long-term changes in the way in which human communities inscribe their presence on the landscape: regional studies, landscape archaeology, spatial archaeology and social theory (fig. 6). After a brief characterization of each approach, an attempt will be made at a theoretical integration of these strands of thinking.

Regional studies are no stranger to archaeologists, even early in the twentieth century (Fox 1923). Coones (1985) has made out a case for regarding the 'region' as more than just an 'area', a convenient sub-natural unit of classification. Regions provide an integrated framework for the exploration of distinctive socio-economic structures and spatial patterns created by the use of the environment over time. A good Balkan example is Cjivić (1922). Regional analysis is, therefore, a realistic scale for study, allowing the deepening of understanding of specific landscapes by concentrating attention on the inter-relationships within the region and facilitating the use of non-landscape concepts of social power within precise contexts of period and place (Coones 1985). In this way, regional analysis serves to unite people and places; by doing so, it penetrates close to the heart of landscape studies.

At their broadest, landscape studies are concerned with the study of human behaviour in an evolving landscape. They are, therefore, generalizing approaches, in which the regional context is an ever-present structure for understanding isolated spatial points such as sites or monuments. The key task of landscape archaeology is the identification of the landscape structures defining each specific region (Braudel 1989). These structural correlates are as distinctive for each region as are the Braudelian temporal divisions of the '*longue durée*', the '*conjoncture*' and the '*évènement*' (Braudel 1972, 1981), to which, in turn, a structured relationship can be discovered. Notions of continuity and tradition are especially relevant to

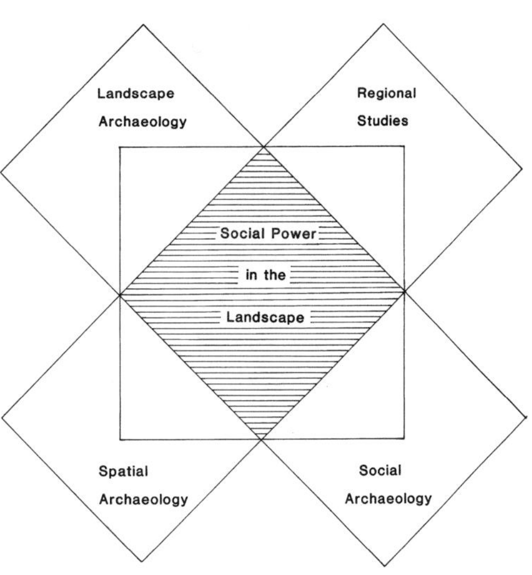

6. Convergent interests of NDP: regional studies, landscape archaeology, spatial archaeology and social archaeology

landscape studies, in which pre-existing monuments are often used by later generations for their own distinctive purposes. Cosgrove (1984) has described the landscape as a 'visual ideology'; in the sense that their object is the study of representations of the exercise of power over space, landscape studies become an inherently ideological research field.

Spatial archaeology interlocks with landscape archaeology in so far as the two research fields use varying approaches to almost identical objects of study. Clarke defined three main interests of spatial archaeology: information from spatial relationships; the spatial consequences of human behaviour; and the flow and articulation of activities within and between sites and structures (Clarke 1977, 9). It was the essentially dynamic content of spatial archaeology which led Clarke to reject static entities such as archaeological cultures in favour of social networks, a term he used in three senses: a network of settlements on the ground, a network of inter-relationships between people both on and off sites, and a dynamic form of network, comparable to an operational system (Clarke 1979). Although he stressed the importance of commercial networks in prehistory, Clarke acknowledged the multiple potentialities of social networks. While Clarke used systems theory as an underpinning for his identification of social networks as the operational systems of prehistoric groups, systems theory is not essential to the notion of social networks, as will become apparent in our consideration of social theory.

An alternative theoretical underpinning of social network theory is drawn from developments of Michael Mann's model of social power (1986). Mann theorizes human communities not as 'culture systems' comprising reified sub-systems, not as 'societies', bounded, totalizing and holistic, not as horizontally cleft into base and superstructure, but rather as social networks. In short, Mann defines societies as 'constituted of multiple, overlapping and intersecting socio-spatial networks of power' (1986, 76). Through these networks, individuals and groups mobilize social power to effect control over people and resources. Four interdependent sources of social power are defined: ideological, economic, military and political (IEMP). Mann's model traces the evolution of power by measuring the socio-spatial capacity of social groups at the leading edge of world history for organization, control, logistics and communication.

Since most other regions in general, and Dalmatia in particular, are not at the leading edge of world history, it is important to contextualize Mann's model. This process begins from Foucault's (1984) idea that the control of space lies at the heart of social power. Since most of the social groups under study are small-scale communities with restricted hierarchical differentiation, networks of social power are most readily related to the social space which they have created. In particular, the idea of 'arenas of social power' leads to a technique for identifying the differentiation of social power through time. We attempt to use spatial data to identify the structures of power in a regional landscape.

Explanatory models

Just as Mann has identified four overlapping networks of social power in the IEMP model, so it is necessary to introduce a series of more specific models by which to investigate social change at different time-scales. In this study, four explanatory models are introduced:

1. The land use capability model (LUC).
2. The cyclic intensification–deintensification model (CID).
3. The communal ownership of property model (COP).
4. The arenas of social power model (ASP).

The LUC model relates to the long time-scale and is based on expectations of land use change in the Neothermal period consequent upon changing land area and soil quality, on climatic fluctuations, and on the technology, crops and animals available. In this model, an attempt is made to define the range of environmental factors which have changed and to assess their interaction with each other and their impact on land use in a non deterministic way. The main nexus of intervening variables concerns land use categories and their distribution, settlement pattern and contemporary land use at the millennial time-scale.

Two models are juxtaposed for an analysis of medium term processes of change. The CID model is an elaboration of Bintliff's (1982) cyclic model of Aegean settlement nucleation and dispersion, in which private land-holding is assumed to be the key variable. By contrast, the COP model is a development of Fleming's (1985) model of communal land-holding, as refined through the course of the Dartmoor Reaves Project (see also Fleming 1988).

Finally, the ASP model is used as a framework for understanding the short to medium time-scale of annual and inter-annual events. This approach relies on the notion that human communities create their own place-based landscapes full not only of meaning but of the opportunities for the development of arenas of social power.

In the case of the first three models, the settlement patterns predicted on the basis of the main assumptions of the model are compared and contrasted with the actual settlement data in an attempt to assess the degree of congruence between the two. 'Residuals' comprise those aspects of the data 'unexplained' by the model in question and provide a starting point for further investigation. In the ASP model, the settlement sequence is taken as the basis for interpretation of changes in the form and frequency of monuments, sites and settlement foci in the light of the creation, maintenance and/or modification of arenas of social power; emphasis is laid on the contrasts between ASPs in the long-term sequence.

Research design

Given that a wide range of settlement, economic, social and environmental evidence is necessary to examine aspects of social power in the landscape, there was an evident need for an integrated programme of inter-disciplinary research. Such a programme could best be developed in the context of a single study region in which there were good conditions for the preservation and discovery of a wide range of sites and monuments as well as deposits containing significant environmental information.

Widespread erosion over the last three millennia (Chapman 1981) limits selection of a viable study region to a handful of lowland basins, the largest of which is the Ravni Kotari or plain of Zadar (fig. 7). In view of the potential significance of upland transhumance and marine resources, an upland component and an offshore island component are essential to the definition of a Dalmatian study region (for uplands, see Dédijer 1916; Carrier 1932; Filipović 1963; for islands, Zadarski Otoci Zbornik 1974). The boundaries of the study region were selected to ensure coverage of a full altitudinal and lateral range of environmental variation, inclusion of several sites of scientific importance with potential for environmental reconstruction, and inclusion of a range of excavated and/or dated sites in sharply contrasting environments. A final but key factor in the choice of the Zadar Lowlands as the NDP study region was the existence of Zadar as the regional capital, with its University Department of Archaeology, its specialist institutes and its two leading Museums (Archaeology and Ethnography).

The research strategy for the project comprised a multi-stage approach, including extensive transect survey, intensive block survey, test and area excavation and environmental analyses. The project proceeded by means of controlled intensification at key sites or areas discovered in the first two seasons.

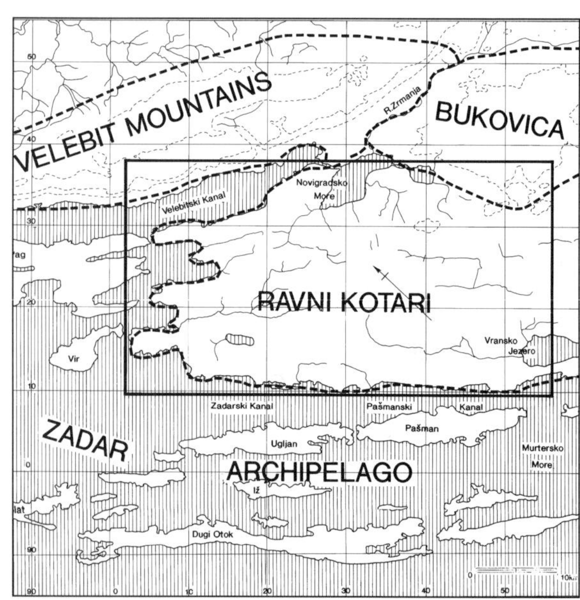

7. The areas of the Study Region: Ravni Kotari, Velebit, Bukovica and the Zadar archipelago

The survey strategy was determined by two stable factors, namely the size of the study area (*c.* 2,200 sq. km) and the high cost and slow speed of intensive archaeological survey (e.g. coverage of 1 sq. km in Dalmatian conditions required between six and ten person-days). Field survey was divided into two phases: extensive transect survey (1982–3) and intensive block survey (1984–6) (fig. 8). Extensive survey was designed to gain an impression of the densities of surviving sites and monuments in various environmental zones in the lowlands. This information led us to the choice of a block of land 11 × 7km for analysis of settlement patterns. A total of *c.* 120 sq km of land was surveyed by the end of the project.

At the more intensive level of analytical survey, tacheometric survey of thirteen sites was completed. These plans of drystone walled monuments provided a basis for a work study, in which estimates of construction time were made for each monument.

8. The NDP grid, with location of Survey Areas

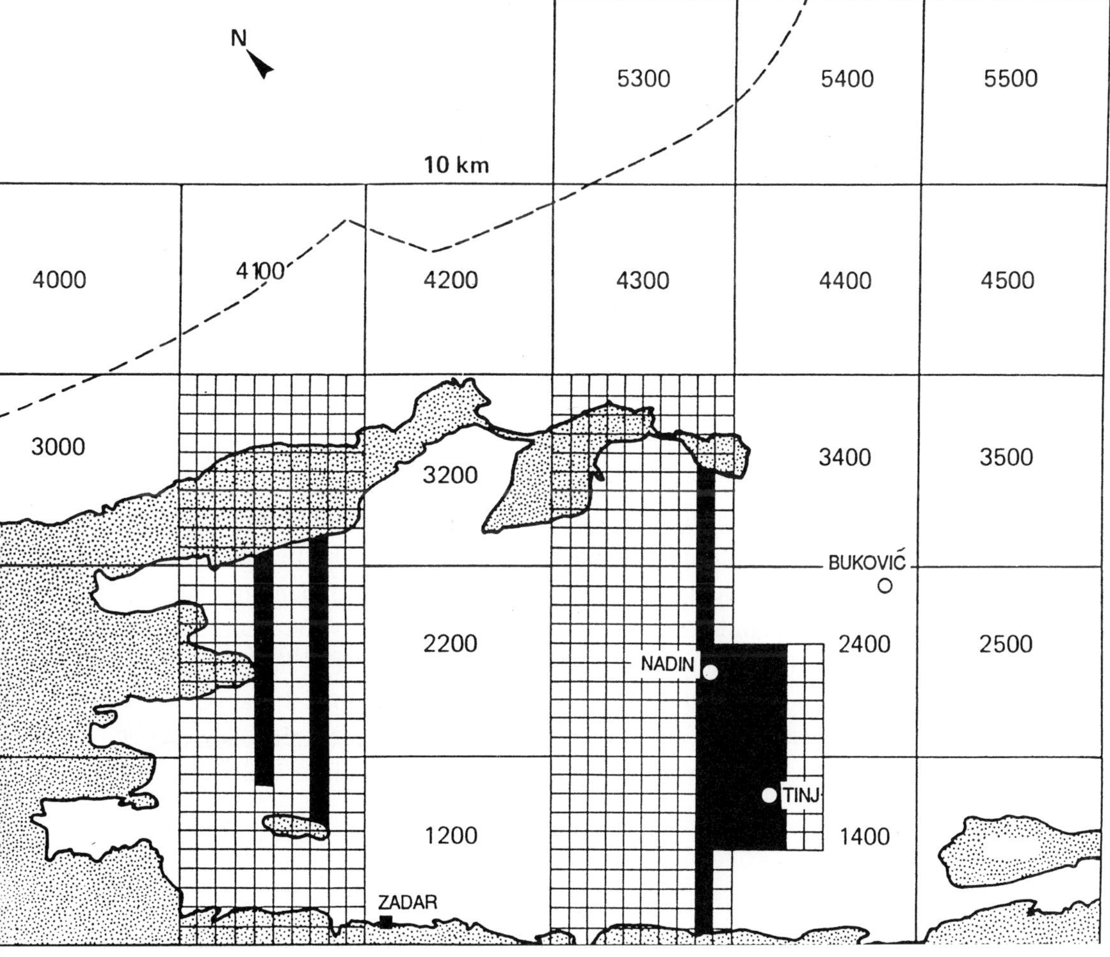

Settlements from most of the main chronological periods were sampled by trial excavation (Early Neolithic, Copper Age, Bronze Age, Iron Age and Roman). The aim of these excavations was to identify the functions of a range of site types, some of which had never been excavated before, through the recovery of a representative sample of structural, artefactual and palaeoeconomic information.

Because of poor modern pollen preservation, vegetational reconstruction was limited to study of pollen cores from Bokanjačko Blato taken by Professor Beug and Dr Grüger in the 1950s before drainage of the lake. In addition, sedimentological studies in the main basins of the study area have provided details of mechanisms of erosion and deposition in the main basins. Soil mapping was completed for the entire area covered in the archaeological survey. In addition, the soils around important sites were examined and detailed soil descriptions have been made. Samples were taken from all soil types for later analysis. Land use maps were prepared of the survey areas.

Ethnographic investigation of the various soils and land use types found in both lowland and upland parts of the study area was conducted and the results were used to develop land use models for the nineteenth and twentieth centuries. For earlier periods, the landscape was reconstructed using geomorphological information as a basis for extending modern land use models backwards in time.

The aim of the NDP's historical research was to collect material for a study of land use and settlement pattern in the territory of Zadar in the sixteenth and seventeenth centuries AD, concentrating on patterns of land tenure, agricultural production and stockherding. A secondary aim was to sample the archive in order to extend the chronological limits of the study to the period AD 1300–1800.

Summary

The intersection of the social environment and the physical environment is one of the most fertile areas of enquiry in the human science. Incorporating the individual social actor, social groups from the size of the family to the state, *conjunctures* of different time-scales and different spatial frameworks, from the micro to the macro, the liminal area of human activity is the locus of multiple meanings whose deciphering is the task of many disciplines (Bintliff 1991). In this book, we attempt to define and explain the changes in social activities over the long time-scale in one particular region – the north Dalmatian area in coastal Yugoslavia. But explaining long-term changes can only be achieved by the dissection of activities framed in several different time-scales – hence the attention to the everyday as well as the millennial. Similarly, the spatial scale of activities radiates out from the hearth and home to the settlement, the river valley, the region and the inter-regional network of social ties and obligations which individuals form and into which individuals are embedded. In this sense, each individual in prehistory is the locus of multiple, pre-existing constraints which form a framework within which choice is made. The least malleable of these constraints is the geomorphological structure, with its enormous time-depth stability; more flexible are the quotidian relationships between neighbours and strangers in social space. What this amounts to is the acceptance of multiple pasts, contradicting or in tension with the 'one' present of modern Dalmatia, and linked to each other in a unique sequence of prehistoric and historic changes.

2 The physical environment

Introduction

The physical environment of an area is a product of the chemical and physical composition of the rocks and soils, of the land form, and of the climate. These various factors must be teased apart, and their inter-relationships considered, before an analytical approach to the settlement and use of an area's resources can be attempted.

1. The chemical nature of the rocks, and to a lesser extent of the soils, determines whether or not ores or rocks of economic value are present.
2. The potential of the rocks and soils as building materials, or as sources of tools and fired clay, depends on a combination of the physical and chemical properties of the materials.
3. The physical nature of the rocks and soils determines, together with the climate, (a) the movement of water within the rocks and soils; (b) the depth of water table, if there is one; and (c) whether or not, and where and when, surface water will occur.
4. The land form and geology, together with climate and vegetation, determine the distribution of surface water over the landscape.
5. The land form affects the ease of movement within an area and with other areas. The presence of surface water, whether fresh or salt, may hinder or facilitate transport.
6. Climate directly influences the attractiveness of a site for settlement. To facilitate habitation the temperature should lie within moderate limits, while water should be available without causing flooding or encouraging disease. To some extent, this is encouraged by land form.
7. All three major factors – climate, land form and composition of soils – influence the biological productivity of the area and the range of species that will grow.

The inter-relationships between factors influencing biological productivity are very complex and the use of an area for this purpose may also be affected by the other aspects of the physical environment, such as ease of transport and the presence of economic rocks. In the succeeding sections the geology and mineral resources, climate, land form and soil in relation to land use are discussed in turn after which the factors influencing vegetation distribution are considered. Finally, the vegetational history of the area, the impact of sea-level change and the ease of communications are discusssed.

Geology

The area consists of a series of folded and faulted strata aligned with their strike north-west to south-east with a general dip to the north-east. The only maps available at a reasonable scale were published in the 1880s at a scale of 1:75,000. With the exception of one or two small areas, these are available for the whole of

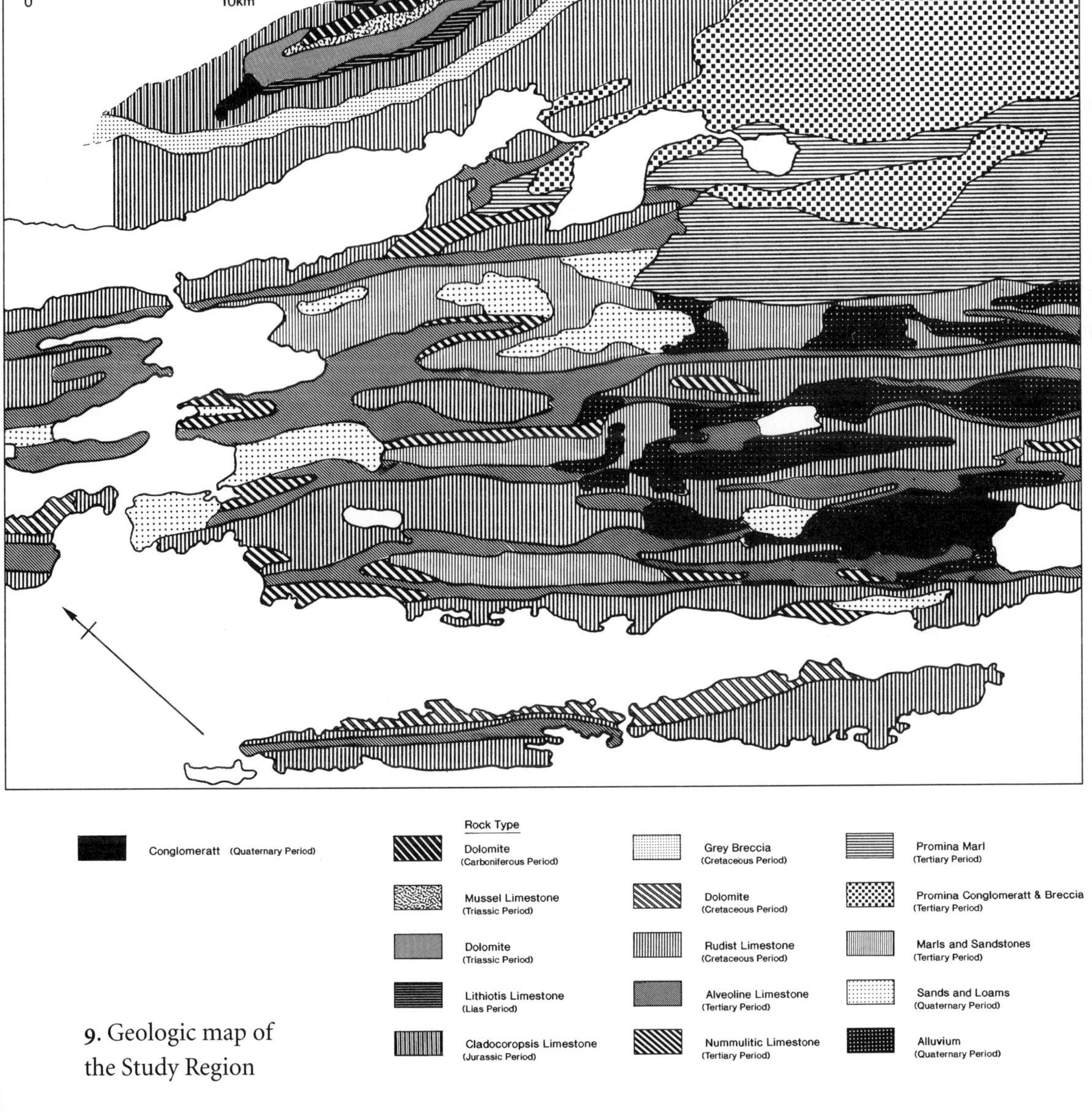

9. Geologic map of the Study Region

the study area. They have been amalgamated, rotated, simplified and reduced (fig. 9). The ridges are mostly of small amplitude (less than 100m) above the valley floor but with a progressive rise in base line height towards Bukovica and Velebit (fig. 10). There are prominent summits rising to some 200m from the valley floors but these are relatively small in extent. The ridges lie about 7km apart and rarely extend along the strike for more than 20km without an interruption. The strike is in fact very nearly horizontal with the result that neither ridges nor valley floors grade clearly in any direction. The result is a series of small seasonal lakes – internal drainage basins known as *blata* – in the higher valleys, and marine flooding, producing elongated islands and extensive promontories, where the valley bottoms are lower. The river pattern is also erratic due to the relatively level valley bottoms, and in some places the rivers flow at right-angles to the strike, effectively crossing the ridges at low points. The most noticeable of these crossings occurs where the Benkovac valley drains into Nadinsko Blato through a deep gorge cut into a limestone ridge at Kličevica. The lack of clear fall along the valleys has led to sedimentation continuing in the valleys starting with the Eocene flysch through a series of Quaternary sands and gravels to modern alluvium. The western faces of valleys, often escarpments, are steeper than the eastern sides.

Rocks and minerals

In the absence of copper, tin and major iron deposits, there do not appear to have been any extractive industries in the area utilizing mineral resources. A variety of low quality flint and chert sources may be hypothesized on the basis of the geological maps; the only one discovered during NDP was the Quaternary sands and gravels and from the Eocene marls near Mataci. The rudist limestone when found in large blocks makes a convenient building stone. The circuit walls at Nadin were built using the larger blocks at the base (0.9m) with smaller blocks for higher courses. Although acceptable ashlar can be wrought from this stone, it is not satisfactory for sculptural use. Elsewhere limestone is also used for building, mostly using a rubble method of construction. Limestone is also used as a temper in pottery, although its use limits the firing temperature to below 800 °C. It is also used for mortar, and more recently for Portland cement manufacture. Clays occur widely, particularly in the blata, and are used for pottery making. The reserves are, however, localized and there is no stable temper available. Bricks never seem to have been made on any scale.

Land use

The use to which any piece of land can be put is limited by the soil, the topography and the climate. For each individual species, the success of growth is determined by whichever growth-controlling factor is present at a limiting level (Liebig 1841). Variation in other growth-controlling factors will not have a significant effect, unless the range of variation is sufficient to render this other growth-controlling factor limiting. Not all species will be affected to the same extent in any given environment; thus wheat is tolerant of frost in winter, while tomato is damaged by temperatures below about 5 °C (Chang 1968). Although an area may be capable of producing one species very well, the environment may be unsuitable for other species; for example, in North-West Europe, coniferous forest and grasses may grow satisfactorily at high elevations where broad leaf woodland, cereals and other arable crops will not grow successfully.

10. Contour plan of Survey Area 1. Transect survey 2. Block survey 3. 0–300m 4. 300–500m 5. 500–1000m 6. Above 1000m

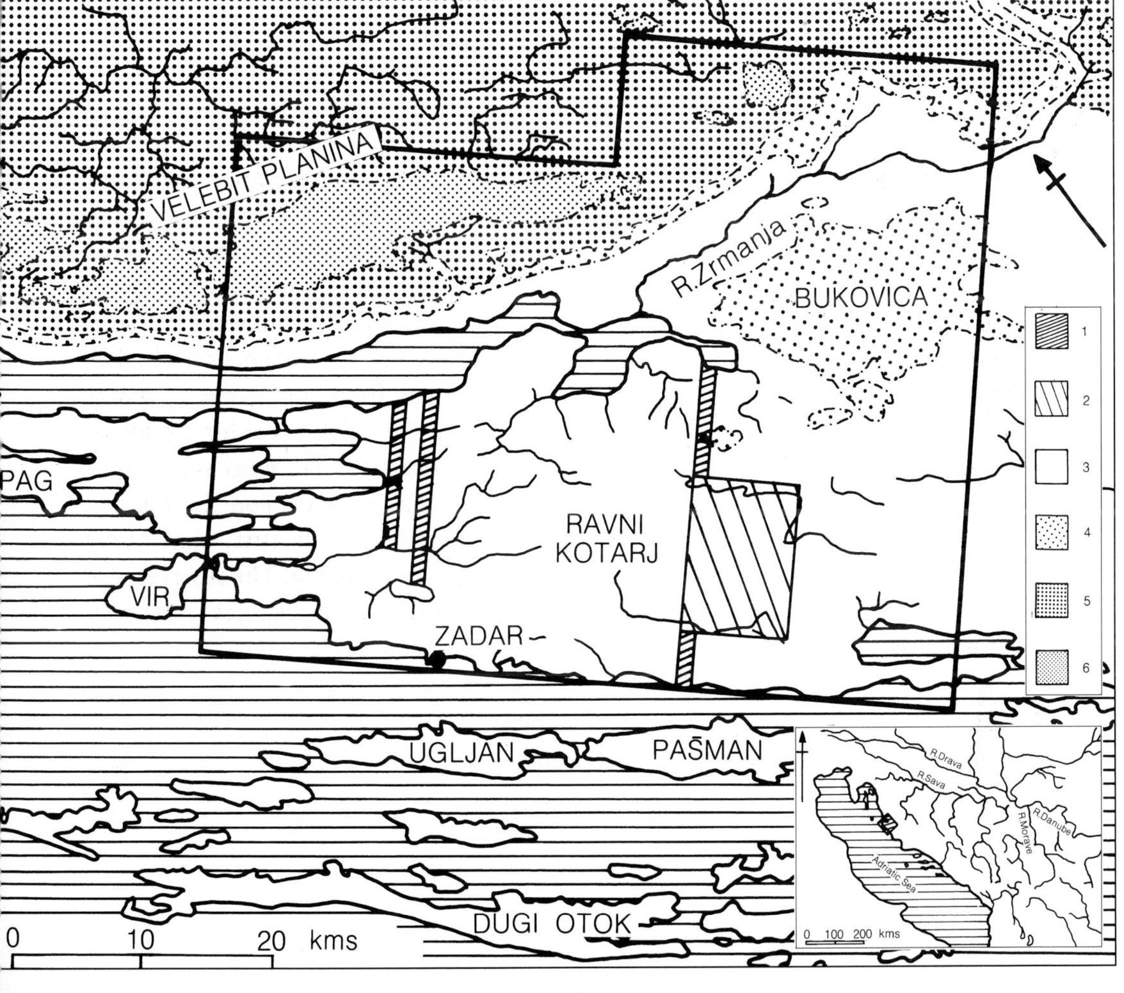

Although perennials such as grasses and trees can occupy land continuously for an extended period, there are major problems of growing a permanent monoculture of most annual species, as has been found at the Broadbalk wheat experiment at Rothamsted Experimental Station (Garner and Dyke 1969). The problems of nutrition, pest, disease and weed management which affect monocultures are minimized by a rotation of species. However, this requires a larger area of land suitable for the production of a species than will be the area of that species which is grown in any year. Because of the value of flexibility, essential for crop rotation, land which is capable of growing a range of crops is perceived as being of greater utility than that suitable only for one use; in modern systems of land classification, this flexibility is given a high priority so that the best, or class 1, land will grow a wide range of crops while the nth class will grow none (Klingebiel and Montgomery 1961).

A distinction must be drawn between land use and land capability. Some users may choose to utilize land as if it were in a poorer class than it actually is; this represents an under-exploitation of the available resource. The explanation of such under-exploitation may be that there is an excess of land or it may depend on the social status of the user. The alternative, in which use and capability coincide, may be due to compulsion, either by a *force majeure*, or by necessity if there is a food shortage. In extreme cases, land may be over-utilized, resulting in erosion and degradation. By comparing actual land use with land capability it may therefore be possible to draw conclusions about the economic and social situation of those using the land.

Past land use can be reconstructed on the basis of subsistence and settlement evidence, while past land capability can be reconstructed from the modern land capability, after moderating this to account for changes in the environment which have affected the productivity of the land. A comparison of these sets of data will allow similar conclusions to be drawn about past users of the landscape as can be drawn concerning the modern users.

In order to reconstruct the past land capability it is necessary first to determine the environmental conditions required for the survival of plants and animals which could have been produced in the area. The changing climate of the area must also be considered over the period since the end of the Pleistocene. If the requirements of a species are fulfilled, then the growth that occurs, and the ease with which the species can be managed, depend on a combination of edaphic factors, which interact with climate and topography, and have changed with time. The impact of the physical resource base, and its changes and interactions with climate change is considered second. Finally, an appropriate system of ranking the capability of past landscapes is developed from the existing present-day land classification system (Chapman *et al.* 1987).

Climate

There is no disagreement over the occurrence of massive climatic changes at the end of the Pleistocene, though views differ on the magnitude of change. Subsequent changes within the Neothermal period are neither global nor of comparable magnitude. Neither of these findings is surprising, as the changes at the end of the Pleistocene varied with proximity to the ice sheets, while subsequent changes depend on air circulation and ocean currents, which are inevitably localized. Even within a locale, weather variation may have been of greater significance to marginal species than were the longer-term changes in climate. Raikes (1978) argues that short-term extremes of weather, particularly when clustered, were more significant than the much smaller long-term changes; Parry (1978) also showed that it was clusters of unusually cold seasons that influenced settlement. Thus, while long-term climate must be considered, the impact of variability and the extreme conditions it brings must also be examined closely. Although historic records can make the distinction clearly, the separation of variability from change in mean palaeoclimatic data may be difficult.

Temperature

The modern temperature regime (table 4) varies with elevation and distance from the Adriatic coast. Moving inland, there is a marked downward trend in winter temperature and a smaller decline in summer temperature. The temperature regime is currently satisfactory at low elevations for cereals, fruit trees, vines and nuts, such as almonds, plus vegetables such as pumpkins. All these crops are also produced at lower latitudes under a higher temperature regime. The only crops that may be considered near their lower temperature limit are almond and olive. For these two crops, the most critical period is probably spring, when low temperature can cause loss of fruit (Money 1978). Winter frost would also limit the maximum elevation at which these crops can be grown (around 250m), and even higher elevations would limit growth of a wider range of crops. These views

Table 4 Mean monthly temperatures across a transect through the study region

Site	Jan	Feb	Mar	Apr	May	Jun	Jul	Aug	Sep	Oct	Nov	Dec
G	6.4	7.6	9.0	13.1	16.9	20.8	23.0	24.1	20.1	16.1	12.8	8.8
B	7.0	6.9	9.3	12.5	17.0	20.7	23.0	22.9	20.5	15.9	11.8	8.9
Z	6.7	7.3	9.4	13.7	18.4	22.3	25.0	24.4	21.2	16.6	11.1	7.7
C	-1.9	-1.2	3.7	8.3	13.1	16.6	18.8	18.2	13.9	9.2	4.5	0.2

G Grpaščak, one of the outermost islands
B Bonaster, an island adjoining the mainland
Z Zadar, on the coast of the mainland
C Gospić, inland and at a high elevation

correspond with the current European distribution of crops. Similarly, pig, sheep and cattle have a distribution today which stretches both north and south from the study area.

Over the period in question, temperatures have varied around the modern value, rising about 2 °C above it during the Altithermal (7000 to 3700 Cal. BC: Frenzel 1991). Between 3700 and 2800 Cal. BC, the temperature dropped by some 2 °C, glaciers advanced and forests retreated (Lamb 1982). During this Piora Oscillation, the weather became much more variable, possibly due to blocking anticyclones (Bintliff 1982a) which persisted through the whole second millennium BC. After 2800 Cal. BC it was at times as warm as the Altithermal, but the weather was more variable. Warm periods were short-lived; the last to be as warm as the Altithermal was around 1600 Cal. BC, immediately before a drop of 2 °C between 1600 and 1200 Cal. BC (Lamb 1982). At about 1000 Cal. BC, there began a deterioration in temperate areas known as the Medithermal (Frenzel 1966), but by 300 BC vine and olive production had extended north of the Alps and beech was considered a mountain species (Lamb 1977). This warming appears to have continued until around AD 500. During the cold periods, olive and almond growth would have been very poor, and even vine productivity may have been reduced. Most fruit types are sensitive to frost, particularly at flowering periods when the weather is cold, or very variable. At such times, the best land will be on a slope where air drainage allows cold air to sink to lower levels. Valley bottoms become frost hollows and should be avoided (MAFF 1964). The period of growth of other species may have altered but it would have required a temperature reduction comparable with that likely to have occurred during the Würm glacial maximum to eliminate cereal growth at low elevations. Equally herbage and tree growth – other than that of eu-Mediterranean-type species – are unlikely to have been affected directly by temperature fluctuations, and herbivorous animals may possibly have benefited from temperature reduction. Increased winter cold would have, however, extended periods of fodder shortage, increasing the need for storage. This problem would have been much more severe inland and at higher

Table 5 Rainfall (R) (mm) and mean rainfall intensity (I) (mm per rainday) in the study region

Site	Data	Jan	Feb	Mar	Apr	May	Jun	Jul	Aug	Sep	Oct	Nov	Dec
Grpaščak	R	82	59	81	75	42	35	34	31	67	90	110	95
	I	9.1	9.8	8.1	9.4	7.0	7.0	6.8	7.7	11.2	11.3	11.0	7.9
Bonaster	R	84	65	103	56	51	39	47	31	91	95	94	110
	I	8.4	9.3	0.3	7.0	7.3	7.8	9.4	7.8	15.2	11.9	9.4	9.2
Zadar	R	87	59	65	56	50	50	36	42	84	125	139	122
	I	7.9	6.6	6.5	6.2	5.6	7.1	7.2	8.4	10.5	12.5	10.7	8.1
Gospić	R	145	139	154	156	118	112	93	92	152	251	211	186
	I	11.2	11.6	11.8	11.1	9.1	10.2	11.6	13.3	15.2	19.3	15.1	2.4

elevations, such as on Velebit. A transhumant system may have been necessary, not so much to avoid low temperatures as to avoid a long period with no herbage.

Water balance

At the present time, a large summer soil water deficit, sufficient to restrict growth of unirrigated crops for several months, occurs in the study region. The drought is unlikely to have a serious effect upon winter cereal growth, as this is largely complete before the drought becomes severe, but it affects growth of spring-sown cereals to a moderate extent and summer growth of vegetables and animal fodder to a very substantial extent. Deep-rooted perennial crops such as vines and fruit trees are affected by drought to a smaller extent than annual crops because of their more extensive root systems. The only soils on which crops avoid this severe drought are those with a high ground water table. Even where there is a large store of available water in the rooting zone of annual crops, this will not be sufficient to offset the drought fully, though it will mitigate the impact of drought. The heavy autumn rain typical of this region may, however, cause flooding in valleys, resulting in severe damage to perennials, or unharvested annuals. There is a risk that such flooding could recur in spring when there are more cereal and fodder crops in the soil. Once the soil has become wet in autumn, management will be difficult on clay-textured soils, as these become very sticky. Cultivation will also be difficult on these soils in summer when they are baked hard.

There is unfortunately little agreement over the change in water balance during the Neothermal. The simple scheme of climatic bands of air circulation which migrate north–south as temperatures rise/fall would suggest that in the Altithermal rainfall should decline, and evaporation incidentally increase. Lamb (1982) suggests that, between the eleventh and fifth millennia Cal. BC, tropical anticyclones penetrated to around 40 degrees N, while storm belts moved far to the north and monsoons penetrated into North Africa. As a result, rainfall in the study area may initially have been lower than today, and evaporation greater. Although it was wetter at lower and higher latitudes there is evidence (Roberts 1989) that some mid latitudes were drier. In any case evaporation was increased by higher temperatures. The rainfall does appear to have increased later in the Altithermal (Bottema 1974), and van Zeist and Bottema (1982) consider that in Greece 'humidity' did not reach modern levels until 2000 Cal. BC. None of these changes appears, however, to have been great enough to cause a break in the local Dalmatian pollen record (see p. 39). Bintliff (1982b) suggests that climatic variation from 3500 to 1100 Cal. BC did not cause modifications in the established woodland of the North Mediterranean area, as this area was not climatically marginal. Lamb (1982) recognizes changes in both temperature and wetness over the period and we follow his suggestion that wetter intervals generally appear to have coincided with lowered temperature. This combination may have been more damaging to tree crops, such as almond or olive, than either factor taken alone (Harding 1982). Periods of increased autumn wetness may also have increased the risk of waterlogging damage in winter cereals as well as damaging perennial crops. If it occurred in late spring or summer, the extra rain would, however, have increased growth of cereals, vegetables and especially fodder. A decrease in rain, especially during winter, would have made yield of cereals less reliable but a fall of more than 50 per cent to less than 300mm would have been required before annual cropping became impractical (Whyte 1963). An increase in precipitation would have benefited soils with a low available water capacity and free drainage, such as sands, while increasing the risk of waterlogging in clays. As management would have been easier on sands, these soils would have been preferred where there was a reliable water supply. Drier weather would have had the opposite effect.

Climatic and weather variability

The problems of variability in crop yield have been admirably discussed by Parry (1978) and Bourke (1984). In the study area, vegetables and cereals may have been affected by fluctuations in rainfall quantity and distribution, which probably corresponded with the temperature fluctuations. An increase in flood risk would suggest a move from valley floor sites, but if a drought occurred instead, a hillside site would have suffered more than the valleys, especially if the soil had a low available water capacity. As a series of droughts may have enticed farmers downhill into the valleys, it can be clearly seen how variable weather created a series of critical management decisions over which land to use. 'Bad' weather may have induced stress on plants, leading to attack by pests and disease, while the time available for cultivation and hence the area of crop sown may have been reduced by unusually dry/wet or cold conditions. However, weather conditions which affected fruit growth would have been unlikely to cause problems in wheat, so only part of the food supply would have been affected, provided there was not a monoculture.

Topography and land classes

Two important factors in successful crop and animal production are slope, which influences site drainage, erosion risk and frost risk, and elevation, which influences water balance and temperature regime. The study area consists of a series of alternating valleys and ridges, parallel to the Adriatic coastline; the ridges increase in elevation with distance inland. To the north-east, the study area is bounded by the Velebit mountains and the Bukovica hills (figs. 7, 11, 13). Here, the land is very steep, and the season short, so the current land use is limited to extensive grazing. To the south and west, the region is bounded by the Adriatic, where flooded valleys

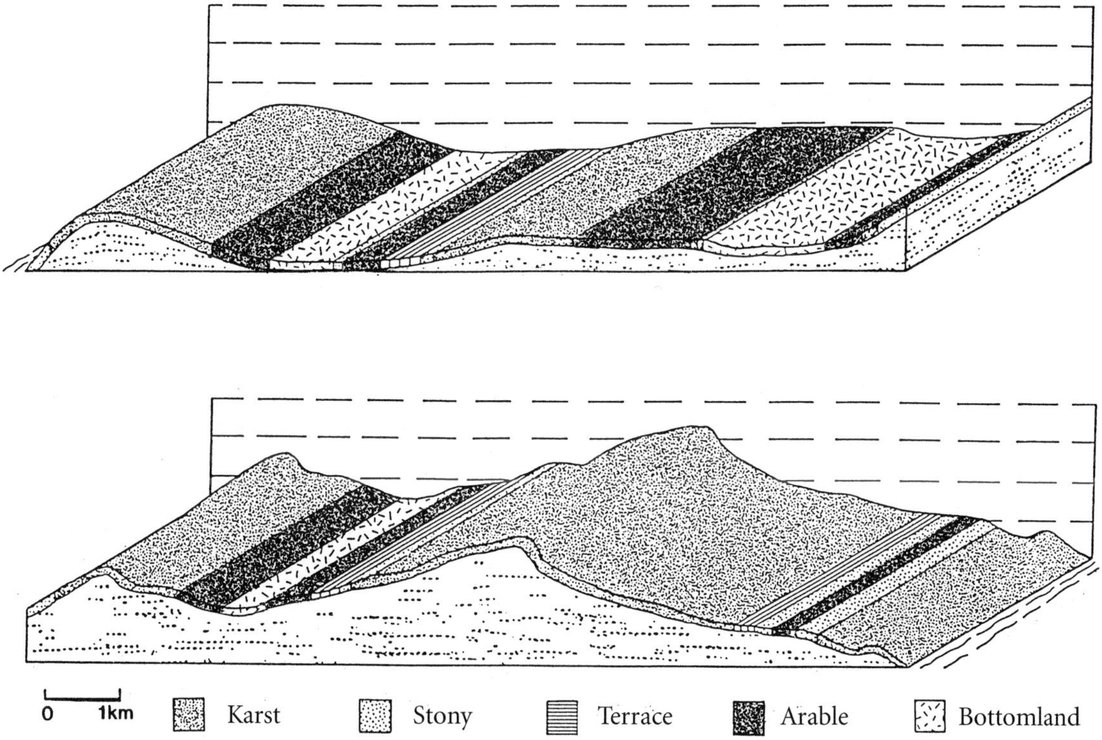

0 1km Karst Stony Terrace Arable Bottomland

11. Vertical section through the Study Region

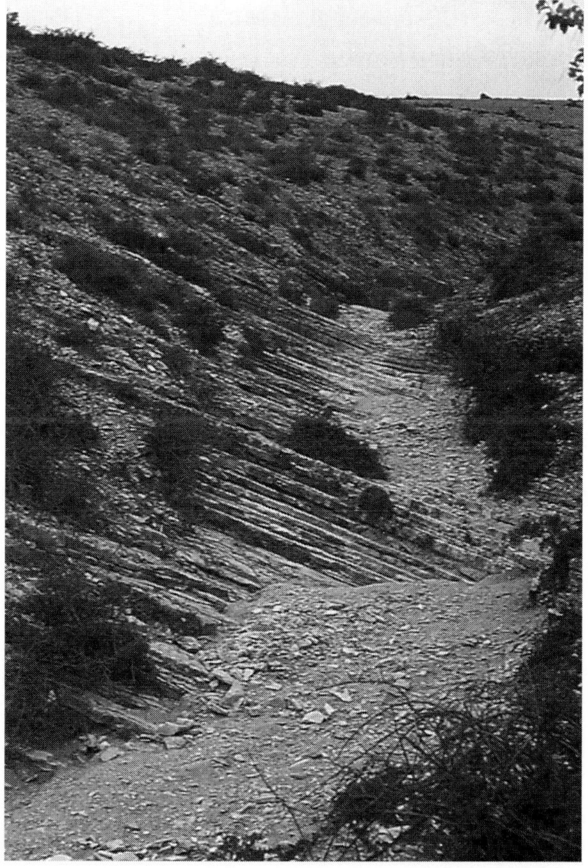

12. Fully developed draga, Ostojići

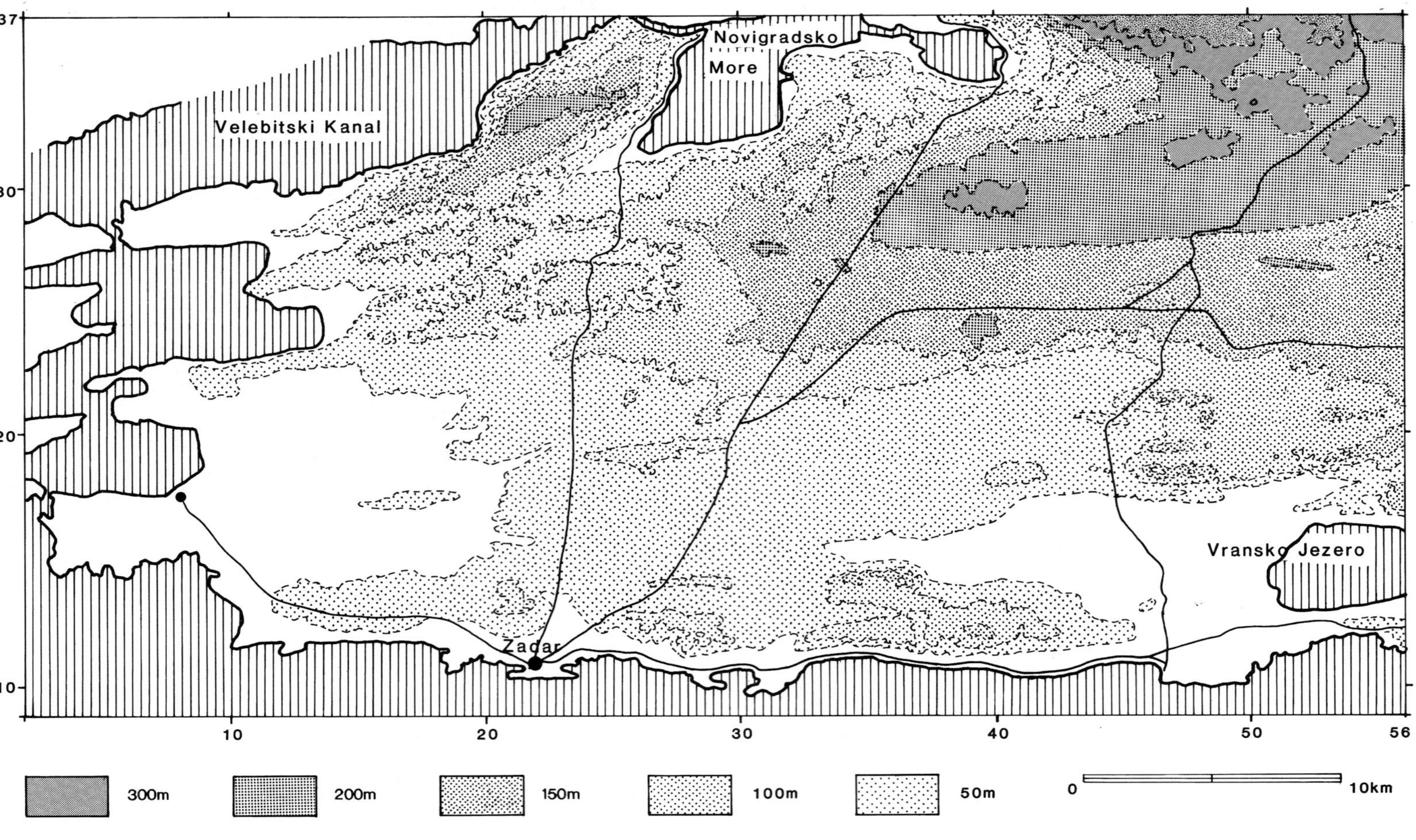

13. Elevation of the land in the Study Region

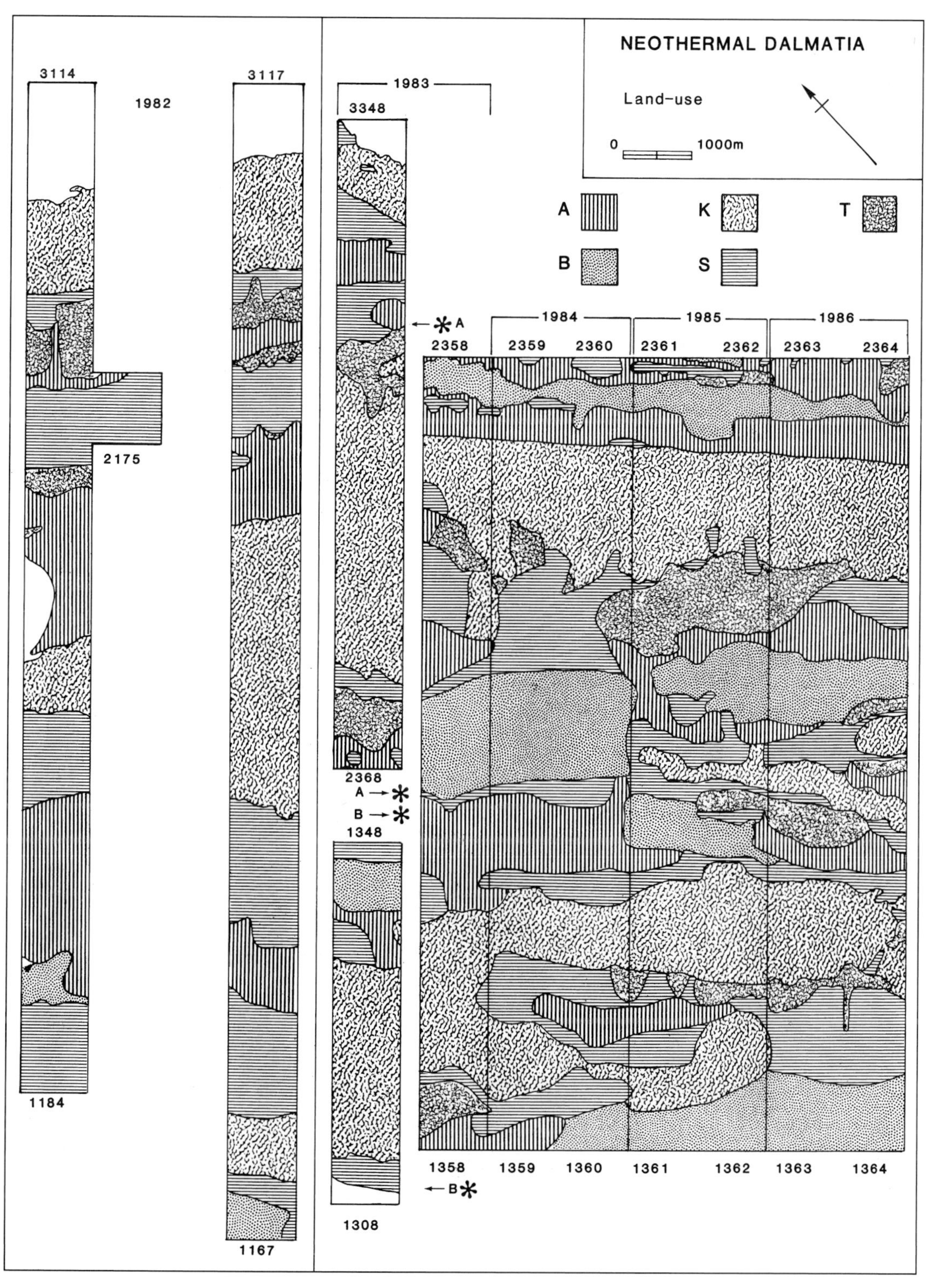

14. Land use classes in the Survey Area A – Arable B – Bottomland K – Karst S – Stony T – Terrace

have created parallel lines of islands. The valley floors are flat with little fall in any direction producing seasonal lakes (or blata) in wet weather. Run-off water from the ridge sides also tends to flood the valley bottoms, creating wide alluvial zones which drain into the blata. The gentle valley slopes provide cultivable land, but the steep valley sides are subject to erosion, creating *dragas* (fig. 12). On the limestone ridges the soil may be 'vertically eroded' into the developing solution voids in the limestone (Shiel and Chapman 1988). The repeated structure of the ridges and valleys provides a convenient set of land classes (table 6 and fig. 14).

Bottomland occurs on the valley floors and is the flattest land in the study area (fig. 15). There are, however, drainage channels which dissect the land and these are frequently several metres in depth and very steep sided. Soils vary from thin (less than 2m) clays in internal drainage basins such as Nadinsko Blato, to deep (more than 5m) sands in steep-sided valleys. The soils are immature, and are (or were, in the case of drained land) flooded annually in autumn. Even in summer the water table is within a few metres of the surface. The soils have a high pH and are, with the exception of the coarsest sands, relatively rich in plant nutrients. The clays are poorly structured due to prolonged wetness and are much more difficult to cultivate than are the sands. Soils vary abruptly from place to place.

Arable land occurs on the lower slopes of the valleys (fig. 16) and is separated from the Bottomland by an abrupt rise of some 2m. The land occurs in broad strips along the valley sides and slopes are less than 5 per cent. The soil, which is a silty clay, is gleyed, and even in summer the water table lies within 2m of the surface. During winter the land will be waterlogged, but in summer there is a good supply of water from the soil pores and from the water table. Due to excessive

15. Karst hillslope above the Bottomland of Nadinsko Blato

16. Level Arable land near Mitrovići, with Neolithic flint scatter in centre of field

wetness the soil tends to be poorly structured and breaks into large clods; it is not easy to cultivate in wet weather. The absence of stones and large patch-size, however, makes the land attractive for cultivation. The supply of nutrients is also good, and the soil is calcareous. As the underlying rock is usually marl (flysch) and erosion is not a problem, this land will have altered little over time.

Stony land occurs on the somewhat steeper slopes of the valley sides (fig. 17). The soils, which are terra rossa, are freely drained and, although they are silty clay in texture, are much better structured than the Arable land. They do, however, contain substantial amounts of stone which can interfere with cultivation. Over large areas these stones have been removed into field walls, which serve to limit erosion and have created substantial lynchets. After clearance the land is easier to cultivate than Arable land, but the nutrient content is less good, and there is a greater drought risk; the water table is at a considerable depth. As the land overlies limestone there is a risk of vertical soil erosion which can lead to reclassification as Karst.

Terrace land. Further up the valley sides are localized small areas of freely drained brown sands, which occur on steep sites that have invariably been terraced; erosion is a major risk (fig. 18). This land is very droughty and any water table is at considerable depth. The soils are easy to cultivate after the land has been formed into terraces. Due to the coarse texture the supply of nutrients is, however, poor.

Karst land occurs where there are substantial outcrops of solid limestone (fig. 15). The amount of outcrop varies, so that the land grades from a rather rocky version of Stony land, to bare limestone pavement with soil restricted to the grykes.

17. Stony degraded to Karst, north slope of Malo Brdo

18. Eroding Terrace land, Ražanac ridge, from the Mataci ridge, with the Velebit Mountains in the background

Table 6 Areas of each land use class in the survey area

Land use class	Percentage of survey area
Arable	19
Stony	24
Karst	34
Terrace	8
Bottomland	14

The similarity to Stony land extends to the soil, which is also a freely drained terra rossa. The available water content varies with the amount of soil, but is small; the water table occurs at depth in the underlying limestone. The nutrient reserve also tends to be small. It is not possible to mechanize cultivation of this land. Karst occurs in a variety of topographic situations, and is progressively extending due to erosion of Stony land; it is the most extensive land type in the study area.

The changing landscape

Until this juncture, the discussion has not incorporated any changes in the landscape. It is clear that, in addition to changes in sea-level discussed later (see p. 43), there have been major geomorphological changes in even the relatively low-lying lowland zone.

Erosion

A great deal of erosion has occurred and is still going on; no good sequences have been found in the study area by which other than a single *terminus post quem* date per site can be given. Chapman and Shiel (1988) have reported numerous sites, mostly from Bronze Age ramparts, where deep soil is preserved beneath the rampart, while in the surrounding landscape the soil is thin and discontinuous (see p. 220). Where there is a substantial slope, soil is found forming terraces against the uphill side of walls, even when, as at Polača-Dražice, this is on the outside of an enclosed area (see p. 227). Unfortunately, these sites have not been reoccupied and hence it is impossible to say when, after the Bronze Age, erosion occurred. The Nadin site was reused and Roman deposits overlie substantially more soil than is present today, suggesting much erosion in post-Roman times (see p. 231).

This view of severe erosion is corroborated by the existence of large, undated but not ancient field systems which now have insufficient soil to justify the labour of enclosure (Shiel and Chapman 1988). Also the landscape is dotted with large *stanovi* (Chapman *et al.* 1987) which were built to house numbers of sheep which the landscape could not now support. These stanovi appear to have remained in use into living memory, indicating that much erosion may have occurred relatively recently. The presence of deeper soil under individual thorn bushes on the karst (Chapman *et al.* 1987) supports this view. The intense rains at the end of the summer and in spring occur respectively when growth has been decimated by drought or grazing, and before spring-sown crops become established. The exposed soil can be easily eroded, leaving prominent gullies, and the even larger draga systems testify to continuing erosion. The occurrence of blocked weather patterns would have led to intense rainfall, precipitating erosion. Wetter summers may have had the opposite effect by maintaining a better crop cover and thus preventing erosion in autumn.

Erosion of Arable land was not seen. Much present-day Karst was considered to be eroded Stony land, but the remaining Stony is largely protected from lateral (but not vertical) erosion by field boundary walls. Terrace land itself was seen actively eroding around the unprotected periphery of terrace-walled areas, which were in general secure. Bottomland was cut by active stream channels, but these were associated with deposition as well as erosion. As each of these classes contains a variety of conditions, care must be taken with comparisons over time, for Karst and Stony land, in particular, have tended to move from the 'better' to the 'worse' extremes of the class, as well as Stony being eroded to Karst.

Deposition

Part of the evidence for erosion comes from the presence of deposited products of erosion in valley sites. These products heighten the level of the land and may effectively improve it although flooding must occur for the material to be deposited. This run-off flooding reduces ground water recharge and may lead to water table depression on ridges, lowering grazing and cropping potential. Before erosion occurred the more extensive soils on ridges would have retained water, making the valleys drier. Several bottomlands – especially the Vrana and Benkovac troughs – appear to have aggraded by many metres. It is possible that these sites were very wet for long periods in the past, and that the rise in land level has increased their productivity substantially. Other areas, such as Nadinsko Blato, have only aggraded by less than 2m, and the material filling the basin is very fine textured. Such basins occur at the end of long drainage channels with little gradient, so that coarse particles presumably have settled out higher up the valley. There has clearly been little scope on such valleys for change in level, so unless the run-off characteristics of the valley have changed the flood risk was climate-dependent.

If deposition occurred on crop land, this would constitute at least temporary downgrading of land quality. There is no evidence that this has been a common occurrence, for, even today, the Bottomland and stream courses lie several metres below the level of the adjacent land. The only evidence of widespread alteration which has affected productivity as a result of deposition is therefore in the Bottomlands. Change has occurred due to soil redistribution on Arable and on Terrace land but, other than over short periods, there is nothing to suggest that productive potential was reduced.

This consideration of erosion and deposition suggests that both the area (table 6) and the quality of the various land types has changed. Arable land appears to have changed hardly at all while the area of Stony land has been progressively reduced and on much of the remaining Stony land soil loss has increased drought risk. The eroded Stony is in some places so eroded that it is downgraded to Karst. The area of Terrace land does not appear to have changed much, though there may have been some movement and redeposition. Karst has increased in area, and has certainly declined in quality with thinner, less extensive soils. Bottomland has deepened and become very slightly more extensive. However, erosion elsewhere has increased water run-off so that flood risk in valleys has increased. This has offset the effects of increased level and thickness of the Bottomland.

Vegetational change

By E. Grüger

Modern vegetation

The modern vegetation of the study region is not 'natural' but the result of human activities, which started during the Neolithic, greatly intensified during the Roman and medieval periods and lasted up to modern times. Except for certain ecologically special sites of relatively small extent (e.g. rocks, coastlines), the whole area would be covered by forests if natural conditions had continued or if man's activities ended.

Horvat *et al.* (1974) distinguish four major vegetation zones in north Dalmatia. The study region falls within three of these:

1. The zone of evergreen forests, which covers a narrow strip of land along the coast and the lower parts of the islands of the Adriatic sea (*Orno-Quercetum ilicis*);
2. The area of deciduous oak-hornbeam forests further inland (*Ostryo-Carpinetum adriaticum*). These deciduous forests grade in the east, with increasing altitude, into:
3. The montane and sub-Alpine beechwoods of the Velebit mountains (*Abieti-Fagetum illyricum, Aceri-Fagetum illyricum*), with *Fagus* and *Abies* as the

main tree species and *Picea*, *Taxus*, *Carpinus*, *Betulus* and others on suitable sites.

The oak-hornbeam forests are characterized by *Carpinus orientalis*, *Ostrya carpinifolia*, *Fraxinus ornus* and deciduous oaks (*Quercus pubescens/robur* pollen type) as the main constituents, but species like *Ulmus*, *Alnus* and others also occur in this zone. The diversified topography of the region favours the formation of a mosaic of stands of trees which would be distributed in the area according to their different ecological requirements (wetness, soil depth, etc.).

Typical members of the evergreen forests are the evergreen oaks (*Quercus ilex/coccifera* pollen type), *Phillyrea latifolia*, *Pistacia lentiscus*, *Juniperus oxycedrus* and others. The olive tree, *Olea europaea*, which is not resistant to frost, also occurs in the region but, for the most part, near the coast only. The boundaries between these forest types are not abrupt.

Earlier studies

Humans alter the vegetation of their surroundings by their activities and they do so particularly intensively in contexts of permanent settlement. Vegetational changes can also be caused by climatic changes. Both of them affect pollen production and hence pollen precipitation. They should therefore be detectable by pollen analysis of sediments containing former pollen precipitation, i.e. in lacustrine or peaty deposits from the study region. If conditions for pollen preservation fluctuate, vegetational 'changes' may be more apparent than real, as pollen deterioration may have altered the pollen assemblages.

Compared to the regions north of the Alps, only a little modern pollen-analytical work has been done in the Mediterranean region. Some of this work is fortunately in the former Yugoslavia and those cores from sites at low elevations close to the Adriatic Sea are of special interest for the purpose of this chapter.

The first modern studies in this area were undertaken by Beug (1961, 1962, 1967) on sediments of Malo Jezero on the island of Mljet (42 degrees 45 min. N, 17 degrees 20 min. E), south of the study area. They permitted the reconstruction of the history of the vegetation on this island during the period 9000–2000 BP. The results of this research have recently been confirmed by Jahns (1990, 1991). According to these studies, deciduous trees, mainly oaks, predominated in the forests of Mljet and the coastal area during Mesolithic and Early Neolithic times. Though evergreen species like *Phillyrea* and *Pistacia* were present, they remained of minor importance until about 7500–7200 BP, when *Juniperus* spread and the importance of *Phillyrea* in the forests increased considerably. These changes are thought to indicate the transition to a Mediterranean type of climate. Evergreen oaks – an important constituent of the modern Mediterranean vegetation – were, however, not yet present. *Quercus ilex* immigrated and spread later; it began to dominate the coastal vegetation only around 5500 BP (Jahns 1991). Pollen analysis does not reveal major changes in pollen precipitation during the following millennia, including Bronze Age times, though the rising *Erica* curve and the first occurrence of some other pollen types were probably related to increasing human impact on the vegetation.

Brande (1973, 1989) continued this work by studying sites on the nearby mainland in the Neretva valley lowlands, about 25km north-east of Mljet. He confirmed the general lines of vegetational development found on Mljet in his own study region and extended the pollen record to recent times. The distribution of the sites allowed the recognition in the pollen diagrams of the vegetational gradient from a eu-Mediterranean type of vegetation along the coast to a sub-Mediterranean one further inland. The study also documented later vegetational changes, especially since Roman times, showing the most characteristic patterns of human impact over the last two millennia.

Later, Beug (1977) added a study on vegetational development during the last 5,000 years in the coastal area of Istria (45 degrees N, 13 degrees 40 min. E, and north of the study region). Here, about 2.5 degrees of latitude further to the north, evergreen species were, for climatic reasons, never as important as on the island of Mljet. Deciduous forests covered the area and a narrow strip of evergreen trees (mainly *Quercus ilex*) existed along the shore of the Adriatic Sea as long as natural conditions prevailed (i.e. until Roman times).

Of special interest are Beug and Brande's results concerning human impact on the natural vegetation of these areas. It was weak during the Neolithic, Bronze Age and Iron Age but devastating in the Roman and medieval periods. Brande (1989) considers the fine charcoal and high non-arboreal pollen sedimentation result from forest clearance by fire in the Middle Neolithic period, with further woodland disturbance in the Later Bronze Age. Such high levels of charcoal may, however, be caused partly by natural forest fires. But it was in the Roman and medieval periods only when human influence started to cause a general spreading of evergreen trees and shrubs – the formation of maquis vegetation (Beug 1975). Cultivation of plants finds its expression in rising pollen curves of specific species, among them *Juglans*, *Castanea*, *Olea* and *Vitis*. Of these, *Olea* and *Vitis* are indigenous to the area. They had probably already been used, though not cultivated, by pre-Roman populations (see p. 241). *Juglans* and *Castanea* are, however, considered to have been introduced by the Romans. On the basis of macro-botanical remains cultivation of cereals can be assumed for the Neolithic (Hopf 1958; Chapman and Müller 1990) and for succeeding periods (Kučan 1984; see also Chapter 6) but it cannot be proven convincingly for the pre-Roman period by pollen analysis.

Bokanjačko Blato

The site

Bokanjačko Blato (44 degrees 11 min. N, 15 degrees 14 min. E) is a former lake in the Neothermal Dalmatia Project study area (fig. 19). This area lies between the palynological reference sites in southern Dalmatia (Mljet and the Neretva lowlands 240km to the south-east) and Istria (150km to the north-west). The site itself lies only 2km from the seashore, at 25masl, in a zone which now supports sub-Mediterranean vegetation. The 10km-wide territory surrounding the lake is dominated by the Karst land use class, with discontinuous patches of Stony land on the south-west side. Two cores were taken from the lake beds. Fluctuations in the pollen counts allow division of the pollen diagrams into five zones. The diagram from core 2 (fig. 20) will be discussed in this chapter. The percentages are based on the pollen sum of all woody species (fig. 20: *Betula* to *Pinus*). Rare pollen types are listed below (table 7).

Stratigraphy

The sediment is a clay-gyttja in the deepest part (Zone 1) and calcareous gyttja in the upper 4m of the profile. The gradual change of sediments is reflected by the values of inorganic carbon, which rise from about 4.5 per cent (dry weight) in Zone 1 to about 11.5 per cent (fig. 20) in Zones 2 to 5. The content of organic-bound carbon varies between 0.1 and 2.2 per cent, due to the occurrence of bigger plant remains here and there in the samples. A thin layer of peaty material was present in Profile 1 and has been used for a radiocarbon determination. The sediments and the algal remains, which have been found in almost all the samples used for pollen analysis (mainly of *Botryococcus*, but also of *Pediastrum* and *Chara*) indicate that there was a lake in the basin all the time, throughout the period.

Radiocarbon dating

Dating of specific levels of the two profiles is difficult, as only two radiocarbon determinations could be made in the entirely calcareous sediments. The sample from the thin layer of peaty material (Profile 1, Zone 3, 2.2–2.26m depth) yielded a radiocarbon date of 3755 ± 120 BP (Hv-4076), which gives a calendrical date, at 95 per cent confidence level, of between 2530 and 1905 Cal. BC (Stuiver and Reimer 1993). Pollen-analytical correlation proved that this Bronze Age horizon is found in both profiles at the same depth. Another radiocarbon determination was done on the directly underlying calcareous gyttja (2.27–2.31m depth). It gave a date of 4455

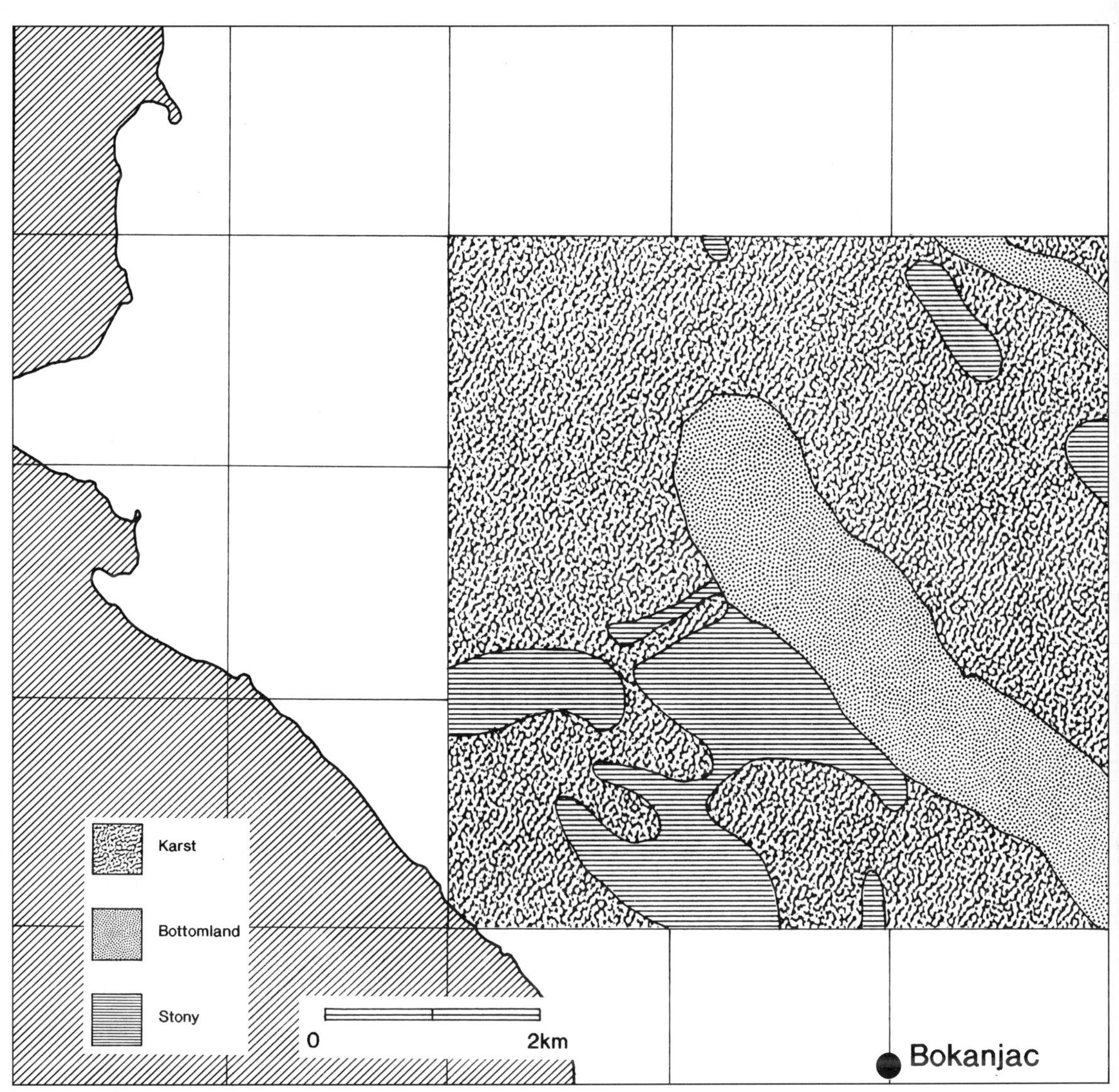

19. Topography of Bokanjačko Blato, with land use classes

± 295 BP (Hv-4077), a value which is perhaps too early due to 'old', geological, carbon in the sample. If this date were correct, one would have to postulate a hiatus of some 700 years between the two dated levels. In addition, some characteristic vegetational changes can be approximately dated by correlation with other dated profiles (see below, pp. 40–1).

Pollen sources

Plant species belonging to different vegetational zones and altitudinal belts contributed to the pollen precipitation preserved in the sediments. Naturally, most

Table 7 Rare pollen types not shown in the Bokanjačko Blato pollen diagram (depth/percentage)

Zone 5 (0.00–0.90m):
Anemone type 24/0.4; 32/1.9; 51/0.9; 71/0.4; *Campanula* 0/0.4; *Centaurea montana* type 51/0.9; *Humulus/Cannabis* type 13/0.3; *Hydrocotyle* 0/0.4; *Ilex* 71/0.4; *Lamiacaeae* p.p. 0/1.7; 40/0.3; *Menyanthes* 24/0.4; *Myrtus* 13/0.9; *Plantago* sp. 24/1.8; 80/0.5; *Polygonum bistorta* type 40/0.3; *Polygonum convolvulus* type 0/1.3; 24/0.4; 71/0.4; *Sphagnum* 71/0.4; *Trifolium* type 13/0.9; 71/0.4; *Xanthium* 0/0.9.

Zone 4 (0.90–1.90m):
Euphorbia 180/0.2; *Hydrocotyle* 140/0.2; *Lamiacaeae* p.p. 100/0.2; *Malvaceae* 160/0.2; *Myrtus* 120/0.2; *Plantago* sp. 100/0.2; 120/0.2; 180/0.2; *Populus* 180/0.2; *Sphagnum* 140/0.2; *Trifolium* type 100/0.2; 120/0.2; 140/0.2.

Zone 3 (1.90–3.22m):
Convolvulus arvensis type 200/0.2; *Humulus/Cannabis* type 200/0.2; *Mercurialis annua* type 295/0.2; *Myrtus* 315/0.2; *Onobrychis* type 220/0.2; *Plantago* sp. 200/0.2; 295/0.2; 315/0.2; *Populus* 240/0.2; *Utricularia* 240/0.2.

Zone 2 (3.22–4.20m):
Cryprogramma 355/0.2; *Echinops* 415/0.2; *Plantago* sp. 331/0.2; 415/0.2; *Polygala* 355/0.3; *Polypodium* 331/0.2; 395/0.3.

Zone 1 (4.20–5.10m):
Anemone type 425/0.2; *Campanula* 510/0.2; *Convolvulus arvensis* type 436/0.2; 455/0.2; 495/0.2; 510/0.2; *Genista* type 510/0.2; *Gentianaceae* p.p. 436/0.2; 455/0.2; *Geranium* 455/0.2; *Malvaceae* 495/0.2; *Plantago* sp. 436/0.4; 455/0.4; *Polygonum convolvulus* type 510/0.4; *Polypodium* 425/0.2; *Valeriana* 436/0.2.

of the pollen comes from the surrounding species-rich sub-Mediterranean vegetation (*Ostryo-Carpinetum adriaticum*) and its degradation forms, from plants growing in the lake (*Nymphaea, Myriophyllum, Potamogeton*) or on its swampy shores (*Cladium, Cyperaceae, Typha* and others) or, in later periods, from species planted by humans (e.g. *Castanea, Juglans, Pinus*). Some pollen derives from the communities of the eu-Mediterranean *Orno-Quercetum ilicis* and its degradation forms, which occupy the nearby offshore islands of the Zadar archipelago and a narrow strip of land along the seashore. In addition, a final contribution of between 10 and 20 per cent of arboreal pollen has been transported to the lake by wind from the forests of the Velebit mountains 25km to the north-east (*Fagus, Taxus, Abies, Picea, Betula*).

Pollen preservation

The reliability of the pollen spectra is certainly not consistent throughout the profile. Pollen preservation was good to excellent in samples from Zones 1 and 3 only. It was poor in the uppermost half metre of the profile and in samples from between 3.3 and 4m depth. It was moderate in the rest of the profile. Well-preserved pollen was, however, present in all samples. The *Indeterminata* curve mirrors these changes. It includes not only pollen with decayed exines but also crumpled grains which, although otherwise well-preserved, did not show the characteristics needed for a safe determination (e.g. tricolpate, reticulate grains of the *Oleaceae* and others).

The quality of preservation is obviously related to changes in the water table of the former lake. Samples with high frequencies of pollen of submerged living water plants (*Myriophyllum*, *Potamogeton*) show the best pollen preservation, those with the highest sedge (*Cyperaceae*) values the worst. In interpreting the pollen diagram, the observed variability in pollen preservation must be taken into consideration.

Vegetational development and dating

Zones 1 and 2

The most characteristic features of Zone 1, with its good pollen preservation, are the occurrence of high values of the *Juniperus* pollen type (which is believed to represent the genus *Juniperus* only) and the low percentages of the deciduous oaks (*Quercus pubescens/robur* type). The representation of the latter, at less than 30 per cent, is lowest in Zone 1. Other deciduous tree species, sub-Mediterranean as well as montane ones, are comparatively well represented at the same time. A species-rich woodland is indicated, which was probably closed on the mesic sites (Stony land) but more open in drier places (Karst or Terrace land), as is shown by the importance of the light-demanding *Juniperus.*

Dramatic changes in the vegetation seem to be indicated in the pollen diagram for the duration of Zone 2. Except for the curves of the montane species and the deciduous oaks, almost all curves of woody species (including *Juniperus*) decline to minimal values. *Tilia* and *Acer* attain somewhat higher, but nevertheless low, percentages. Those of the *Quercus pubescens/robur* type increase from about 25 per cent to almost 70 per cent of the total arboreal pollen count, allowing only 15 per cent to the other sub-Mediterranean shrubs and trees. Whereas the decrease of the juniper curve and the beginning of the increase of the *Quercus pubescens/robur* type are expressed in samples with good pollen preservation, the extremely low values of taxa with thin-walled pollen grains and the height of the peaks of the deciduous oaks curve, as well as those of pine, *Artemisia*, *Cichoriaceae* and others in the upper part of Zone 2, are intimately connected with the decay of pollen in the now shallower lake, a condition indicated in the pollen diagram by the high *Cladium* and *Cyperaceae* values.

Deciduous oaks must have dominated the forests of the Zone 2 period, which were most likely richer in species than the pollen diagram would suggest.

The occurrence of so many woody species with different ecological requirements together in the same area during the period of Zone 1 indicates a

20. Bokanjačko Blato pollen diagram (E. Grüger)

great variety of site environments and vegetational patterns. Though warm, the climate must have been moist enough for all of them during the summer and not too cold in winter (cold-sensitive species include *Phillyrea* and *Pistacia*). A change to drier conditions in Zone 2 may be inferred from the rising curves of the *Cyperaceae* and of *Cladium* (sedges and sedge saw), which indicate that the extent of swampy areas around the lake edge had increased. While this may have been caused by silting up of the lake, finds of *Ephedra* pollen and the increase of the composites (*Asteraceae, Cichoriaceae, Artemisia*) and of the *Chenopodiaceae/ Amaranthaceae* would be consistent with the assumption of a now drier climate.

The best way to correlate pollen Zones 1 and 2 with other diagrams is by comparison of the pollen strengths of the regionally important species, which are, in our case, the oaks and juniper.

Juniperus was an important constituent of the vegetation recorded in the southern Dalmatian sites, especially during the period from 7000 to 4500 BP (Beug 1961, 1967; Brande 1973, 1989; Jahns 1991). The Bokanjačko Blato diagrams show its decline at the Zones 1/2 boundary. Assuming that the decline of juniper was a contemporary process throughout Dalmatia, the latter date can be taken as the approximate age of the sediments at the Zones 1/2 boundary. Evergreen oaks spread throughout the southern part of the region earlier. They became dominant around 5500 BP (Jahns 1991) and displaced the shade-intolerant junipers. Evergreen oaks were never dominant in the Bokanjac area but a rise of their curve from values below 2 per cent in Zone 1 (Profile 1, unpubl.) to about 5 per cent in the upper part of this zone and to 15 per cent in Zone 3 can be seen in the Bokanjačko Blato diagrams. The date of 5500 BP can therefore be attributed to either the earlier part of Zone 1 (before the juniper decline) or to the Zones 2/3 boundary (after the juniper decline), where the most pronounced increase can be seen. The latter possibility is unlikely, as the *Quercus ilex* pollen values are certainly affected (reduced) by the poor pollen preservation of Zone 2. The sediments near the base of Profile 2 are certainly older than 6000 BP.

Zone 3

This zone has good to excellent pollen preservation in all samples. It is similar to Zone 1 in composition of the forest vegetation. Except for *Juniperus*, all tree species are again as well represented as in Zone 1 of the pollen diagram. Deciduous oaks dominate, though their values decrease to 30 per cent. *Juniperus* remains uncommon. The percentages of the evergreen oaks (*Quercus ilex/coccifera* type) increase from 5 to about 15 per cent and *Pistacia* and *Phillyrea* were of importance at the same time. This is sound evidence for a warm climate and especially for mild winters. The lake level must have been higher at this time, as sedges became insignificant. Submerged living water plants were present and *Myriophyllum* was even more important than before. If this is not a local phenomenon, caused, for example, by a sudden sinking of the lake bottom, it must indicate increased precipitation. The forests of this time must have been rich in species and dense, as is shown by the conspicuously low values of most of the non-arboreal curves.

The samples for the two radiocarbon determinations came from the upper part of this zone (see above). Using the 3755 BP date for interpolation, one can estimate the age of the sediments at the upper boundary of Zone 3 at *c.* 3200 BP. Sediments from its lower boundary must have an age of at least 4500 BP. Therefore, Zone 3 is coeval with the Eneolithic period and Earlier Bronze Ages.

Zones 4 and 5

The doubling of the percentages of the deciduous oaks at the beginning of Zone 4 and the reduction in many of the deciduous woody species at the Zones 3/4 boundary can certainly be partially explained as an effect of worsened pollen preservation. Increased values of light-demanding taxa, such as *Artemisia*, *Asteraceae*, *Cichoriaceae*, *Chenopodiaceae/Amaranthaceae*, *Juniperus*, *Pinus* and others could also indicate growing human impact on the local vegetation. The period under consideration spans the Later Bronze Age to modern times.

The Zones 4/5 boundary is defined by the start of the continuous *Castanea* curve. This horizon can be dated by interpolation to between AD 150 and 400, if it is assumed that the sedimentation rate remained constant above the radiocarbon-dated level. The equivalent process in the Neretva lowlands has a radiocarbon date of 1785 ± 200 BP (boundary of Zones 2b/3a: Brande 1973), calibrated to AD 22–495 (Stuiver and Reimer 1993). The uppermost sample comes from the modern surface of the lake, which must have been almost completely filled up before drainage in the twentieth century.

Zones 4 and 5 mark the time of the final filling-up of the lake basin. This is indicated by the curves of *Cyperaceae*, *Cladium* and *Typha* and by the finds of typical members of communities growing on swampy land – *Lythrum*, *Lysimachia*, *Mentha* and some species of *Ranunculus*.

Anthropogenic indicators and cultivated plants

Human communities used and influenced the natural vegetation in many ways. People cut down the forests, promoted plants native to their surroundings, or introduced new species to cultivate them. They also let their animals graze in the forests and coppiced trees both to feed them and for fuel and construction timber. Weeds could spread on the man-made clearings and shrub communities developed where forests grew before. As a consequence of such activities, the quantities of certain pollen types (the so-called 'anthropogenic indicators') must change in pollen diagrams, or additional ones should occur in sediments coeval with periods of human occupation. As climatic changes may cause similar effects, it is often not easy to prove human influence with palynological data. In the present case, interpretation of the pollen diagram is also hampered by the changing quality of pollen preservation. Critical surveys and examples of research on anthropogenic indicators in pollen diagrams are given in the publications of Behre, Beug, Bottema and Brande (cited below).

The pollen spectra of Zone 1 with its good preservation most likely reflect natural conditions, undisturbed by human activity. Those of Zone 2 are influenced by climatic fluctuations towards increasing dryness, which causes the decay of pollen, so that possible indicators of human activity remain hidden. The pollen spectra of Zone 3 should, however, show the impact of Bronze Age societies on the local vegetation.

Degradation of the natural forest vegetation is usually indicated in Mediterranean pollen diagrams by rising values of *Fraxinus ornus* and of species with unpalatable green leaves (such as *Juniperus*, *Phillyrea*, *Pistacia* and others). *Paliurus* pollen would indicate even more disturbed conditions and that of members of the *Cistus* family and of *Erica* the formation of garrigue. But, as all of these species are native to the area, small quantities of their pollen can be expected in all samples of the profile. Some of these pollen types, however, are important in Zone 3, the zone in which also most of the *Plantago lanceolata* type pollen grains are registered. This pollen type is considered to be a reliable indicator of human activity in many regions (Behre 1989). Therefore, its occurrence together with that of other species indicating disturbance proves that there has been forest clearance during the period of Zone 3, in the Eneolithic and the Earlier Bronze Age.

At the lower boundary of Zone 4, the pollen curves of *Artemisia*, *Asteraceae*, *Centaurea jacea* type, *Cichoriaceae*, *Chenopodiaceae/Amaranthaceae*, *Apiaceae* and others start to rise. The members of these taxa do not usually grow in forests, but on open ground (Bottema 1982, 1989). Therefore, this change could be related to human activity during the Later Bronze Age. The same pollen diagrams also record high values in earlier zones, especially in Zone 2, dating to the Neolithic period. Human impact cannot be ruled out in these older levels, but a climatic reason for this earlier process is more likely, as the observed changes can be connected to a lowering of the water table indicated in the frequency of swamp plants. This could support the view expressed above (see p. 23) that the Altithermal period in coastal Dalmatia was dry.

Of the crop plants cultivated today in the region, only cereals, *Juglans* (walnut), *Castanea* (chestnut), *Vitis* (grape) and *Olea* (olive) are represented in the Bokanjačko Blato pollen diagram. Some of them are represented by a few pollen grains only. Most indicative is the *Castanea* curve, which starts and increases to relatively high values (4.5 per cent) in Zone 5. This tree has apparently been cultivated in the area since Roman or, more likely, post-Roman times only. *Juglans* pollen has been found occasionally but, except for one grain found in the deeper part of Zone 1, always in sediments dating from classical or later periods. *Olea* and *Vitis* are native to the region but the distribution of their pollen grains in the profile shows a distinct tendency towards higher values in the upper part of the profile (Zones 4 and 5). This certainly indicates the increasing use of these species by local societies but it is not possible to infer the earliest date of their cultivation from their low pollen values. The *Cerealia* type curve shows the same trend but its values are very low, when present at all. This pollen type also includes the pollen grains of some wild grasses. The absence of abundant cereal pollen is perhaps not surprising, in view of the paucity of Arable land suitable for cropping in the vicinity of the lake (fig. 19).

Conclusions

In summary, one may conclude that human influence in the Bokanjac area started in the Eneolithic or Earlier Bronze Age – the third to second millennia Cal. BC. Traces of agriculture are weak or missing in the pollen diagram but grazing is indicated. Chestnut and walnut were introduced by humans to the area in classical times. These findings are in general agreement with the results of earlier studies at coastal sites north-west and south-east of Bokanjačko Blato.

Sea-level change

There are two main schools of thought on sea level change. Van Andel and Sutton (1987) are representatives of the majority, which assumes a continuous rise since the end of the last Glacial period, with a maximum rate of rise at 6600 Cal. BC and a progressively declining rate, with only a relatively small change (1.6m: Jelgersma 1966) over the last 4,000 years. The alternative view (Fairbridge 1977) envisages a rapid rise to some 3m above the present level, at 3500 Cal. BC, or possibly 1–2m above present at 2300 Cal. BC (Lamb 1982), and a subsequent decline to the present level. The models disagree by a maximum of about 12m at around 3500 Cal. BC. This difference, though apparently large, only influences the date at which loss of land to the sea occurs, and it does not affect areas well away from the modern coast-line. There is also a small possibility of relative sea-level change of geologic or isostatic origin. As there was no major ice cap nearby, isostatic compensation is unlikely to have been substantial in the Study Area, and there is no local record of seismic uplift or settlement. The effect of the pre-3500 Cal. BC rise in sea level would have been the preferential flooding of Bottomland and Arable. As the ridge–valley structures occur at a variety of levels, sea-level rise would have had a different effect in each partially flooded valley. To seaward, Bottomland and Arable would already have been lost, resulting in the creation of islands, so subsequent

Table 8 Sea level and areas of land and water within the study region since 14,000 BP

Date 000 BP	Sea level m	Climatic period	Rate of change mm/year	Area of water km²	Area of land km²
14	-75	Younger Dryas	–	200	3300
11	-50	Anathermal	8.3	630	2870
8.8	-30	Altithermal	9.1	980	2520
6.7	-10	Medithermal	7.7	1400	2100
0	0	Modern	1.6	1540	1960

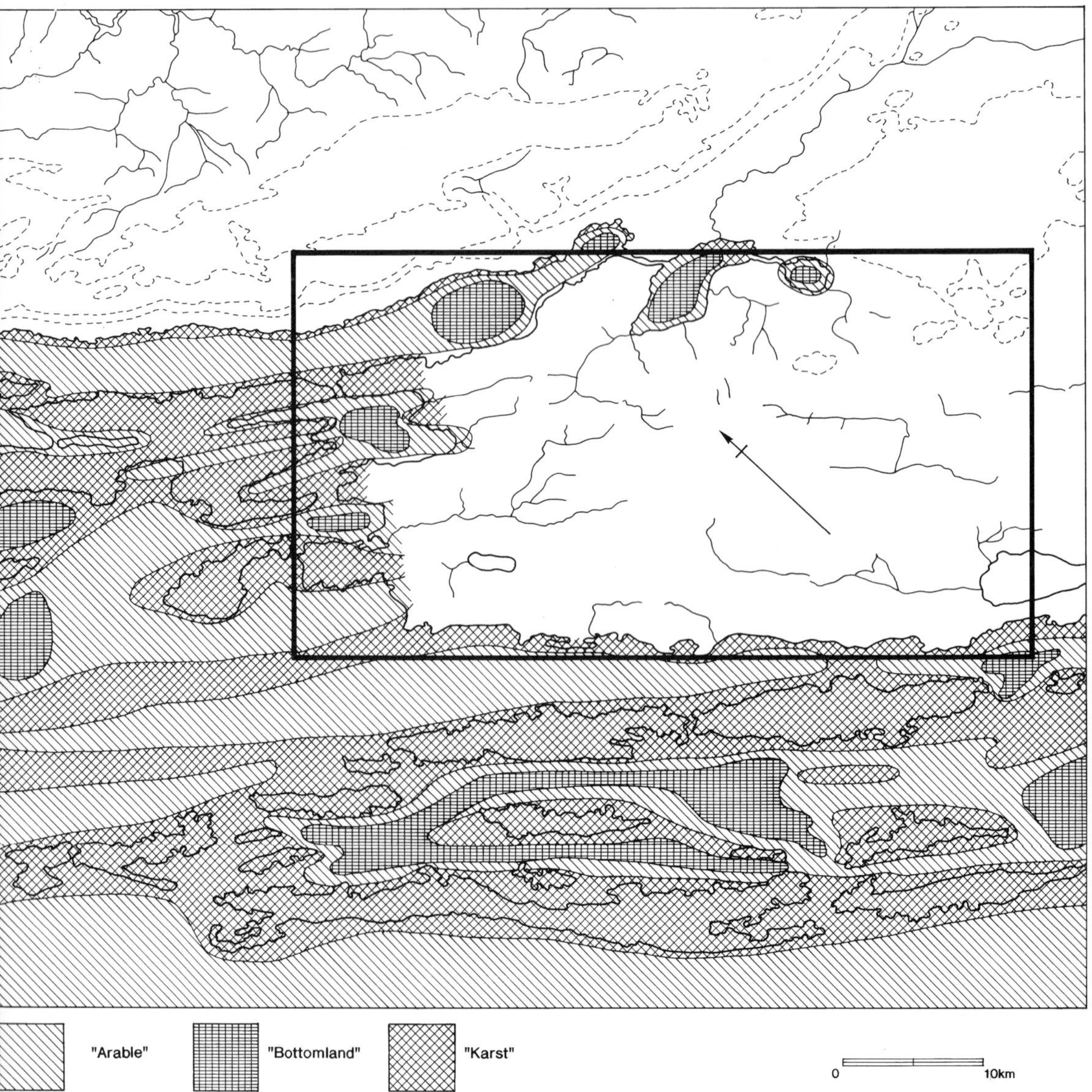

21. Proposed distribution of land between modern sea level and -50m

sea-level rise would only have a marginal effect on the area of steeply sloping Karst and Stony land. In intermediate valleys, Bottomland would have been lost already so a small rise in sea level would cause substantial flooding of Arable and the less steep lower areas of Stony land. Further inland, Bottomland would be affected by seasonal flooding, but not marine incursion. For any particular ridge–valley structure, this suggests initial impoverishment due to loss of the better land, with subsequent losses locally dominated by poorer land, and occurring more slowly per millimetre of sea-level rise. The main difference between the two models' predictions of the effects of sea-level rise is that Fairbridge predicts an earlier loss of present shallow areas of sea, such as Pasmanski Kanal. As an effect on the total land resource, losses over the whole period amount to several hundred square kilometres on the basis of either model (table 8). Areas most likely to have emerged, in Fairbridge's model, would be around Nin and Vrana, where silting has in any case had a massive overriding effect.

In attempting to quantify the type of land lost as a result of sea-level rise, the major difficulty is that of separating the classes only on the basis of topography. In particular it is difficult to distinguish Karst, Terrace and Stony land, or to separate the more level areas of Stony from Arable. In figure 21, 'Bottomland' therefore consists of about 75 per cent Bottomland, 10 per cent Arable, 10 per cent Karst and 5 per cent Stony; 'Arable' is 40 per cent Arable, 10 per cent Karst, 35 per cent Stony and 15 per cent Bottomland; 'Karst' is 50 per cent Karst, 35 per cent Stony, 10 per cent Terrace and 5 per cent Arable. Clearly a huge resource of land with large agricultural potential was lost in the Early Neothermal period. To these losses must be added those due to erosion, which have degraded large areas of formerly Stony land (see p. 29). Taken together, these losses have seriously reduced the productive potential of the region.

Water resources

In the major valleys, water is available even in summer within 5m of the surface. Open pits and lined wells are in use, as well as modern pumped pipe-wells. In winter, the water table rose to the surface over much of the low-lying land though such formerly flooded areas – blata – have now mostly been drained. Although the limestone is well jointed, the flat valley bottoms and limited scale of ridges has prevented the development of classical karstic features: only one sink hole was found in the study area. On the ridges and valley sides, water is less easily available today, though when soils were thicker and more continuous there may have been some semi-permanent streams on the lower slopes. No travertine was seen, however, suggesting that there were not springs in former times which have subsequently dried up.

Communications and settlement

The topography within the study area creates few communications problems, particularly if a boat is available. With rising sea level, the offshore ridges would have become separated as islands and routes would have become more circuitous on the mainland. The blata would also force detours in winter. None of the ridges is insurmountable, though again a detour of a few kilometres might be advisable. On the other hand, Velebit is a major obstacle, though once again there are passes such as that afforded by the Zrmanja river. Movement from north to south is much easier than from east to west.

Conclusion

The area has a range of resources which might be best described as modest. Nevertheless conditions for life and survival appear to have been adequate throughout the Neothermal period, although the best situation has probably changed with time. In order to decide what is the 'best' situation, it is necessary to consider all the resources available at each period and, using a general model, produce some prediction of the problems and advantages of each site at that period. It will clearly be necessary to validate this, and both model creation and validation are to be found in chapter 7.

3 The archaeological field survey

Introduction

In this summary of the survey results of the NDP, an attempt is made to characterize the settlement forms and structures which have left material traces on the landscape of north Dalmatia. Amidst the plethora of empirical data, the selection of what appears to us to be the most significant patterning in the settlement information has taken precedence over an exhaustive catalogue of 'facts'. In this, we follow Sheppard Frere's (1988) call for the use of archaeological judgement in the identification of differences with significant meaning.

The four basic questions to which intensive field survey can provide at least partial answers have been defined by Cherry, Gamble and Shennan (1978) as: the number of sites in the area, the number of sites by period and function, the relationship between archaeological sites and environmental variables, and the inter-relationships between archaeological sites. The initial survey stage of medium intensity transect survey across the grain of the countryside was designed to establish the relative density of settlement in each landscape unit by coverage of as many different landscape units as possible. The 1km width of the transects represents a compromise between pure quadrats (often 0.5 × 0.5 or 1 × 1km in area) and pure transects (rarely more than 300m in width) and provides greater control over environmental variations within the sampled area than could otherwise have been achieved. Once a preliminary idea of site densities was established by transect survey, a shift to block survey provided more intensive coverage of areas of particular interest. This second phase utilized survey of a larger block of land to provide the potential for settlement pattern data. A total area of 50.6 sq km was walked by transect in 1982–3, while the survey block of 66 sq km (plus 11 sq km of the 1983 transect) was completed in 1984–6. The total area surveyed was 120 sq km, at an average rate of 5.5 people-days per sq km (fig. 8).

Given that the largest available scale of map cover was 1:25,000, fieldwalking across individual fields was impractical and so the alternative technique of walking across the countryside on fixed compass bearings, at 25m or 50m spacings, was adopted (fig. 22). Findspots and single finds are located, for the most part, to within 100 m of their actual location, while monuments are accurately plotted to within 25m. Given the potential language problems of an Anglo-Yugoslav team, a bilingual recording form was designed (fig. 23), primarily for recording finds but also as a field dictionary. A standard terminology was introduced for all archaeological remains found in the field. Three terms were defined for the

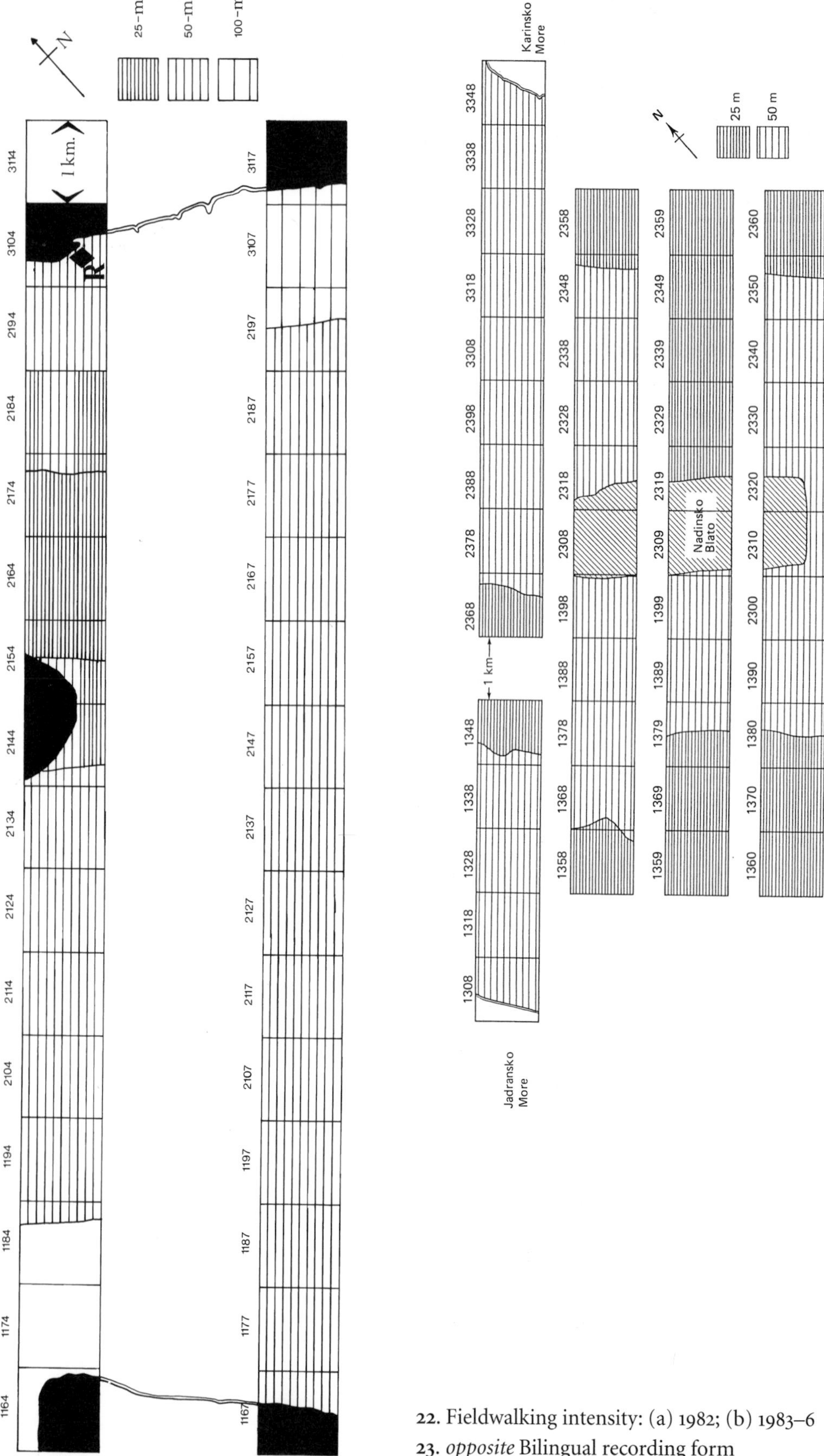

22. Fieldwalking intensity: (a) 1982; (b) 1983–6

23. *opposite* Bilingual recording form

NEOTHERMAL DALMATIA SITE SURVEY - BILINGUAL RECORDING FORM

1. GRID SQUARE/SITE DATUM □□□□/□□□□ 2. MAP REFERENCE □□□□/□□□□
1. KVADRATNI BROJ/BROJ LOKALITETA 2. BROJ KVADRATA NA MAPI
3. VILLAGE/LOCALITY NAME ________________ 4. DATE RECORDED □□ □□ 199_
3 SELO/LOKALITET ________________ 4. DATUM NALAZISTA
5. RECORDED BY ________________
5. IME PRONALAZACA ________________
6. LOCAL INFORMANTS ________________
6. IME SELJACI ________________

---

7. TYPE OF REMAINS ISOLATED TOMB □ CEMETERY □ SINGLE FIND □
7. VRSTA LOKALITETA IZOLOVAN GROB □ NEKROPOL □ IZOLOVAN NALAZ □
SCATTER □ SETTLEMENT □ SETTLEMENT + CEMETERY □
GRUPA NALAZE □ NALAZISTA □ NALAZISTA + NEKROPOL □
SANCTUARY/SHRINE □ OTHER ________________
CRKVA □ DRUGO VRSTA ________________
8. PERIOD OF OCCUPATION PALAEOLITHIC □ MESOLITHIC □ NEOLITHIC □
8. PERIODA OKUPACIJE PALEOLIT □ MEZOLIT □ NEOLIT □
BRONZE AGE □ IRON AGE □ ROMAN □ MEDIEVAL □ UNKNOWN □
BRONZANO DOBA □ ZELEZNO DOBA □ RIM □ SREDNJI VEK □ NEPOZNAT □

---

9. LOCATION ________________
9. PRONALAZAK ________________
10. TOPOGRAPHY ________________
10. TOPOGRAFIJA ________________
11. SURFACE SLOPE NONE □ LIMITED □ MODERATE □ STEEP □
11. UGAO ZEMLJISTA NEMA □ MALO □ VECI □ STRM □
12. AMOUNT OF EROSION NONE □ LIMITED □ MODERATE □ EXTENSIVE □
12. PROCENAT EROZIJE NEMA □ MALO □ VECI □ IAKO □
13. TERRACING PRESENT □ ABSENT □
13. TERASE IMA □ NEMA □
14. OTHER DAMAGE ________________
14. DRUGA VRSTA OSTECENJA ________________
15. FUTURE THREATS ________________
15. KOJA VRSTA OPASNOSTI PRETI LOKALITETU ? ________________
16. GEOLOGY ________________
16. GEOLOGIJA ________________
17. SOIL TYPE MUNSELL COLOUR □□ ________________
17. PEDOLOSKI TYP MUNSELL BOJA □□ ________________
18. pH READING SAMPLE 1 □ 2 □ 3 □
18. PEDOLOSKA KISELINA KVADRAT 1 □ 2 □ 3 □
19. HYDROLOGY ________________
19. HIDROLOGIJA ________________
20. WATER SOURCE (DISTANCE, SEASONALITY) ________________
20. RESERVE VODE (KOLIKO ? SEZONSKA UPOTREBA) ________________
21. DIRECTION OF PREVAILING WIND □
21. VRSTA VETRA □
22. EXPOSURE TO WIND SHELTERED □ EXPOSED □
22. NA UDARU VETRA ZAKLONJEN □ NEZAKLONJEN □
23. VEGETATION SCRUB/BUSH □ SCRUB/TREES □ SCATTERED TREES □ FOREST □
23. VEGETACIJE SIBLJAK □ MAQUIS □ RETKO DRVECE □ SUMA □
ORCHARD □ VINEYARD □ PASTURE □ ARABLE □ OTHER □
VOCNJAK □ VINOGRAD □ TRAVA □ OBRADIVA ZEMLJA □ DRUGO VRSTA □
24. CULTIVATION FALLOW □ CEREALS □ FRUIT □ OLIVES □
24. OBRADA TRAVA □ ZITARICA □ VOCE □ MASLINE □
CITRUS □TOBACCO □ ALMONDS □ POTATOES □
POMORANJE/LIMUN□ DUVAN □ BADEMI □ KROMPIR □
OTHER VEGITABLES □ OTHER □
DRUGO VRSTA POVRCE □ DRUGO VISTE □

---

25. REF. NO OF SAMPLE UNITS ________________
25. BROJ KVADRATA ZA SKUPLJENJE ________________
26. REF. NO(S) OF PHOTOGRAPHS B & W ____________ COLOUR ____________
26.BROJ FOTOGRAFIJE CRNO-BELO____________ BOJI ____________
27. % MATERIAL COLLECTED ________ 28. % MATERIAL LEFT ________
27. % MATERIJAL DONET ________ 28. % MATERIJAL OSTAVLJEN ________

wide range of categories of remains; these terms were designed for on-site implementation:

1. Standing monuments (cists, tumuli, clearance cairns, linear features, walls, enclosures, hill-forts, villas, deserted medieval villages, etc.)
2. Findspots (defined arbitrarily by the presence of a minimum of 4 artefacts within a 5 × 5m collection quadrat)
3. Single finds (defined arbitrarily by the presence of 1–3 artefacts within a 5 × 5m collection quadrat).

The functional connotations of these categories vary widely and their interpretations will be discussed below (see pp. 53–5). Following recognition of field remains, each fieldwalker attempted to define the limit of the scatter or surviving structures. Next, surface finds were collected from finds quadrats. All artefacts within a randomly located 5 × 5m quadrat were collected, unless otherwise recorded (e.g. large quantities of Roman/medieval tile were not all collected but an estimate of the proportions collected was made). The number of quadrats varied according to the size of the scatter (1 for scatters up to 20 × 20m, 2 for 40 × 40m scatters, etc.). This technique for quantification permitted rapid and standardized collection of surface finds from a small proportion of any given site (generally 5–10 per cent).

In summary, since no intensive, systematic survey had been conducted in north Dalmatia before NDP, it was decided to opt for a medium- to high-intensity strategy designed to provide settlement pattern data over a reasonably large area.

Interpretation

The interpretation of archaeological survey results falls into two overlapping stages: pattern validation and interpretation of meaning. By 'validation', we address the question to what extent the survey data are a complete and representative sample of past residues of human activities; by 'meaning', we address the question of the classes of activity which have produced those material residues.

Validation

The quantity of material collected in a typical Mediterranean zone survey is so great that it can sometimes blind us to the material remains which have not survived or been discovered. Do these gaps on survey maps constitute evidence of absence or the converse?

It is widely recognized that the archaeological material discovered in survey is the outcome of a series of transformations of the archaeological record, termed by

Schiffer (1976, 1987) cultural and natural transforms. Although the plain of Zadar comprises a more stable geomorphological zone than other parts of Dalmatia (Chapman 1981), on a smaller scale both natural and cultural transforms are responsible for creating patterning in the surviving archaeological record. In this section, we examine the effects of transforms on the archaeological record.

In terms of natural transforms, erosion, deposition, flooding, degradation and destruction are the five critical processes. The main impact of erosion upon the archaeological record would seem to be confined to limestone hills, especially those with well-developed draga systems. The absence of steep slopes and gullying on most hills make it unlikely for artefacts to have been lost from much of the area; rather there has been localized erosion close to Bronze Age and later settlements. So far, the project has identified discontinuous, repeated episodes of deposition of materials burying archaeological sites from the Early Neolithic onwards in several valley bottoms. Hence early prehistoric sites in the valleys may well have been buried under erosion products.

Flooding of Early Neothermal coastal sites during the expansion of the Adriatic Sea between 8000 and 5500 BC is a well known phenomenon (van Straaten 1965, 1970; see fig. 21); in the study region, valley flooding may have continued even later (see p. 43), submerging a very large total area. In the study region, the equivalent of Taylor's (1971) north-west European 'Zone of Preservation' is the limestone uplands, which have resisted all but the most extensive forms of cultivation. Perhaps the most significant positive feature affecting site preservation is the lack of extensive land forming in the area over much of the last millennium (contrast Italy or France, with their heavily terraced hillscapes). The significance of medieval and post-medieval agricultural under-exploitation is a legacy of Venetian, Ottoman and successive imperial occupations from which the archaeological record has benefited. This accounts for the good preservation of Neolithic sites buried less than 1m beneath the surface, rendering talk of a corresponding 'Zone of Destruction' inexact. The bottomland, where most deposition has occurred, was never a very attractive settlement zone because of the flood risk (see p. 32). There are cases of differential survival of earthworks on uncultivated heathland, but when a landscape feature such as a dry-stone wall is built, there are rarely sufficient reasons to go to the trouble of removing it. Remains far less massive than the Roman centuriated field systems near Zadar (Bradford 1957, 178–83) remain as permanent landscape features.

In terms of cultural transforms, the frequent difficulties of pit-digging on limestone sites is compensated by the good preservation of finds under drystone remains. The impact of curation strategies awaits detailed analysis for this region.

In short, definition of the natural and cultural transforms relevant to the Zadar area provides a provisional framework for the interpretation and comparison of survey and excavation results.

Meaning

Human behaviour which produces material residues occurs both within and outside habitation sites (Gaffney *et al.* 1985). Survey archaeologists recognize that the often greater densities of surface remains on or near habitation sites are a reflection of the spatial concentration of activities (Thomas 1975). The continuous mapping of finds densities across the countryside has produced estimates of discard rates, currently divided into 'background noise' and 'site' patterning (Gallant 1982). The finds density at which 'background noise' becomes 'site' is not only region-specific (Bintliff and Snodgrass 1988) but also varies through time within a region (e.g. the *Ager Tarraconensis* survey: Keay 1991; Millett 1991). The definition of mean and higher-than-average levels of finds discard for each period has been attempted for NDP (table 9). This procedure enables a more objective definition of 'sites' and 'non-sites', without being tied to the assumption that variation in quantity of discard necessarily reflects variations in nothing but pottery production. The quantities of pottery on site by period is the result of the interaction of many complex behavioural patterns through time.

There are a wide variety of mechanisms by which artefacts can appear in the countryside surrounding habitation sites. Most of these mechanisms contribute to either a stochastic or a fall-off discard pattern. Fall-off patterns of surface pottery with distance from a settlement may be explained by several processes – manuring, seasonal use of field huts or facilities, field cooking and eating, etc.

The interpretation of the activities which produce surface artefact distributions relies to a greater or lesser extent on multiple calibrations of 'raw' survey data (cf. Millett 1986). Broadly, two solutions to this dilemma are possible: increasingly detailed surveys of progressively smaller areas, in which multiple regression analyses provide a mathematical basis for adjustments to increasingly

Table 9 Density of surface finds per collection unit by period

Period	Palaeolithic	Neolithic/ Eneolithic	Bronze Age	Iron Age	Roman	Medieval	Iška	Later
N	44	42	283	109	226	70	119	207
Upper octile	12	30	47	20	11	7	5	15
Upper quartile	6	16	17	11	7	5	4	8
Median	5	5	5	5	4	4	3	4
Lower quartile	3	3	3	3	2	2	2	2
Lower octile	1	1	1	1	1	1	1	1

'cooked' survey data, or regional level survey which attempts to deal with broader questions of settlement pattern change at a higher level of generality, taking into account the transformations of the data base as far as possible. Bearing in mind the attendant loss of information at the site level, the second strategy was selected.

The survey data

The NDP survey data fall into two categories: transect data and the results of the block survey. In this review, the survey data will be presented through a series of maps, while data from both transect and block survey will form the basis of the statistical treatment of the results. Initial consideration will be given to the density of finds in collection units, as a preliminary aspect of quantification.

Because the density of surface finds was mapped within 5 × 5m collection quadrats, it has proved difficult to provide estimates of overall densities of classes of finds per sq km (Shennan 1985; Keay 1991). However, analysis of finds densities in the collection units provides a comparable picture of discard by period and enables a distinction between 'sites' and 'non-sites'. The technique of calculating means, quartiles and octiles of finds density per collection unit gives a conservative estimate of surface distributions, while at the same time highlighting period-by-period differences in surface finds density (table 9).

The results of this analysis indicate that, in all periods, there is a low level of artefact density across parts of the landscape which corresponds partly to our category of 'single finds', partly to 'findspots'. In even larger parts of the surveyed area, no surface finds were recovered at all. Given the pragmatic need to classify

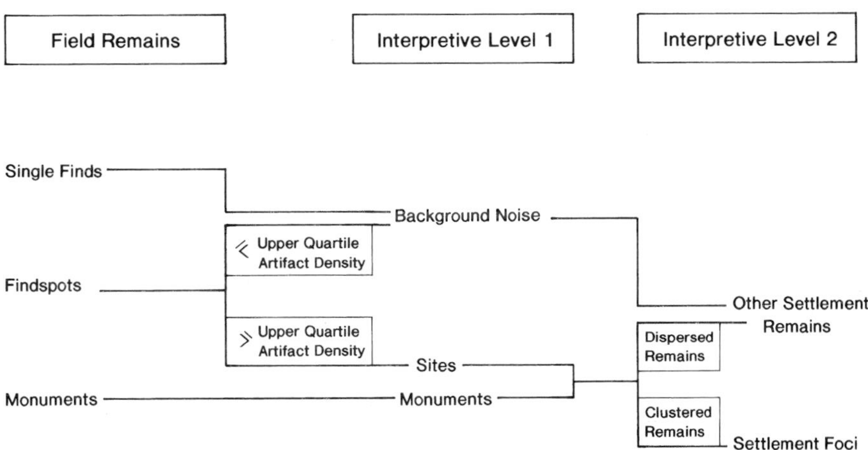

24. Archaeological interpretation: field and interpretative categories

Table 10 Summary of previously known finds from the study region

Class of remains	Ravni Kotari	Zadar Archipelago	Velebit	Bukovica	Total
M Palaeolithic lithics					5
U Palaeolithic lithics					8
Palaeolithic cave			1		1
Mesolithic lithics	1	–	–	–	1
Mesolithic cave	–	–	1	–	1
E Neolithic pottery	8	–	–	–	8
E Neolithic cave	1	–	1	–	2
M Neolithic pottery	5	–	–	–	5
M Neolithic cave	–	–	1	–	1
L Neolithic pottery	5	–	–	–	5
L Neolithic cave	–	–	1	–	1
Copper Age pottery	3	–	–	–	3
Copper Age cave	–	–	2	–	2
Neo/CA stray finds	3 hoards 2 axes	1 axe	–	–	6
EBA pottery	1				
EBA cave	–	–	3		
EBA hoard	? 1				
EBA enclosure	–	–	–	1	1
EBA cairn/cairnfield	3	–			
LBA enclosures/hill-forts	5	4	1	4	14
LBA pottery	4	2	3	1	10
LBA cairn/cairnfield	16/7	2	–	1	19/7
LBA hoard/stray find	7	?1	1	2	11
Later Chipped Stone	20	9	5	6	40
EIA hill-fort	–	1	–	–	1
LIA hill-fort	9	4	1	4	18
EIA + LIA hill-fort	6	2	1	1	10
undated hill-fort	41	34	18	24	117
IA cairn/cairnfield	6	21	1	–	28
IA flat grave cemetery	5	–	–	–	5
IA isolated grave	3	1	–	1	5
LIA coin hoard	7	2	–	2	11
LIA stray find	6	–	2	5	13
Roman *colonia*	1	–	–	–	1
Roman *municipia*	6	–	–	–	6
Roman minor hill-forts	4	1	4	–	9
Roman centuriation	1	–	–	–	1
Roman farms	>30	>16	–	?1	>47
Ostrogothic cemetery	6	–	–	–	6
Avar finds	2	–	–	–	2
E Croatian cemetery	11	–	–	–	11

surface remains into those areas which reflect habitation and those which do not, it is proposed here to define as residential 'sites' those scatters whose value exceeds the mean value in the relevant time period. One further concept used in interpretation of surface remains is the 'settlement focus'. The focus is taken to mean locations defined by monuments and/or high-density scatters, as well as those surface remains discovered within a 1km radius of the centre of the focus. The only exception to the size of the focus territory as 1km radius is the Roman *municipium* of Nedinum, the largest site in the survey area, where a territory of 2km radius has been assigned. Thus, three key units of analysis – 'site', 'monument' and 'settlement focus' – provide the building blocks for an understanding of regional settlement pattern from the Neolithic to the Roman period (fig. 24).

Previous results

Previous research in north Dalmatia over the last century has yielded a sizeable crop of sites and monuments of all periods. The number of previous discoveries made within the study region is presented above (table 10).

Survey results

The settlement results of the NDP survey are summarized below (table 11).

The dated remains form the basis for a period-by-period summary of results. Each period description of the survey results includes an analysis of the settlement foci and their basic characteristics. In this overall interpretation, the aim is to compare and contrast the settlement foci and the monuments and sites which have led to their definition. Before summarizing the NDP survey results (see p. 58), the findings of the Southern Velebit Survey (S. Forenbaher and P. Vranjičan) are presented (cf. Forenbaher 1987). This survey represents the results of six seasons of judgemental reconnaissance and collection in the most important adjacent upland zone.

Table 11 Summary of NDP survey results by period

Period	Single finds	Findspots	Monuments	Monument-based settlement foci	Site-based settlement foci	Total sett foci
Palaeolithic	24	17	0	0	2	2
Neolithic/ Copper Age	18	22	0	0	6	6
Bronze Age	62	155	48	12	11	23
Iron Age	23	36	52	14	6	20
Roman	202	123	97	31	14	45
Medieval	37	22	15	9	0	9
Iška	86	35	0	0	0	0
Undated	61	113	443	0	0	0

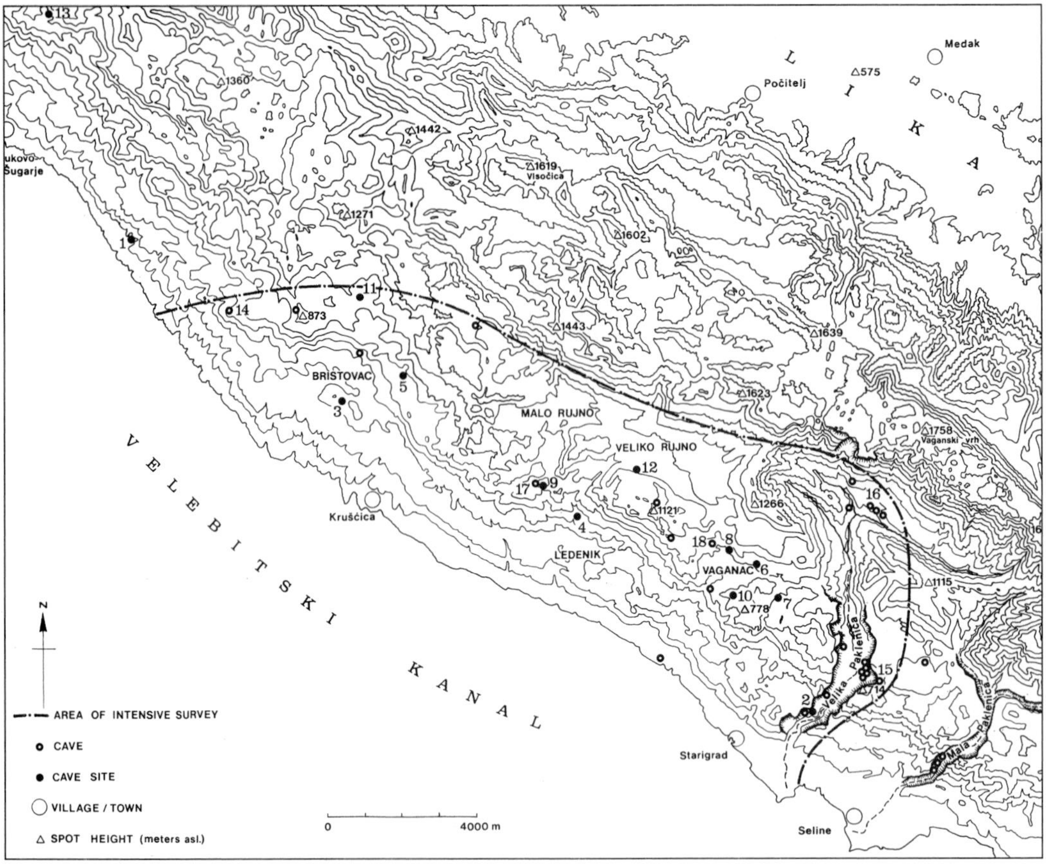

13
△1360
△1442
Medak
△575
Počitelj
L I K A
ukovo-
Šugarje
△1619
Visočica
△1271
△1602
1
11
14
△873
△1443
△1639
BRISTOVAC
5
3
△1623
MALO RUJNO
△1758
Vaganski vrh
VELIKO RUJNO
12
17 9
△1266
16
Kruščica
4
△1121
18 8
LEDENIK
VAGANAC 6
△1115
10
△778
7
VELEBITSKI KANAL
Velika Paklenica
15
2
Mala Paklenica
Starigrad
Seline

AREA OF INTENSIVE SURVEY
CAVE
CAVE SITE
VILLAGE / TOWN
SPOT HEIGHT (meters asl.)

0 4000 m

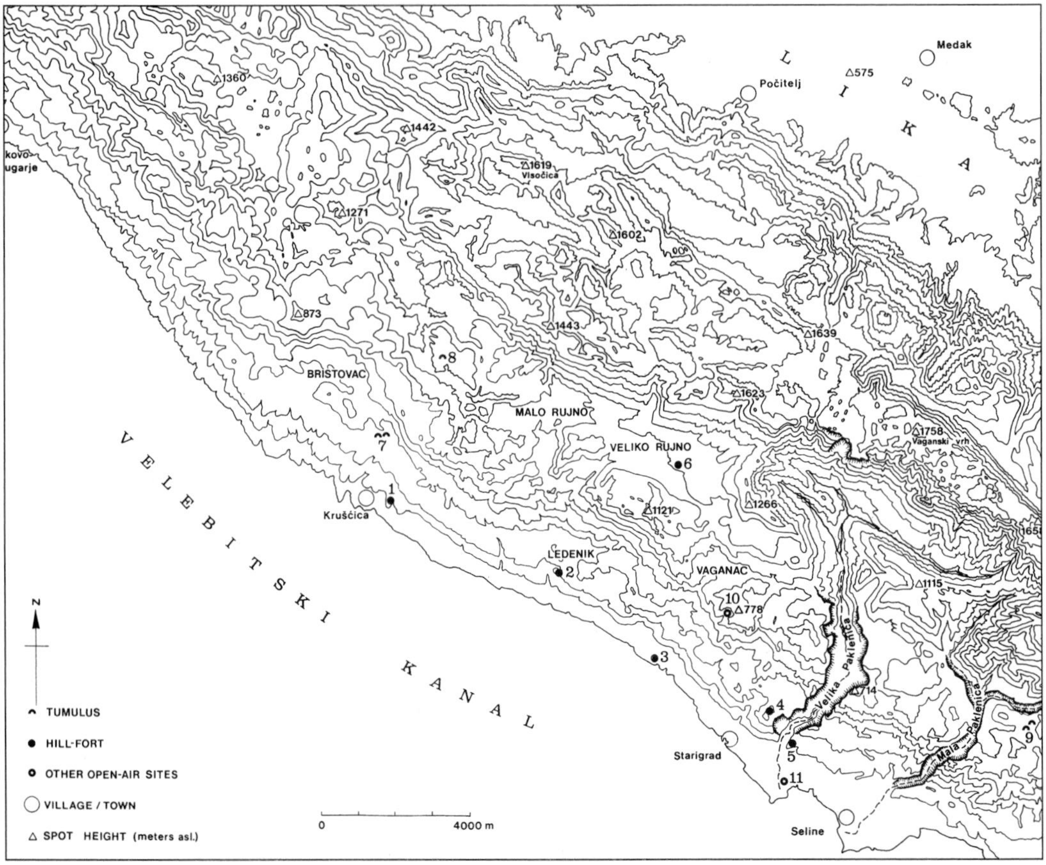

△1360
Medak
△575
Počitelj
L I K A
△1442
kovo-
ugarje
△1619
Visočica
△1271
△1602
△873
△1443
△1639

8
BRISTOVAC
△1623
MALO RUJNO
△1758
Vaganski vrh
VELIKO RUJNO

7
6
1
Kruščica
△1266
△1121
LEDENIK

2
VAGANAC
△1115

10
△778
VELEBITSKI KANAL
Velika Paklenica

3
△714
4
Mala Paklenica
9
Starigrad

5
11
Seline

TUMULUS
HILL-FORT
OTHER OPEN-AIR SITES
VILLAGE / TOWN
SPOT HEIGHT (meters asl.)
0 4000 m

Southern Velebit Survey (Mesolithic–Iron Age: figs. 25–7)

By S. Forenbaher and P. Vranjičan

> Survey of all caves and selected open-air sites in Southern Velebit Mountains up to 1000masl (1980–7). 41 caves surveyed; 13 with evidence of prehistoric occupation (figs. 25–6)

Open-air sites include: *Hill-forts*: concentration on first row of rocky hilltops inland from Velebitski Kanal (up to 200masl) (e.g. Sveta Trojica), but with exceptions as high as 925masl (e.g. Veliko Rujno, with Later Bronze and Iron Age occupation level). Most hill-forts have surface remains of Iron Age pottery; *Cairns*: according to Glavičić (1983), fewer than 20 cairns in 100km length of maritime side of Velebit: generally 10m in diameter, 2m high, with 1 cist grave inside: mostly Iron Age surface material; *Later chipped stone*: lithic scatter at Stapič-Dolac (fig. 27); *Stray finds*: Seline hoard, dated to Later Bronze Age (Batović 1965b).

25. *opposite above* Distribution of cave sites in the Southern Velebit Mountains

26. *opposite below* Distribution of other sites in the Southern Velebit Mountains

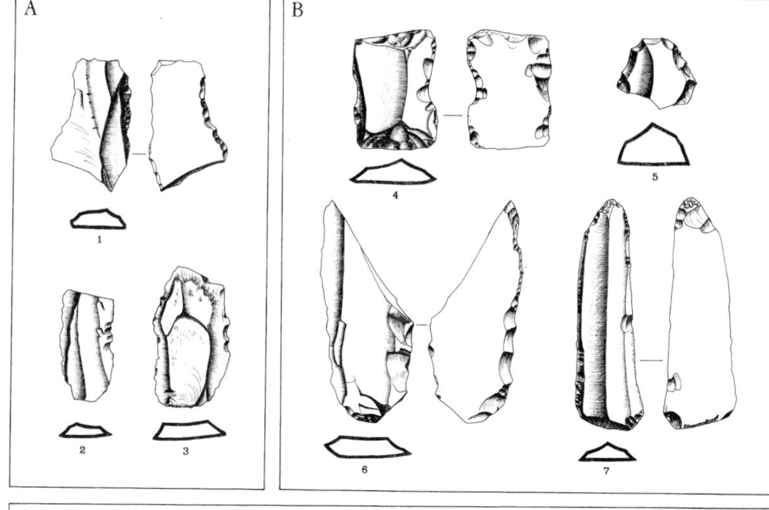

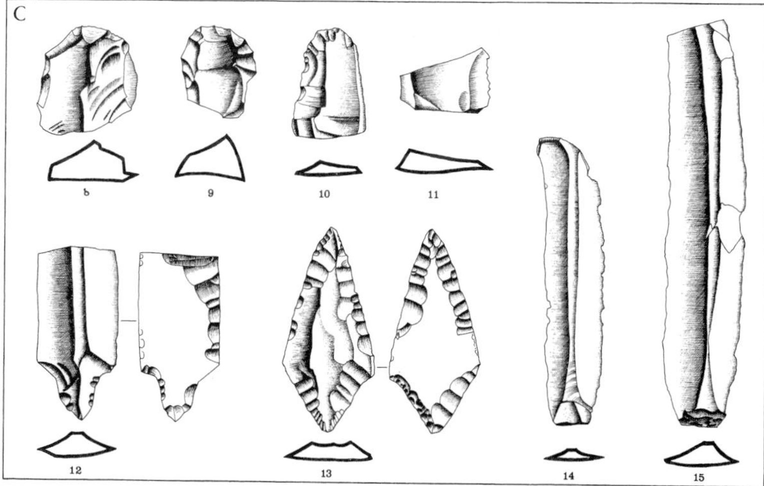

27. Lithic assemblages in the Southern Velebit Mountains

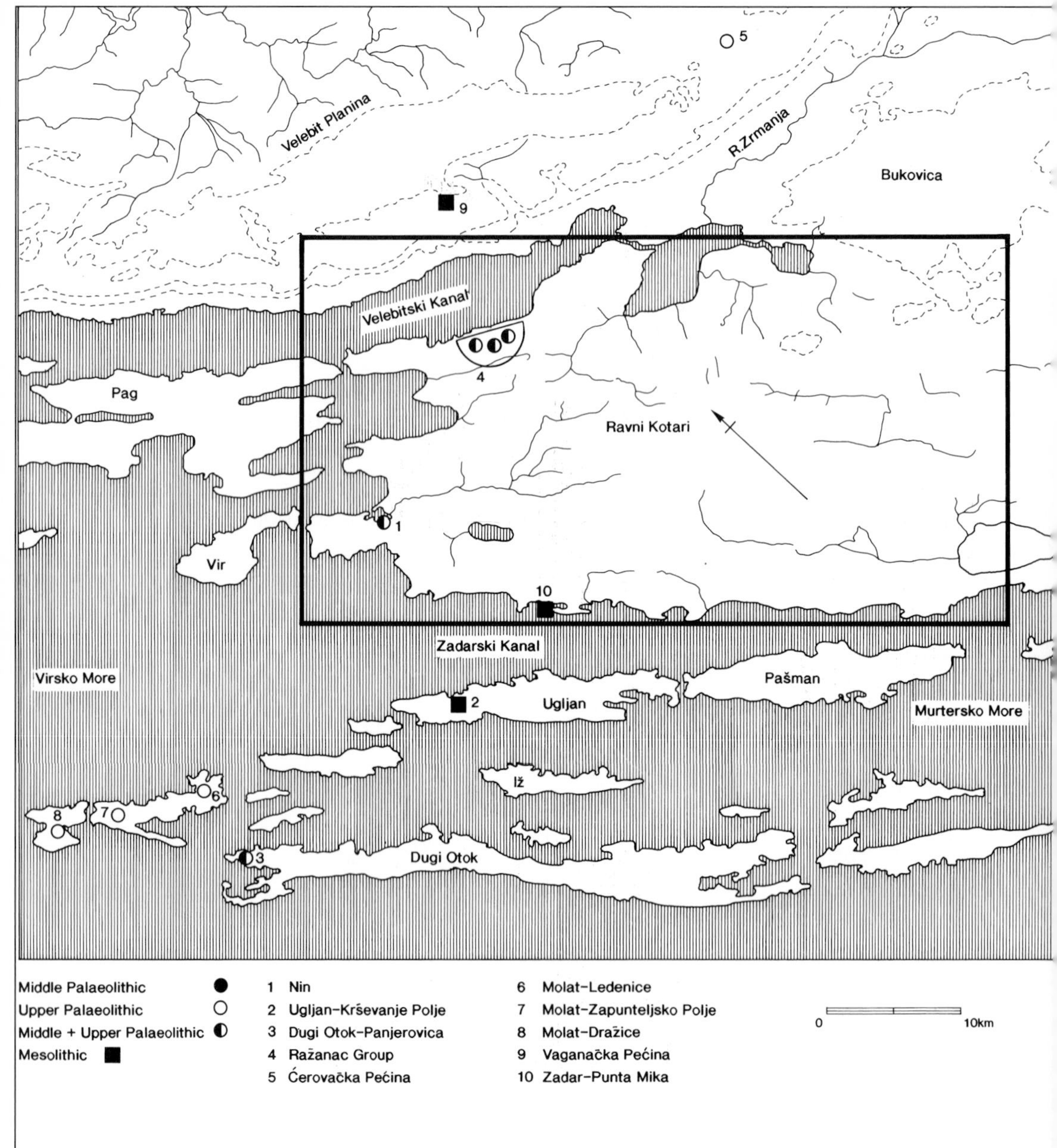

28. Previously known Palaeolithic and Mesolithic sites in the Study Region

The Palaeolithic (50,000–9000 Cal. BC. figs. 28–9)

Survey results: 44 findspots, represented by lithic scatters in 2 clusters: Mataci-Stojici Ridge and the Bay of Ljubac. All retouched pieces (5 per cent of assemblages) date to Middle Palaeolithic; lithics based on locally available pebble flint, with various reduction stages.

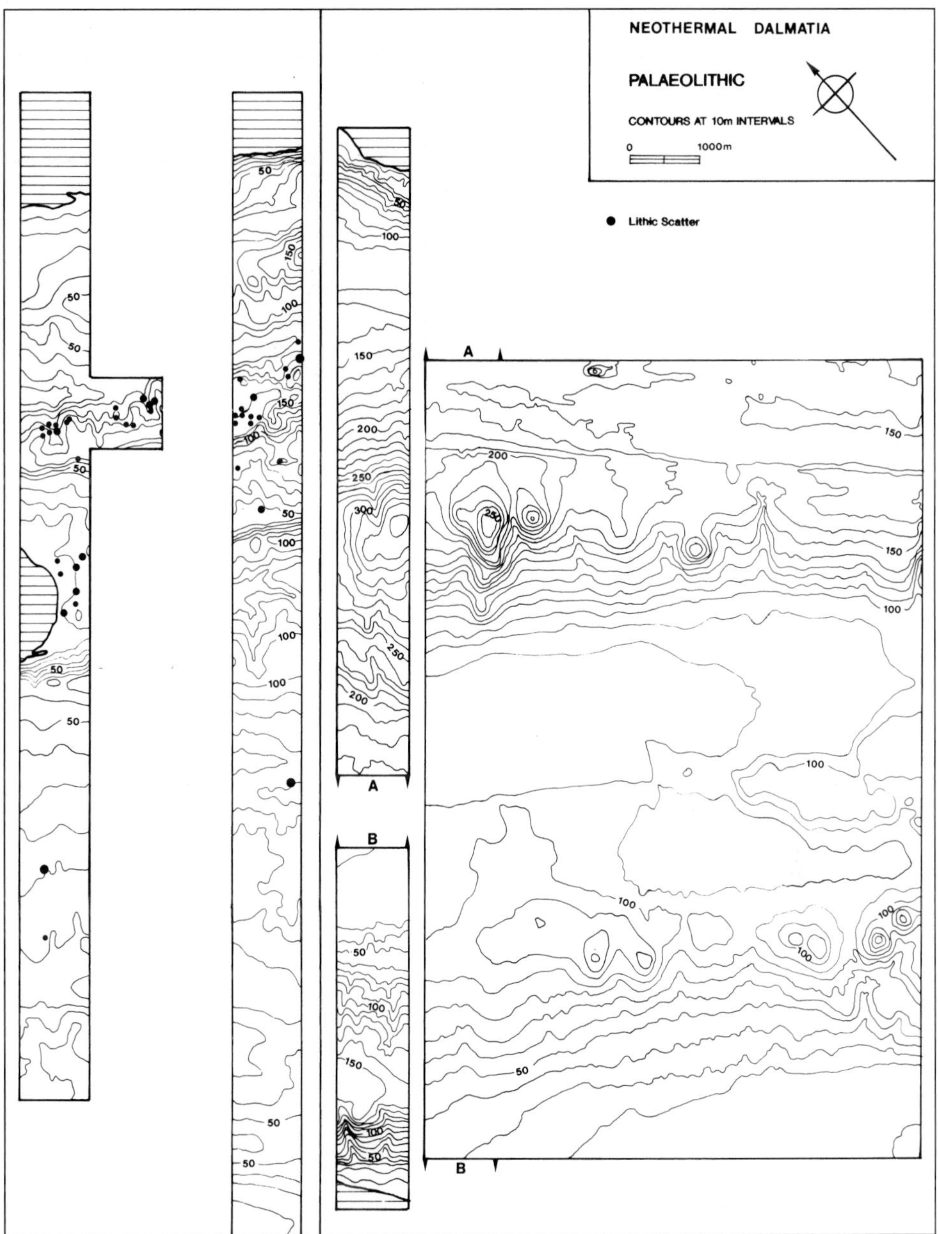

29. Palaeolithic remains in the Survey Area

The restriction of Palaeolithic flints and cherts to the Middle Palaeolithic period and the clustering of remains within 7km of usable pebble raw material on the Mataci-Stojici ridge (fig. 30) indicate a selection of both time and space which in itself is rather remarkable. Large areas of the north Dalmatian lowlands would

30. The Mataci-Stojići ridge, from the south-west

31. The Ljubac lowlands, from the Mataci-Stojići ridge, from north

have been at the least potential settlement zones for migratory hunter-gatherers, yet no remains were found in 80 per cent of the surveyed areas (cf. concentration of Palaeolithic finds in the Ražanac area: Batović 1965a). The depressed sea level current in the Upper Palaeolithic period would have converted the Ravni Kotari into a series of ranges of coastal hills from 300 to 650masl, with most of the survey block lying between 400 and 550masl and a coastline west of Dugi Otok (p.44). It is interesting that Upper Palaeolithic remains occur in profusion at the far higher site of Čerovačka pećina (Lika) but not on the intermediate slopes. In the Middle Palaeolithic, the chipping-floors on the Mataci-Stojici ridge represent opportunistic exploitation of the local low-quality pebble flint and chert. These sites would have been close to the current coastline, as would have been the Ljubac Bay cluster (fig. 31); the migration across the Velebit to Čerovačka pećina would have represented a two- to three-day walk, presumably in the early summer.

A final restriction, as much through palaeoenvironmental as archaeological evidence, is the lack of impact on the landscape of the hunter-gatherers in north Dalmatia. The absence of any human modification in the vegetation recorded by pollen diagrams in the Quaternary of Yugoslavia (Šercelj 1979) is suggestive of a human presence where the local landscape is settled and resources extracted in a low-intensity manner before resettlement elsewhere. The likelihood of low population densities in the Middle Palaeolithic implies, *pace* Wobst (1974, 1975, 1976), the existence of a large, open breeding network covering not only north Dalmatia but also Lika and perhaps central Dalmatia. Mobility was the key to the minimal exploitation of prized lithics and forest and marine resources, as well as maintenance of kinship relations in extensive breeding networks.

The Mesolithic (9000–6000 Cal. BC)

Survey results: no new sites or findspots

Three factors contribute to the elusiveness of the regional Mesolithic in north Dalmatia. First, large-scale sea-level changes affected the Adriatic Sea between 10,000 and 5000 Cal. BC, flooding many coastal sites (see p. 43). Secondly, post-Neolithic deposition of >1m of sediments has covered areas of Bottomland in the valleys (see p. 32), a zone potentially attractive to foraging groups. Thirdly, the absence of retouched artefacts diagnostic of the Mesolithic period inhibits the identification of dated sites. There are two components to this problem: those geometric microliths which characterize the Mesolithic in much of Europe (Rozoy 1989) are dated from the Mesolithic to the Bronze Age in north Dalmatia. The remaining finds are part of a lithic 'Dark Age' which, in other regions of Europe, is explained by a decline in the need for maintainable and reliable tools in the face of increasing subsistence security and predictability (Myers 1989; Torrence 1989).

The most likely settlement pattern in the Mesolithic period, therefore, is an extension of the Upper Palaeolithic seasonal pattern of winter–spring occupation on the now-flooded coastal plains and summer–autumn occupations in the lush pastures of the Velebit uplands. The evidence for the summer–autumn phase comes solely from the Velebit cave of Vaganačka pećina, where the thick layer of marine molluscs demonstrates movement between coast and hills. The possibility of wild caprine bones amongst the fauna from the cave's occupation level raises interesting possibilities of local domestication, but contrasts with Geddes' (1985) argument against native caprine populations in the central and west Mediterranean. The selectivity of settlement zones in the Mesolithic appears to exceed even that of the Upper Palaeolithic but geomorphological factors probably distort this interpretation. As with the Palaeolithic, there is no evidence either way for any anthropogenic modification of the vegetation in this period.

The Neolithic and Copper Age (6000–2400 Cal. BC*: figs. 32–6)*

> Survey results: 42 findspots in 6 settlement foci: Early Neolithic Tinj, Early–Middle Neolithic Kamenta, Late Neolithic–Copper Age Miljovići, Early Neolithic Jagodnja, Copper Age Nadin-Vratarica and Early–Middle Neolithic Kula Atlagić (fig. 35); short-term use of coastal cave of Buta Jama (fig. 36). 9 findspots between settlement foci. 11 dated findspots with Later Chipped Stone, with a total of 27 per cent of retouched pieces and no cores.

Given the absence of Mesolithic data, the origins of farming in the study region are a matter of uncertainty. Perhaps the clearest indicator of continuity of settlement is provided by the Velebit site of Vaganačka pećina, where short-term, perhaps seasonal, occupations recur in each period from the Mesolithic until the Late Copper Age.

The continuity in use of Velebit caves, repeated throughout the Neolithic and Copper Age, is paralleled by the use of open-air domestic sites in these periods. However, domestic space is partitioned as early as the Early Neolithic into two classes of site, the nucleated site and the dispersed site (table 12).

While dissimilar in scale from the dispersed tells and nucleated villages in temperate south-east Europe (Chapman 1989), there is a contrast between dispersed and nucleated settlements in the Dalmatian Neolithic and Copper Age. At one end of the continuum, we find the concentration of all settlement activity into a small segment of the landscape (e.g. 1.25ha at Tinj), at the other, the dispersion of settlement activities over a far wider area (e.g. the 5–10ha site of Miljovići). This latter resembles the Extended Village concept of a village of relatively scattered houses with a central focus (Howell 1983).

Away from the main settlements, a low density of non-site discard is

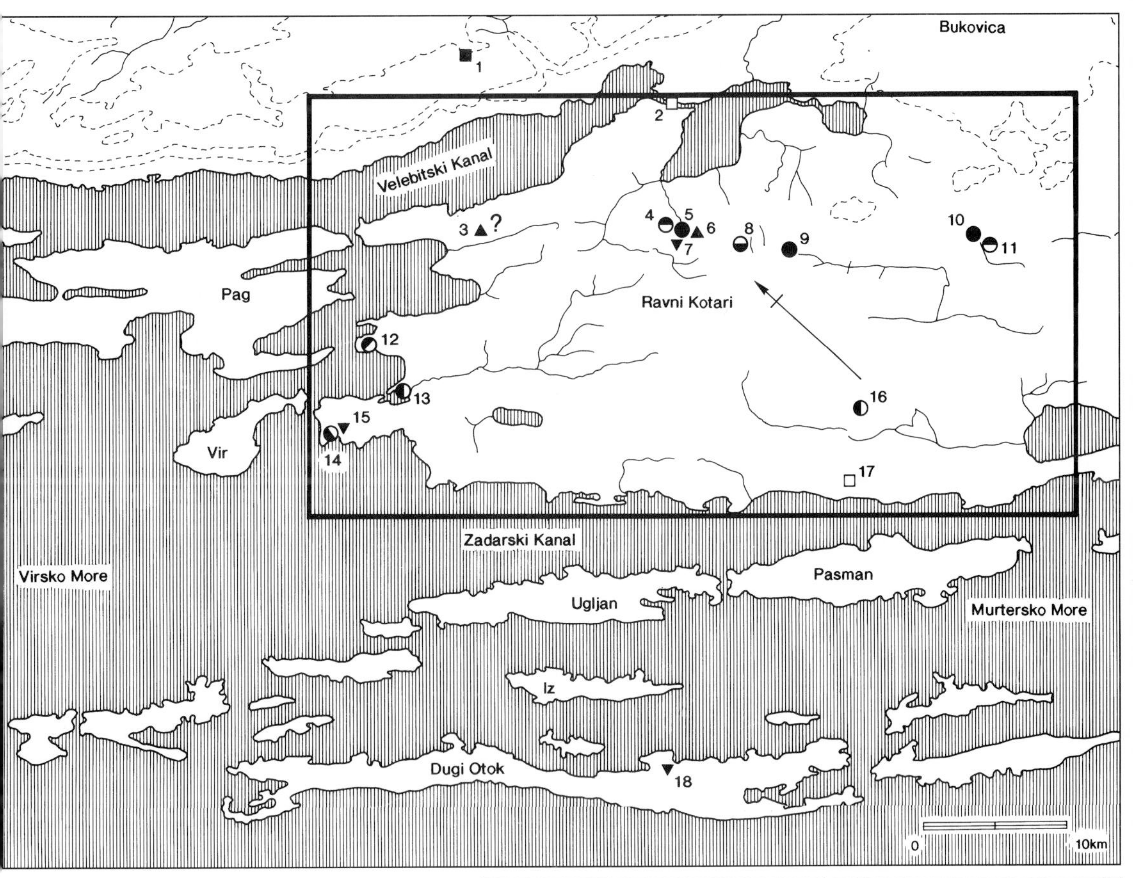

32. Previously known Neolithic and Copper Age sites in the Study Region

Table 12 Classes of Neolithic and Copper Age settlement

Dispersed settlement	Early Neolithic Jagodnja Late Neolithic/Copper Age Miljovići
Nucleated settlement	Early Neolithic Tinj Early–?Middle Neolithic Kamenta Late Neolithic Stapić Copper Age Nadin-Vratarica
Cave settlement	Early Neolithic–Copper Age Vaganačka pećina Early Neolithic Buta Jama Late Neolithic Pažjanice and Stolačká peć

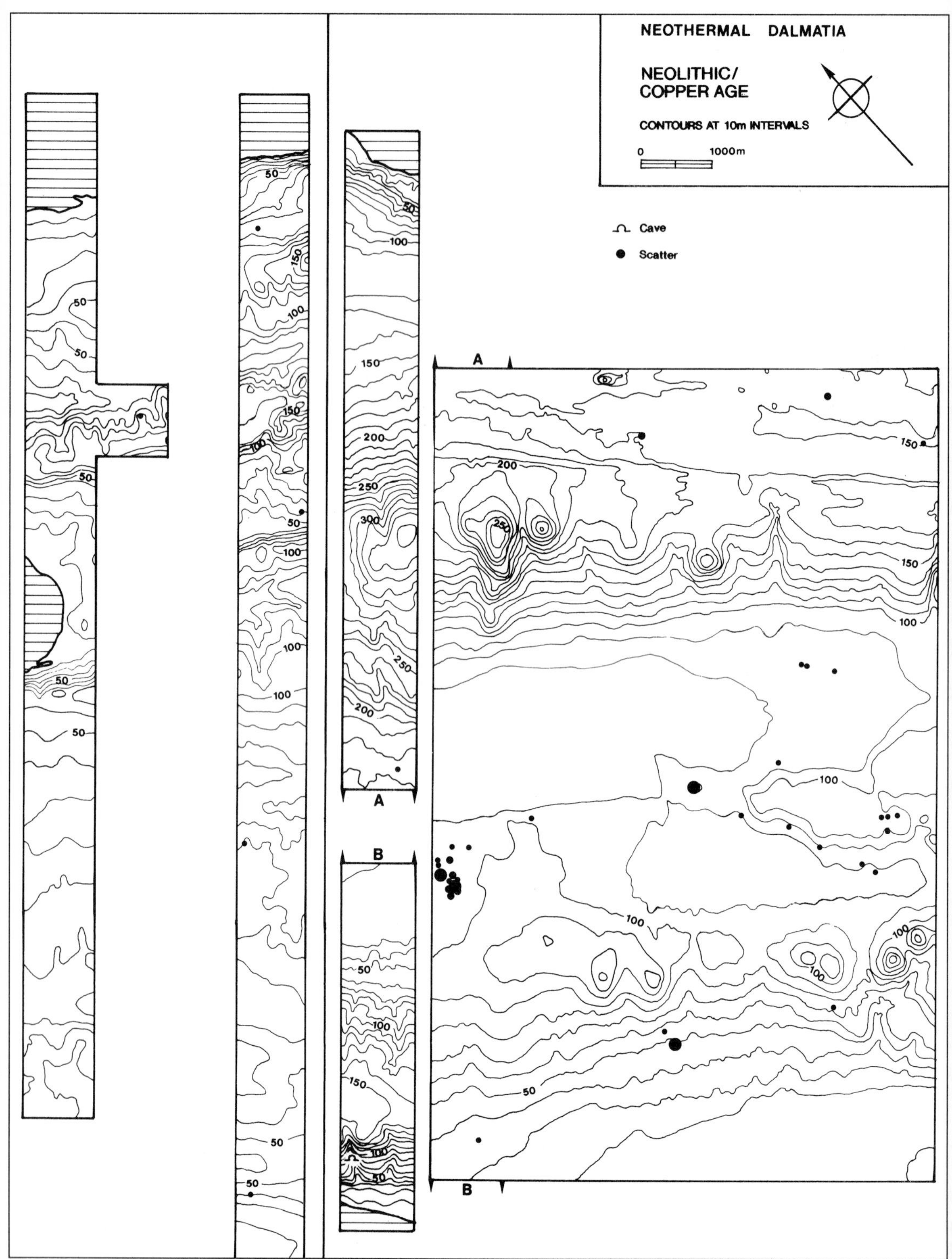

33. Neolithic and Copper Age remains in the Survey Area

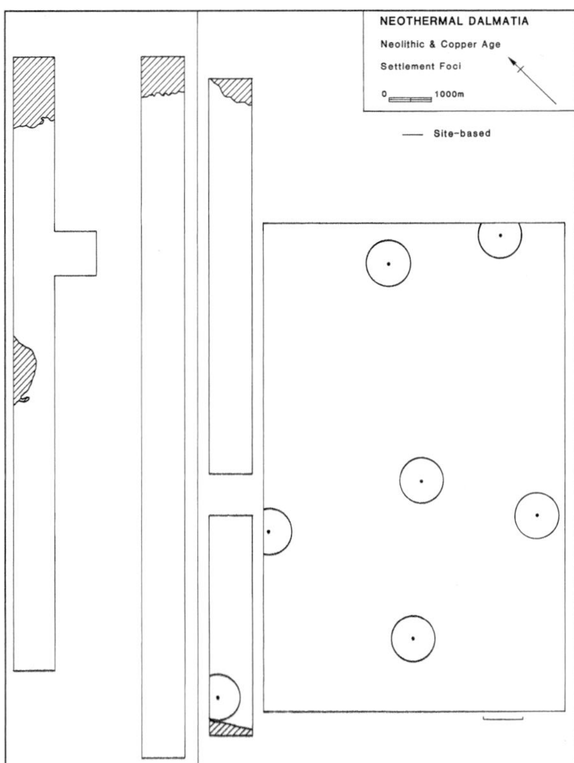

34. Neolithic and Copper Age settlement foci in the Survey Area

35. Kula Atlagić, from north-east, looking across Benkovac Trough to Nadin Ridge; site by spoil heap in centre

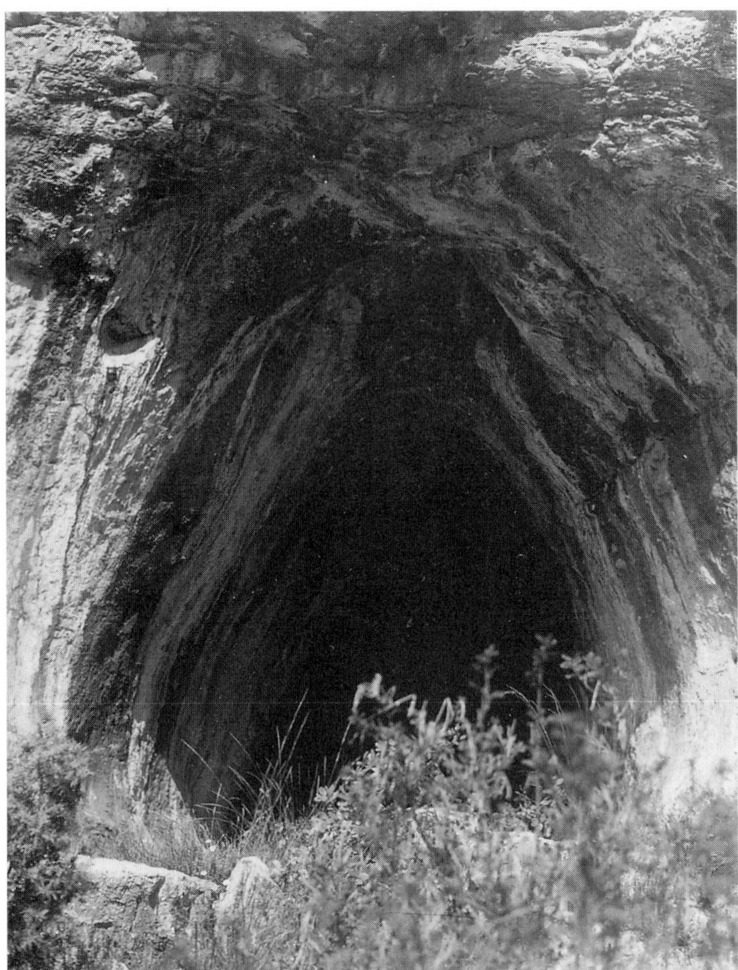

36. Buta Jama, from south-east

encountered. While some of this 'background noise' occurs close to the six settlement foci defined in the lowlands for this long period, several single finds lie some distance from any focus (including perforated polished stone axes on the lower slopes of the Velebit). There can be no doubt that the higher densities of population in the early farming periods led to smaller and more compact breeding networks, where the importance for exchange increased concomitantly with a greater degree of sedentism. Except in the Early Neolithic, however, the settlement network appears to have been rather thin. In this period, the mean distance between sites was 5km, assuming contemporaneity at some point in a period of 500 years. In the Middle and Late Neolithic and the Copper Age, settlement foci were so few that interaction networks appear thin and poorly developed. A singular absence of socio-economic development appears to characterize much of the fifth to third millennia Cal. BC in this area.

The Bronze Age (2400–800 Cal. BC: figs. 37–42)

Survey results: 155 findspots and 48 monuments, grouped into 23 settlement foci (11 site-based, 12 monument-based). Monuments clustered into 7 topographical units: *Mataci-Stojići Ridge:* (a) 3 Later Bronze Age enclosed settlements with internal cairns and linear features (1 surveyed and excavated: see Chapters 4 and 7), (b) a linear cairnfield of over 100 Bronze–Iron Age cairns, (c) 55 findspots between (a) and (b), with Later Bronze Age pottery and lithic remains (on-site blank and tool production, with 4 per cent retouched pieces). *Bokanjac Ridge:* hill-fort with internal cairn. *Pridraga hillslope:* (a) cairnfield of Later Bronze Age cairns, (b) Later Bronze Age linear feature dividing cairnfield, (c) 12 Later Bronze Age pot scatters on the periphery of (a), (d) 6 limestone cists, north of (a) (fig. 41). *Nadin Ridge:* (a) Vijenac hill-fort (main enclosure with central cairn, subsidiary enclosure, and terraces, (b) Čauševica farmstead (4 linked enclosures, with cairns, structures and trackways), (c) Kutlovica hill-fort (single rampart with interior scooped houses). *Prtenjača Ridge* (fig. 42): (a) Mutvica hill-fort (single rampart), (b) Strkovača hill-fort (?double rampart with central cairn), (c) Kruglas hill-fort (single rampart, internal structures on terraces and rock-cut approach track to south gate; extensive off-site discard to south-west). *Tinj Ridge:* (a) Polača-Dražice (field system with linear drystone wall 1.23km in length and cairns), (b) Muvača hill-fort (single enclosure wall with small field and cairns, with cairns and linear features on adjoining summit), (c) Vinculja hill-fort (single rampart, with internal structures on terrace). *Vrana Valley:* the Kakma-Mitrovići cairnfield (193 cairns in area of 4 sq km, 8 dated to Bronze Age, some juxtaposed with linear features to form ?field systems). *Other:* 11 site-based foci (7 pottery scatters, 1 pot scatter with Linear Feature, 1 pot scatter with cairns, 1 cairn with high density of pottery, 1 drystone enclosure with pottery.

The relatively low proportion of the landscape intensively utilized by Neolithic and Copper Age groups in north Dalmatia gives rise to an impression of widespread colonization of land in the succeeding Bronze Age. Hillslopes, ridge tops and hilltops were settled, seemingly for the first time, and occupation continued in the main valleys of the Ravni Kotari.

Before the NDP, it was clear that the Bronze Age was characterized by a greater variety of archaeological remains. Known site classes included *gradine* (comprising both enclosed sites and hill-forts), open sites, caves, hoards, tumuli, barrows and flat cist graves (Batović 1983; Čović 1983a). All of these site classes were known from the Earlier Bronze Age but in small numbers and from only certain areas. Evidence for the first use of large cairnfields comes from the Ravni Kotari only (Nin: Batović 1968a), while gradine appear to begin in the Bukovica (e.g. Medvidje-Gradina: Batović 1987). In the Later Bronze Age, larger numbers of each

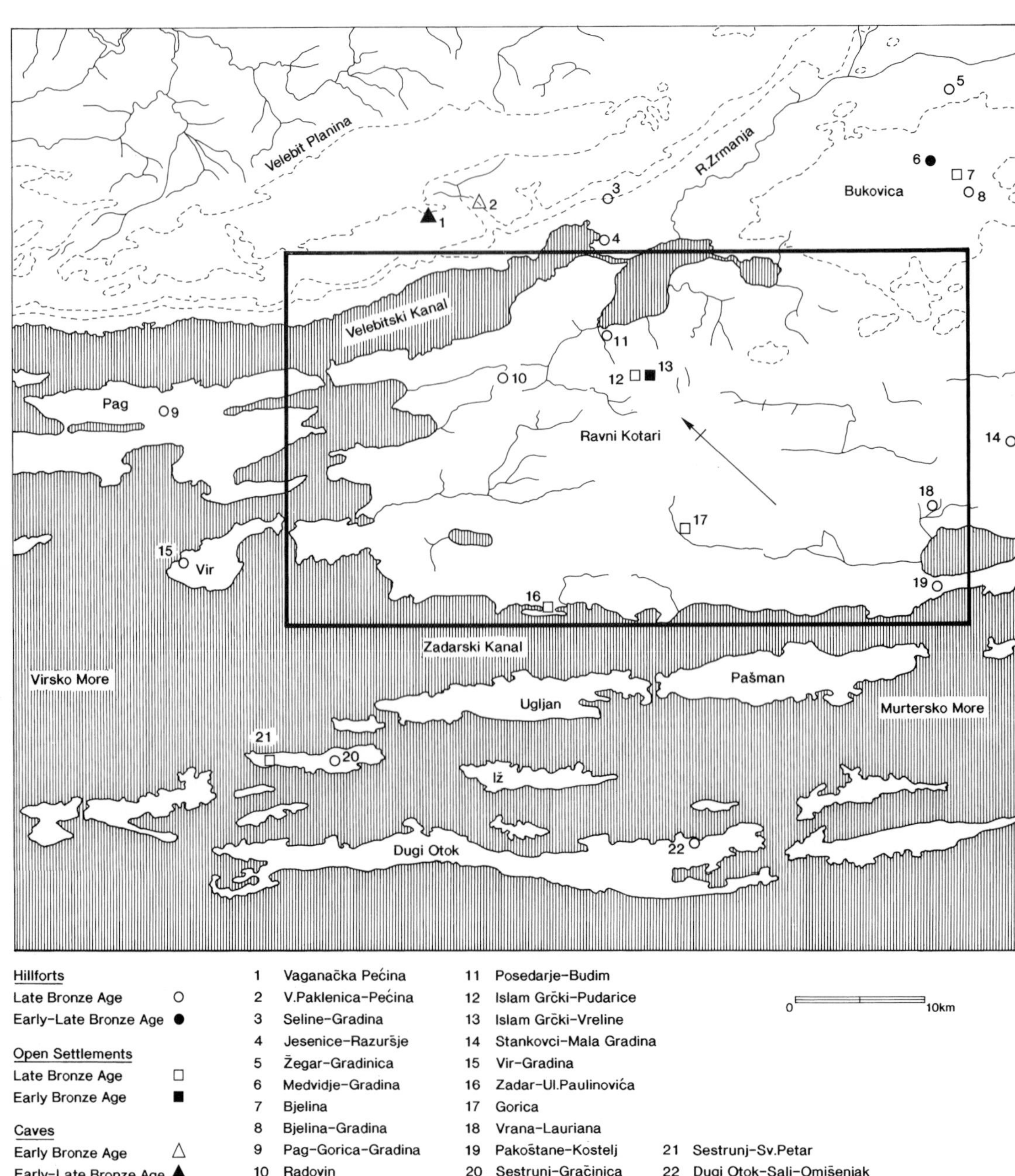

37. Previously known Bronze Age settlements in the Study Region

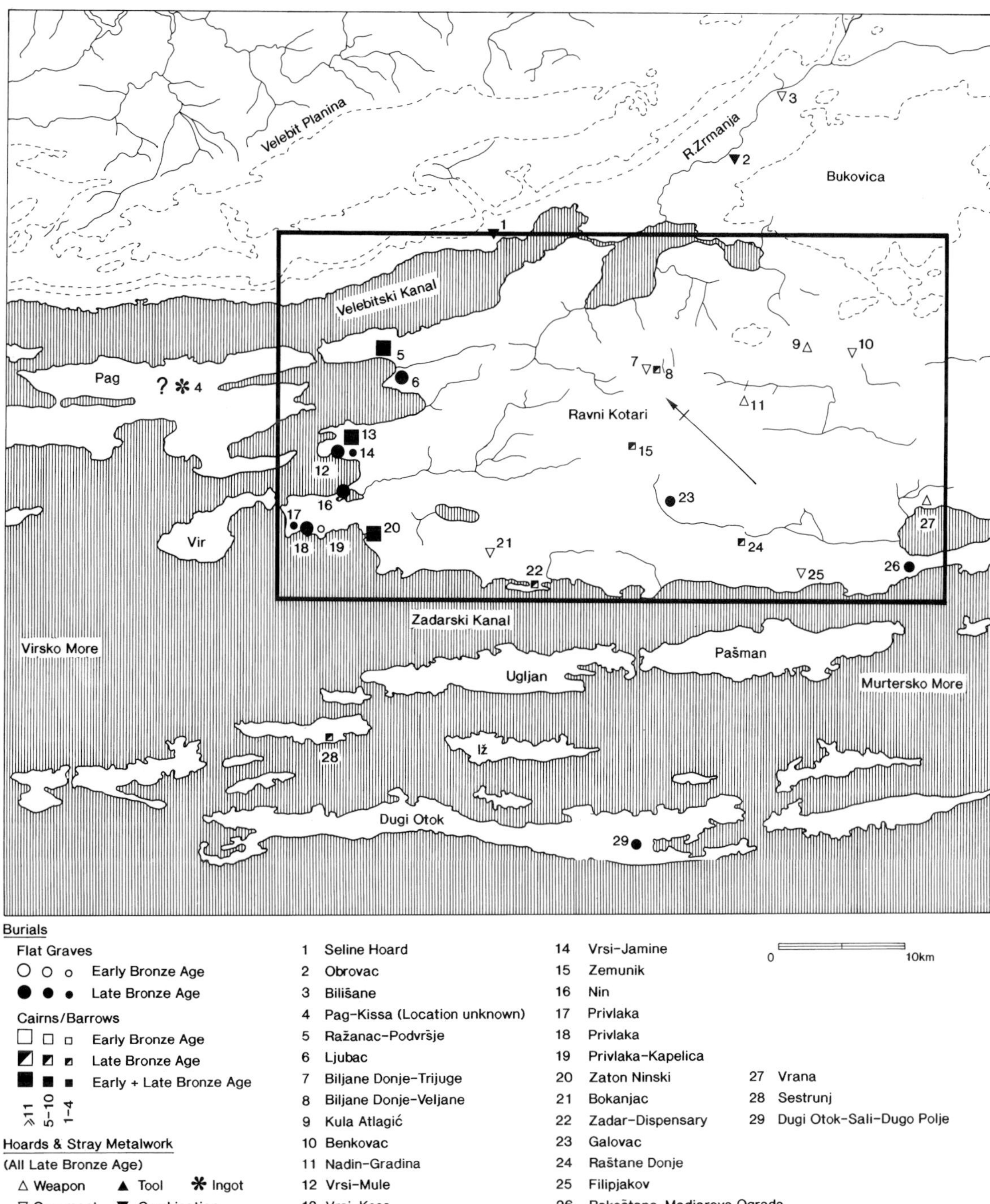
Velebit Planina
R.Zrmanja
Bukovica
Velebitski Kanal
Pag
Ravni Kotari
Vir
Zadarski Kanal
Virsko More
Pašman
Ugljan
Murtersko More
Iž
Dugi Otok
Burials
Flat Graves
Early Bronze Age
Late Bronze Age
Cairns/Barrows
Early Bronze Age
Late Bronze Age
Early + Late Bronze Age
≥11
5–10
1–4
Hoards & Stray Metalwork
(All Late Bronze Age)
Weapon
Tool
Ingot
Ornament
Combination
1 Seline Hoard
2 Obrovac
3 Bilišane
4 Pag-Kissa (Location unknown)
5 Ražanac-Podvršje
6 Ljubac
7 Biljane Donje-Trijuge
8 Biljane Donje-Veljane
9 Kula Atlagić
10 Benkovac
11 Nadin-Gradina
12 Vrsi-Mule
13 Vrsi-Kosa
14 Vrsi-Jamine
15 Zemunik
16 Nin
17 Privlaka
18 Privlaka
19 Privlaka-Kapelica
20 Zaton Ninski
21 Bokanjac
22 Zadar-Dispensary
23 Galovac
24 Raštane Donje
25 Filipjakov
26 Pakoštane-Madjarova Ograda
27 Vrana
28 Sestrunj
29 Dugi Otok-Sali-Dugo Polje
0
10km

38. Previously known Bronze Age burials and hoards in the Study Region

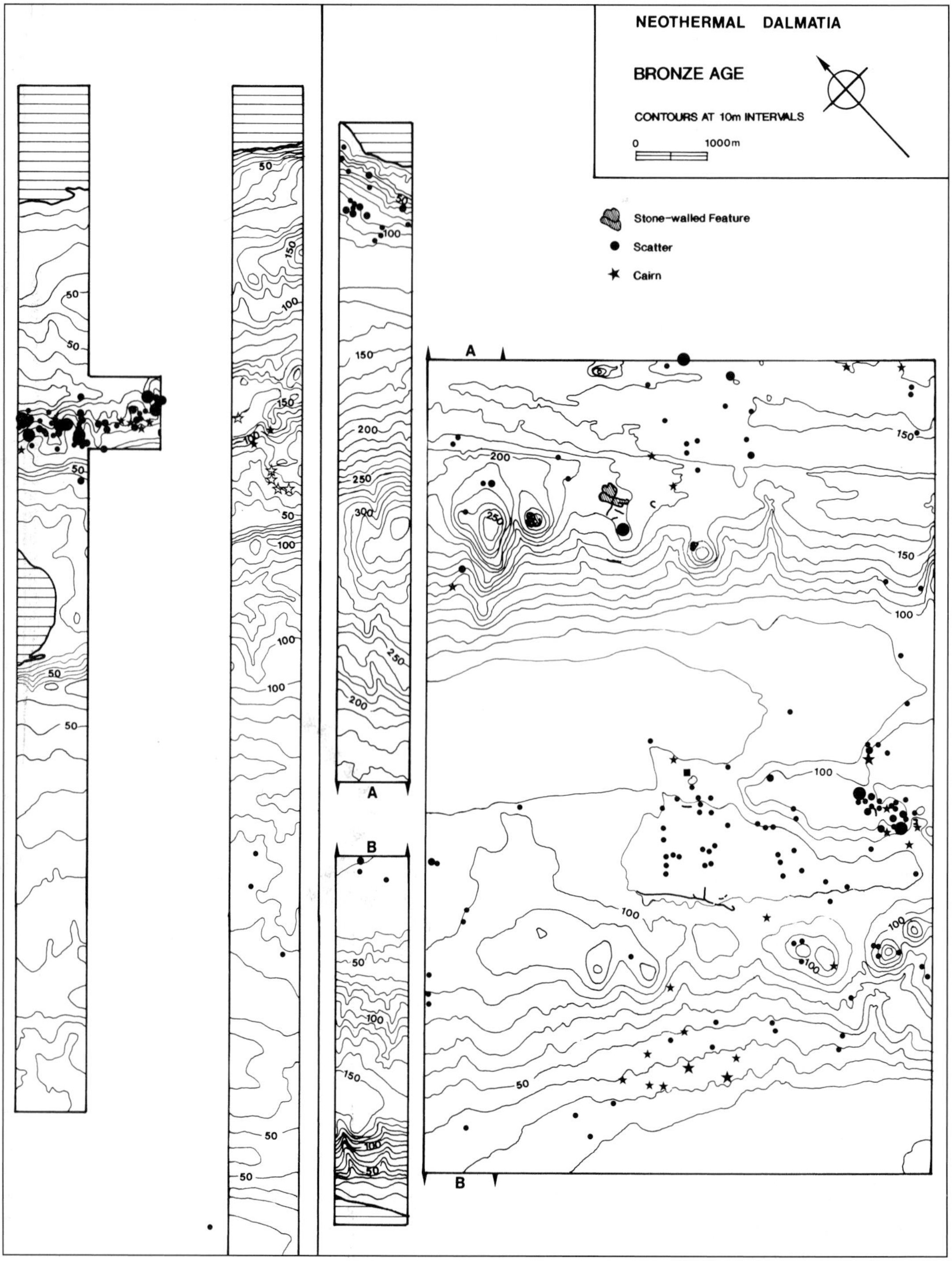

39. Bronze Age remains in the Survey Area

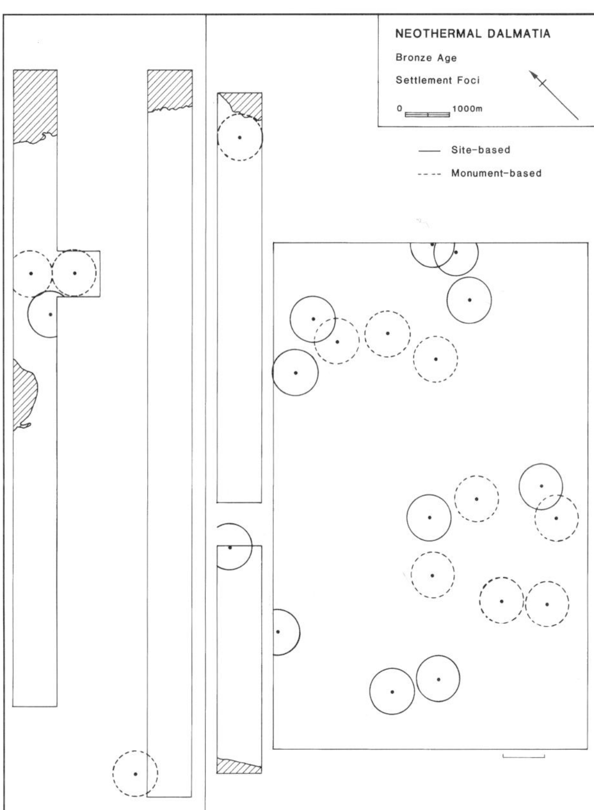

40. Bronze Age settlement foci in the Survey Area

41. Cairns on natural terraces at Pridraga, above Karinsko More, from south-west

42. Prtenjača Ridge, from Vinculja, from south; second from left: Mutvica; extreme left: Strkovača

site class appear and in each zone of the study region. Thus the elements of the pattern had been identified, but what was not clear was the diversity of the patterns composed of the various elements. The primacy of stone in Bronze Age monument-building leads to an extraordinary variety of remains, created by combination and re-combination of a relatively small number of basic elements (table 13). If the Iron Age is, *pace* Neustupny (1977), 'the time of the hill-forts', then the Bronze Age in the Mediterranean is 'the time of stone monuments'.

It should be noted that, three 'simple' hill-forts apart, every major Bronze Age focus has a different monumental combination from every other focus. Yet the scale of monument construction is of a kind, perhaps an indication of groups whose size and complexity is not markedly different. On another spatial scale, Bronze Age settlement foci can be grouped into similar classes of settlement as those of the Neolithic and Copper Age: those foci which are more nucleated and those which are more dispersed.

The variation in domestic settlement space is noted on Velebit as much as in the plains. It takes the form of continued occupation of caves such as Vaganačka pećina and the construction of new open sites such as the high-level Veliko Rujno and new hill-forts such as the high-level Kruščica and the lower-level Marašovići. However, the Southern Velebit landscape differs from the Ravni Kotari in its

Table 13 Bronze Age settlement foci by monument class

	Drystone feature					
Settlement foci	Linear feature	Cairn	Cairn field	Field system	Enclosure	Hill-fort
Kakma-Mitrovići	*	–	*	*	–	–
Pridraga	*	–	*	–	–	–
Čauševica	*	*	–	*	*	–
Polača-Dražice	*	*	–	*	–	–
Mataci	*	*	*	–	*	–
Strkovača/Kruglas	*	*	–	–	–	**
Vijenac	–	*	–	–	–	*
Kutlovica	–	–	–	–	–	*
Bokanjac	–	*	–	–	–	*
Muvača	*	*	–	–	–	*
Mutvica	–	–	–	–	–	*
Vinculja	–	–	–	–	–	*

apparent paucity of cairns. This decreases the potential combinations and recombinations of drystone features in the mountain zone.

The increased number of settlement foci, both on the Ravni Kotari and on the Velebit Mountains, generates a denser interaction network, whether for breeding purposes or for access to exotic prestige materials, such as bronze, copper or tin. The location of some of the Velebit sites implies seasonal occupation, so there is a presumption of vertical summer movement from the coastal plain and/or from Lika. In the main lowland survey block, the mean distance between the twenty-three settlement foci was 6.8km, indicating a wider spread of settlements than in previous periods, as well as the possibility for more intensive interaction across the whole lowland area.

The Iron Age (800–15 BC: figs. 43–51)

Survey results: 36 findspots and 52 monuments, grouped in 20 settlement foci (14 monument-based, 6 site-based). Foci clustered into 7 topographic units, all but one used in the Bronze Age. *Mataci-Stojici Ridge*: continued use of linear cairnfield, with small-scale lithic production. *Bokanjac Ridge:* continued use of hill-fort. *Nadin Ridge* (fig. 47): (a) Krizova Glava hill-fort (?single rampart), (b) Nadin-Gradina (fig. 48) (single rampart of 'megalithic' blocks, with external occupation on terraces), (c) Vijenac hill-fort (continues in use), (d) Kutlovica hill-fort (still in use: fig. 49). *Prtenjača Ridge:* (a) Kamenta hill-fort (small site with ?rampart, possibly a look-out fort), (b) Mutvica hill-fort (continues in use), (c) Smiljevac hill-fort (single rampart with central cairn and one terrace), (d) Kruglas hill-fort (continues in use, with relatively high off-site discard). *Tinj Ridge:* (a) Tinj hill-fort (badly damaged; ?ditch sector surviving), (b) Muvača (cairns still in use), (c) Vinculja hill-fort (continues in use), (d) Trojan hill-fort (defences of drystone wall, megalithic wall and rampart on

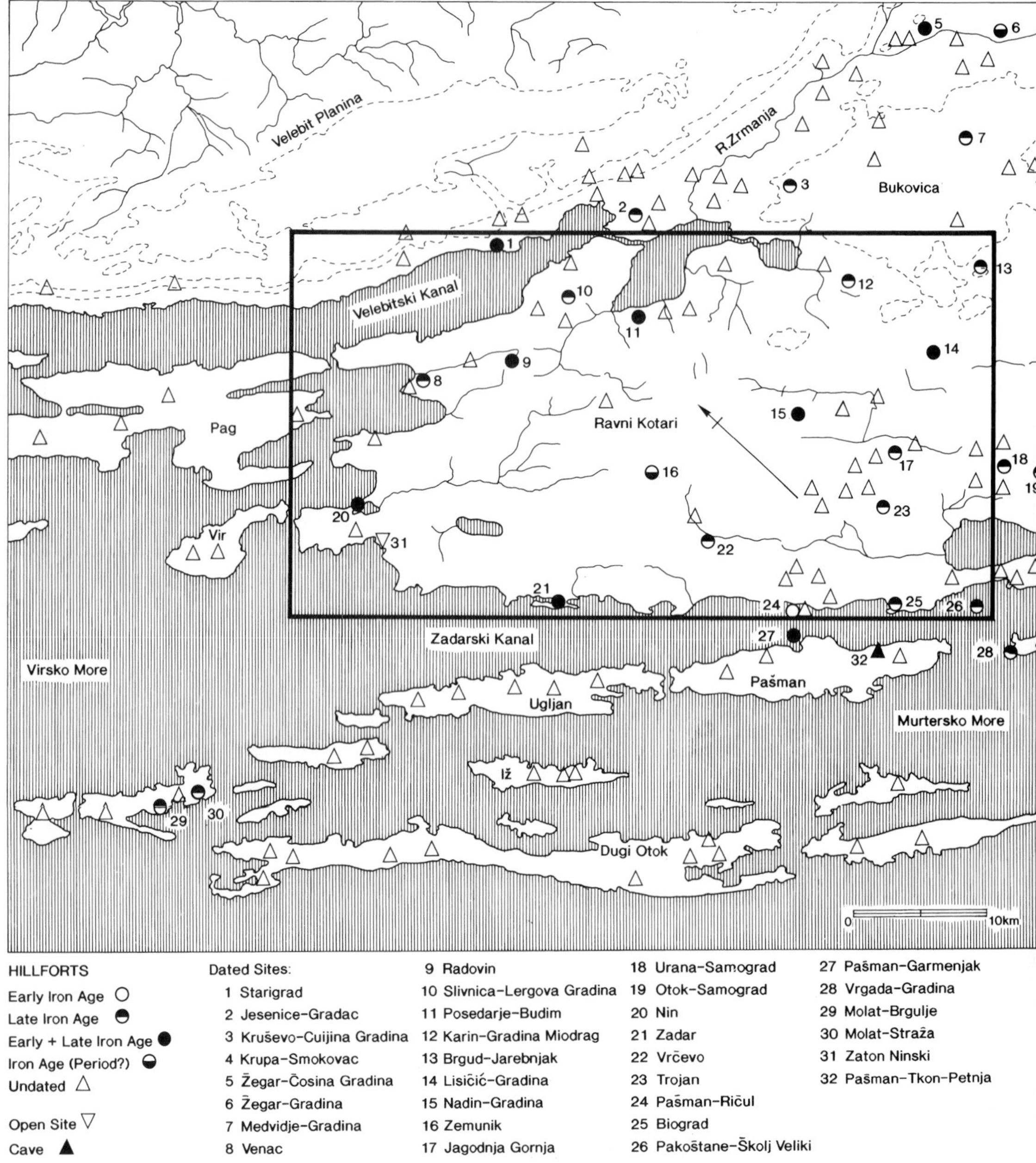

Velebit Planina
R.Zrmanja
Bukovica
Velebitski Kanal
Pag
Ravni Kotari
Vir
Zadarski Kanal
Virsko More
Pašman
Ugljan
Murtersko More
Iž
Dugi Otok
0
10km
HILLFORTS
Early Iron Age
Late Iron Age
Early + Late Iron Age
Iron Age (Period?)
Undated
Open Site
Cave
Dated Sites:
1 Starigrad
2 Jesenice-Gradac
3 Kruševo-Cuijina Gradina
4 Krupa-Smokovac
5 Žegar-Čosina Gradina
6 Žegar-Gradina
7 Medvidje-Gradina
8 Venac
9 Radovin
10 Slivnica-Lergova Gradina
11 Posedarje-Budim
12 Karin-Gradina Miodrag
13 Brgud-Jarebnjak
14 Lisičić-Gradina
15 Nadin-Gradina
16 Zemunik
17 Jagodnja Gornja
18 Urana-Samograd
19 Otok-Samograd
20 Nin
21 Zadar
22 Vrčevo
23 Trojan
24 Pašman-Ričul
25 Biograd
26 Pakoštane-Školj Veliki
27 Pašman-Garmenjak
28 Vrgada-Gradina
29 Molat-Brgulje
30 Molat-Straža
31 Zaton Ninski
32 Pašman-Tkon-Petnja

43. Previously known Iron Age settlements in the Study Region

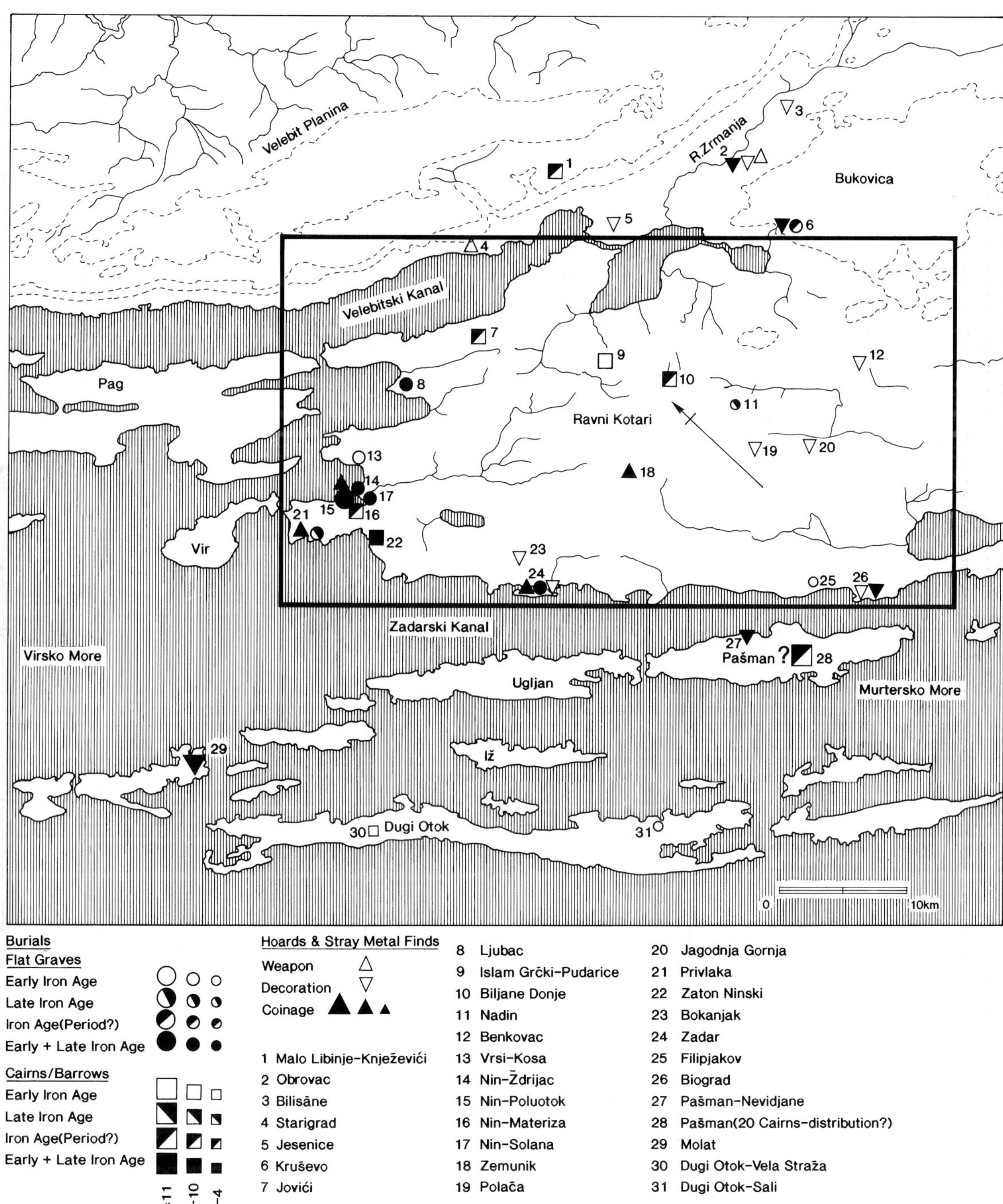
Velebit Planina
R.Zrmanja
Bukovica
Velebitski Kanal
Pag
Ravni Kotari
Vir
Zadarski Kanal
Virsko More
Pašman
Ugljan
Murtersko More
Iž
Dugi Otok
0
10km
Burials
Flat Graves
Early Iron Age
Late Iron Age
Iron Age(Period?)
Early + Late Iron Age
Cairns/Barrows
Early Iron Age
Late Iron Age
Iron Age(Period?)
Early + Late Iron Age
≥11
5–10
1–4
Hoards & Stray Metal Finds
Weapon
Decoration
Coinage
1 Malo Libinje-Knježevići
2 Obrovac
3 Bilisâne
4 Starigrad
5 Jesenice
6 Kruševo
7 Jovići
8 Ljubac
9 Islam Grčki-Pudarice
10 Biljane Donje
11 Nadin
12 Benkovac
13 Vrsi-Kosa
14 Nin-Ždrijac
15 Nin-Poluotok
16 Nin-Materiza
17 Nin-Solana
18 Zemunik
19 Polača
20 Jagodnja Gornja
21 Privlaka
22 Zaton Ninski
23 Bokanjak
24 Zadar
25 Filipjakov
26 Biograd
27 Pašman-Nevidjane
28 Pašman(20 Cairns-distribution?)
29 Molat
30 Dugi Otok-Vela Straža
31 Dugi Otok-Sali

44. Previously known Iron Age burials and hoards in the Study Region

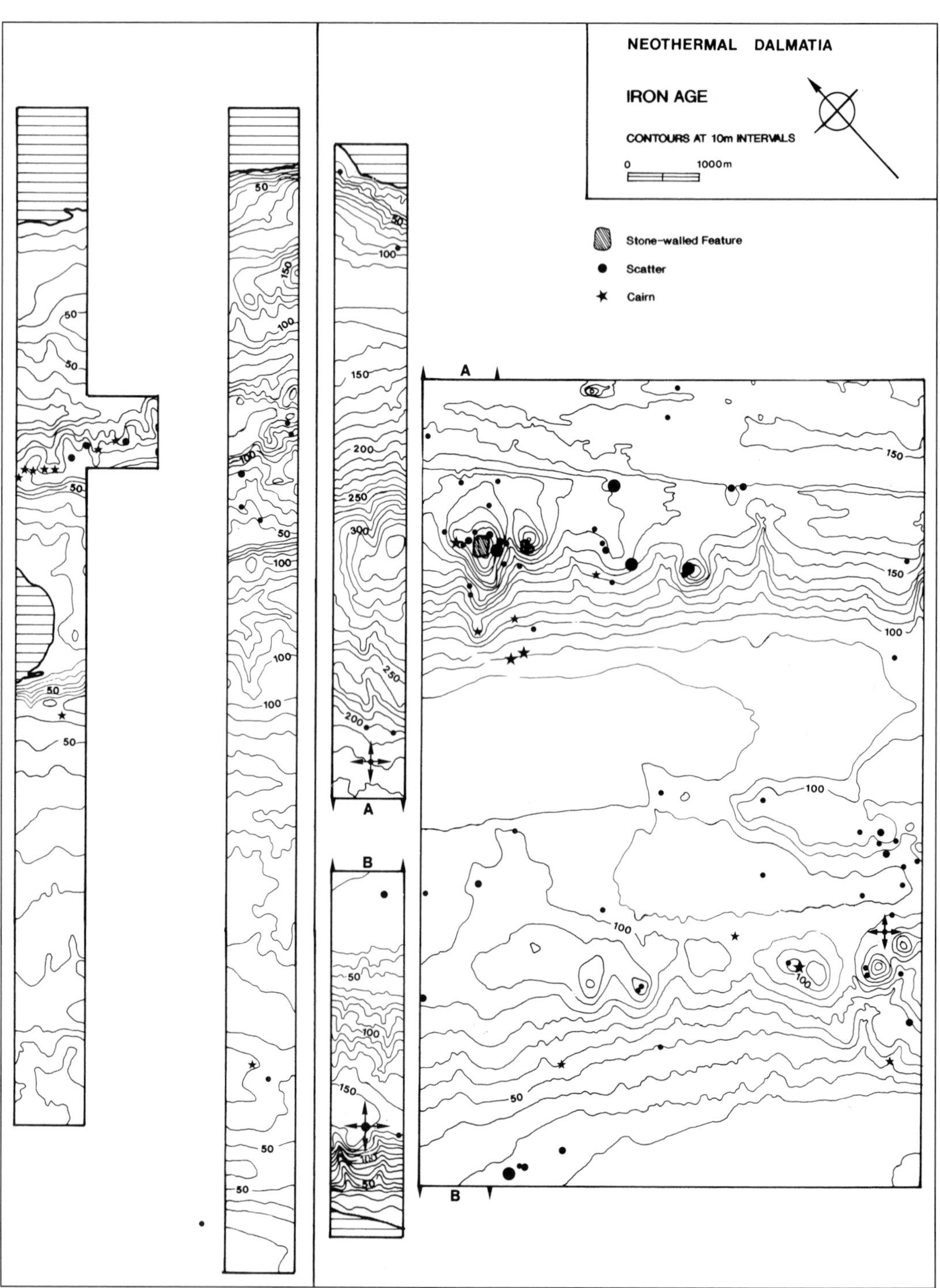

45. Iron Age remains in the Survey Area

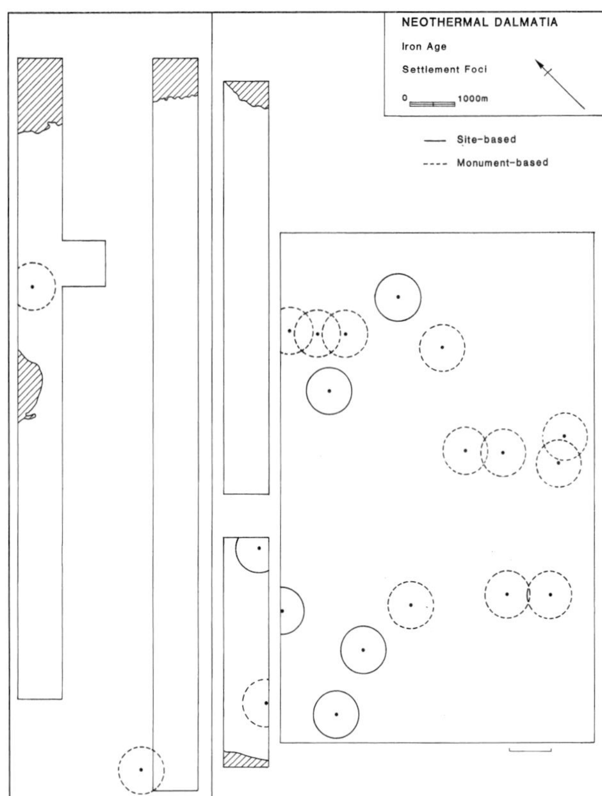

46. Iron Age settlement foci in the Survey Area

47. The Nadin ridge, from south-west, looking across Nadinsko Blato, with Nadin-Gradina as main summit

48. Nadin-Gradina, from across the Benkovac trough

49. Kutlovica, from Nadinsko Blato, from south

earthen mound; many internal structures: fig. 50). *Vrana Valley:* Kakma-Mitrovići cairnfield (continues in use). *Coastal Ridge:* Krmčina hill-fort (massive single rampart: fig. 51). *Other:* 6 site-based foci (4 pottery scatters, one group of cairns with pottery, one linear feature with pottery).

The Iron Age in north Dalmatia is characterized by a different balance between domestic and mortuary arenas from that of the Bronze Age. Whereas Bronze Age

50. The Trojan group, from north-east: Trojan is the lower summit, to right of Petrim

51. Krmčina-Pećinska gradina, north-west rampart from north-east, looking over part of the Zadar Archipelago

monuments tended to be small and dispersed across much of the landscape, in the Iron Age a concentration on hill-fort architecture, with associated cemeteries, and reduced construction of other site classes produced a radically different kind of cultural landscape.

The gross contrasts between monument-free tracts of land and settlement foci, defined by the combination of hill-fort and rich cemetery, were already clear from previous research (Suić 1974; Čače 1985; Batović 1987). The NDP survey has provided a clearer definition of the components of the various settlement foci, which appear to be grouped in several distinct settlement clusters each in contrasting landscapes.

Five settlement clusters can be defined in the survey area, three in the survey block and one bisected by each of two transects. The Nadin Ridge cluster comprises six settlement foci (one major hill-fort, three minor hill-forts, one cairnfield and a pot scatter) and a certain amount of off-site discard. In the Prtenjaća Ridge cluster, five minor hill-forts occur with very few other monuments (one cairn on top of Smiljevac) and off-site discard within the Kruglas territory only. The Vrana/Tinj cluster is far less dominated by hill-forts, with only the Tinj hill-fort amongst five settlement foci (three pottery scatters and minor use of nothing but cairns at the Kakma-Mitrovići cairnfield). The Mataci-Stojići Ridge cluster continues to be a significant zone of settlement, with the linear cairnfield occurring within the survey transect and a major hill-fort with allied flat cemetery and mortuary enclosure further north on the Ridge. Finally, the Coastal Ridge cluster is hill-fort-dominated, with four hill-forts on the first limestone ridge inland from the coast, located to control offshore maritime movement, and one dense pot scatter on the narrow coastal plain.

Four of the five settlement clusters have the settlement of their chosen areas rooted in the Bronze Age (the exception is the Coastal Ridge). The variety of combinations and recombinations of stone features in the Iron Age is greatly diminished. The greatest range of monuments is found on the Mataci-Stojići Ridge, where the newly constructed mortuary enclosure and the continued use of the linear cairnfield contrast with the massive Venac hill-fort, with its 8m high rampart.

In the Velebit Mountains, the focus on hill-fort occupation is as strong as in the Ravni Kotari and most hill-forts are dated to the Iron Age. The more elaborate hill-forts are located at lower altitudes, nearer the Velebitski Kanal, with its access to the Adriatic Sea. Only a small number of caves have remains of Iron Age pottery, while the density of Iron Age graves is as yet uninvestigated. The existence of a small number of high-altitude hill-forts and open sites is suggestive of the continuation of seasonal transhumance, despite climatic deterioration in this region (see p. 22).

The number of settlement foci in the Iron Age is broadly comparable to that in the Bronze Age, both in the Ravni Kotari and on Velebit. It is perhaps not surprising that the mean distance between Iron Age settlement foci in the survey block (7.4km) is slightly higher than the comparable Bronze Age figure. The trans-Velebit links to the continental and Bosnian sources of iron, as well as the Central European sources of bronze continued to be significant components of inter-regional exchange networks in this period, although never as important as the trans-Adriatic routes.

The Roman period (15 BC–AD 500; figs. 52–4)

Survey results: 123 findspots and 97 monuments, grouped into comprising one *municipium* (Nadin-Gradina or *Nedinum*), 5 minor hill-forts, 16 farms, 3 enclosures, 5 platform structures, one shepherds' cave and 14 sites. Monuments are clustered in 12 topographical units, 5 of which were used in the Iron Age: *Bay of Ljubac*: one tile scatter. *Miljašić Valley:* clearance cairns with pottery. *Pridraga Hillslope:* one enclosure. *Benkovac Trough:* 2 farms, one hut and 4 pottery scatters. *Nadin Ridge:* (a) *Nedinum* (expansion of intramural and extramural settlement, with quarries, road network, terraces, enclosures and structures), (b) Vijenac hill-fort (sporadic use), (c) one enclosure near Čauševica, and (d) 3 pottery scatters near the Roman road (Zadar–Asseria). *Zagrad Hillslope:* 3 farms, one hut and one pot/tile scatter. *Nadinsko Blato Basin:* one pottery scatter. *Prtenjača Ridge:* (a) Mutvica hill-fort (sporadic use), (b) Kruglas hill-fort (reuse, with farm to south-west and dense off-site discard), (c) Smiljevac hill-fort (sporadic use). *Polača Valley:* 2 farms, one cairn with pot/tile, one pot/tile scatter. *Tinj Ridge:* 3 farms, one cairn with pot/tile and 3 pot/tile and one pot/tile scatter. *Krmčine Unit:* re-occupation of Buta Jama cave.

The Roman period is marked by a major expansion of settlement into all the available Land Use Classes (as defined earlier: see p. 24). This expansion is seen both in the number and diversity of settlement remains. Since the overall structure of the province of Dalmatia is well enough known from past research (Wilkes 1969; Suić 1974, 1981), the most useful novel information from the NDP concerns the relationship between *municipia* and rural settlement. The widespread use of almost all the available land in the survey block (but not in the survey transects!) carries with it a sense of recolonization of land unused or underused in the Iron Age. Interestingly, the local farmers used much the same kinds of monuments which Bronze Age groups had used when they expanded onto the Karst and Stony land of the Ravni Kotari. Drystone monuments such as linear features and clearance cairns occur widely across the landscape, usually within the 0.5km territory of lowland farms but sometimes forming their own agricultural foci. The frequency of linear features and cairns dated to the Roman period betokens an increase in land management comparable to that of the Bronze Age.

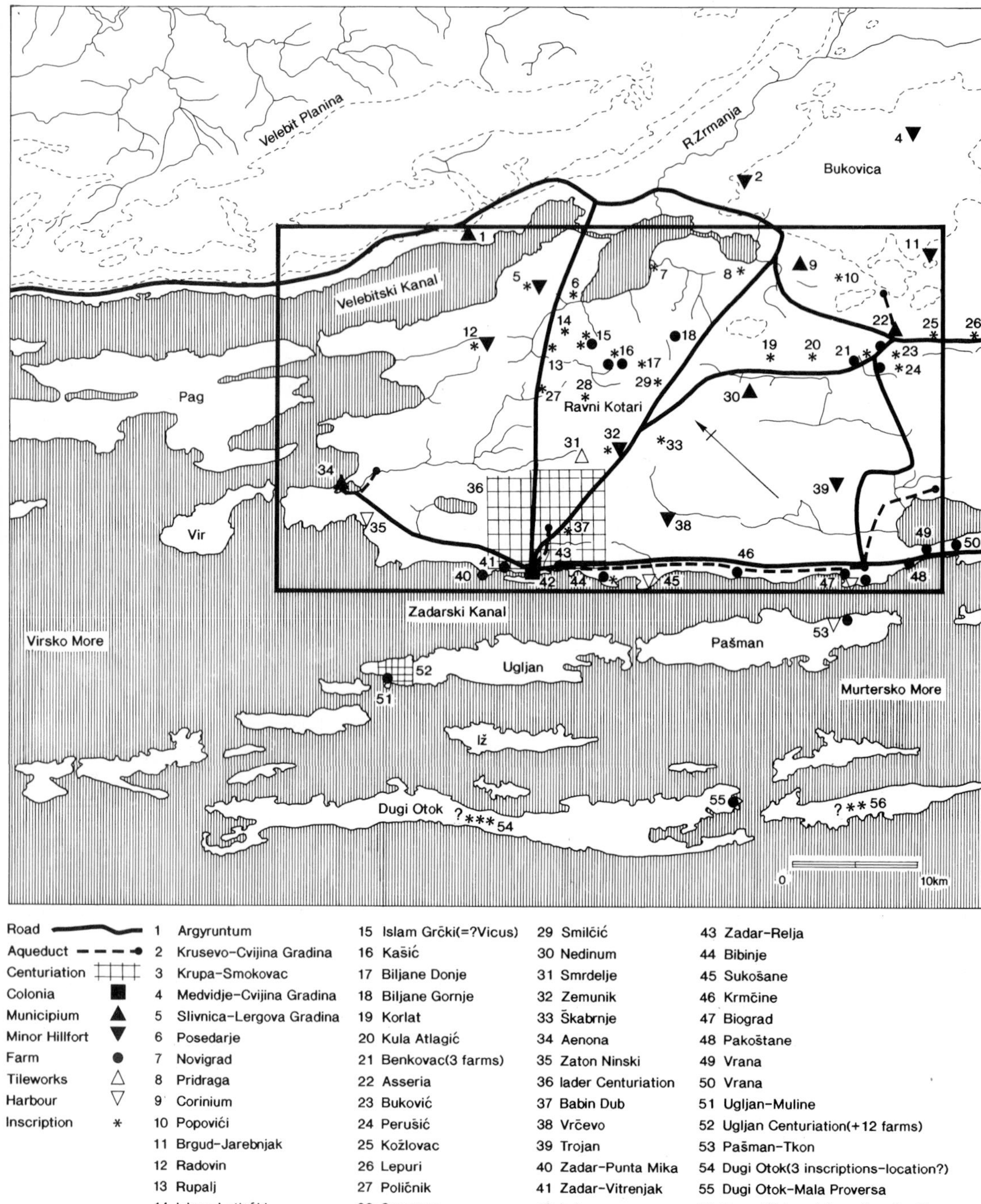

52. Previously known Roman sites in the Study Region

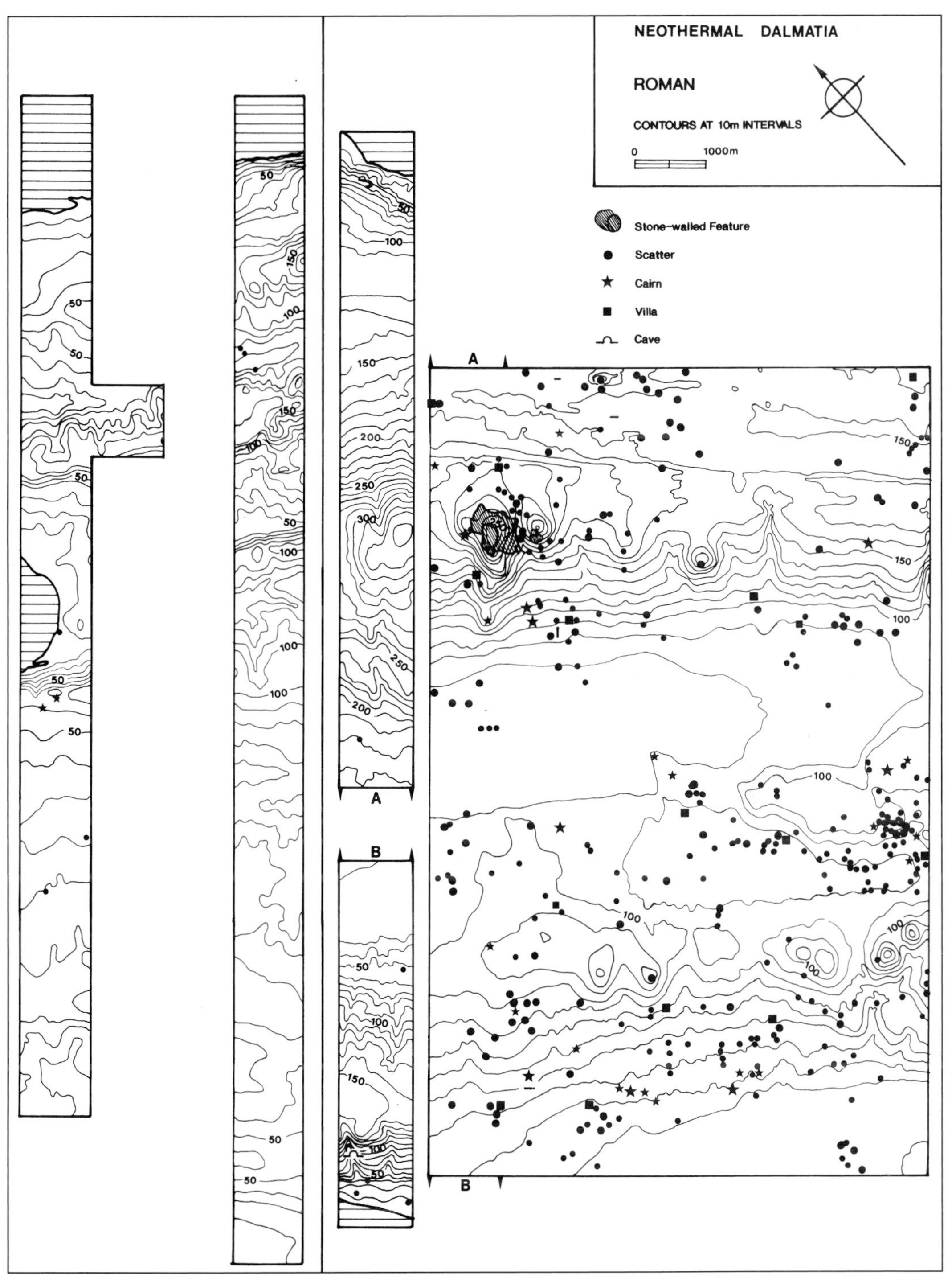

53. Roman remains in the Survey Area

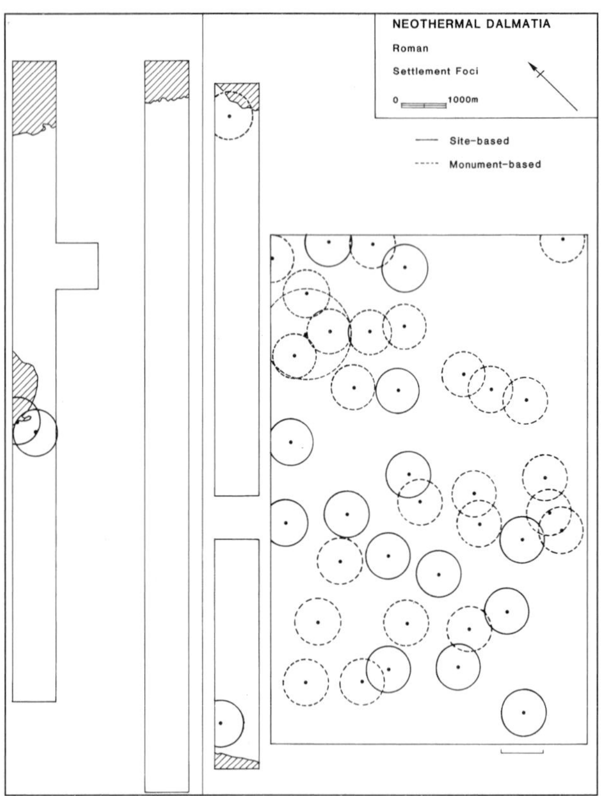

54. Roman settlement foci in the Survey Area

The medieval period (AD 500–1400: figs. 55–61)

Survey results: 22 findspots and 15 monuments, grouped into 9 settlement foci (all monument-based): (a) 2 churches at Ljubac-Manisice, (b) one deserted village at Jovići (fig. 59), (c) one deserted village and church with cemetery at Tinjski Lišane (figs. 60–1), (d) 1 deserted village at Prtenjača, one church at Polača (recorded but now destroyed), (f) one church with house platform at Tinj-Sv. Ivan, (g) one church at Jagodnja, (h) reuse of Vinculja hill-fort, (i) reuse of Nadin-Gradina

The medieval period encompasses two trends in settlement pattern; an initial contraction in early medieval settlement in comparison with the Roman period, and a gradual spreading of occupation from the seventh–ninth centuries clusters (fig. 55) to the widespread occupation of the plains found by AD 1400 (fig. 56) (Klaić and Petricioli 1976). The small cluster of early settlements with churches indicates a dispersed population in much of the Ravni Kotari; the main population nucleations were at the ecclesiastical centres of Zadar and Nin, with a focus near Kašić-Biljane Donje and a scatter of finds in the southern Ravni Kotari. The development of alternative arenas of social power in the medieval period –

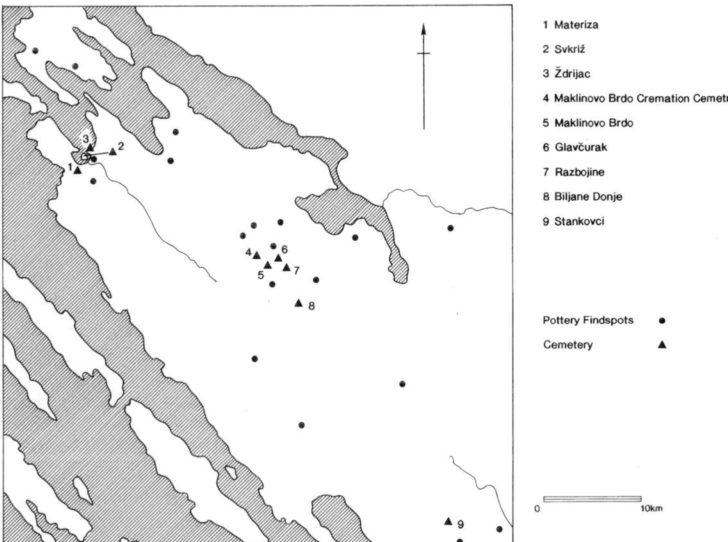

55. Previously known Slavic sites in the Study Region (after Belošević 1980, Tab. C1)

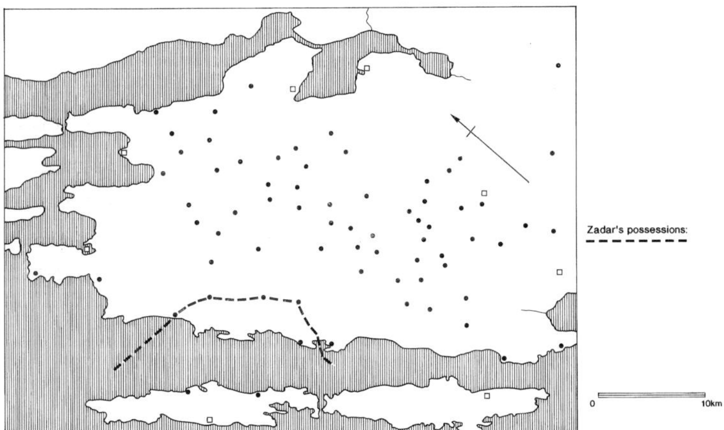

56. Settlements on the Ravni Kotari during the late medieval period (after Klaić and Petricioli 1976, 600–1)

churches – permits a differentiation of the relations of social power and the development of new forms of relationships with the ancestors. By the tenth century, churches are found dispersed throughout the Ravni Kotari (Evans 1989). The continued use of hill-forts indicated the importance of traditional monuments to medieval societies in the midst of the great military upheavals of the period. In the late medieval period, the main concentration of finds in the region shifts away from the plains, to Knin and Biskupija, although populations are still found at Nin and Kašić-Biljane Donje. By the fifteenth century, the population clusters have shifted back to the centre of the plain, with less dense remains on the periphery.

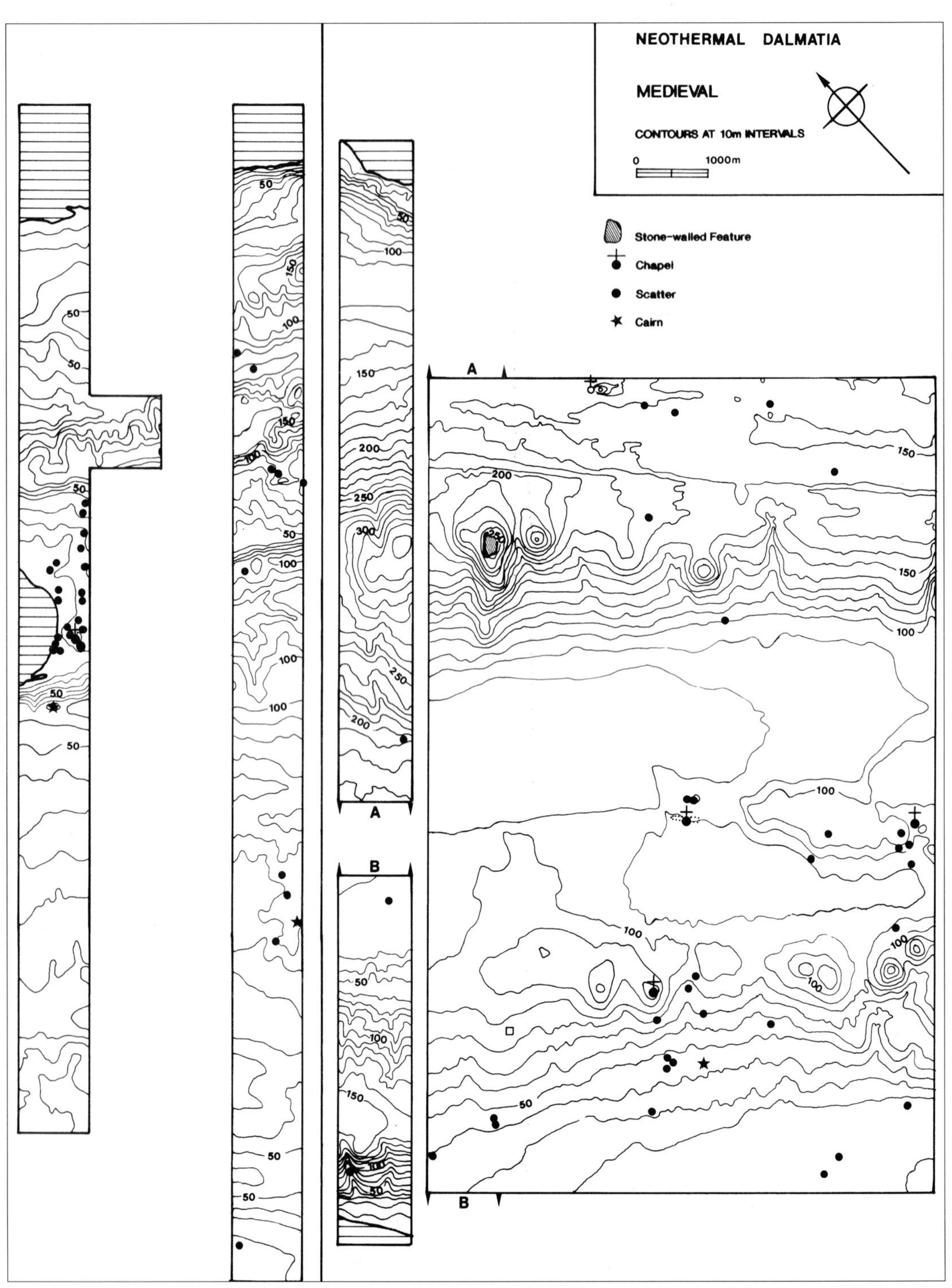

57. Medieval remains in the Survey Area

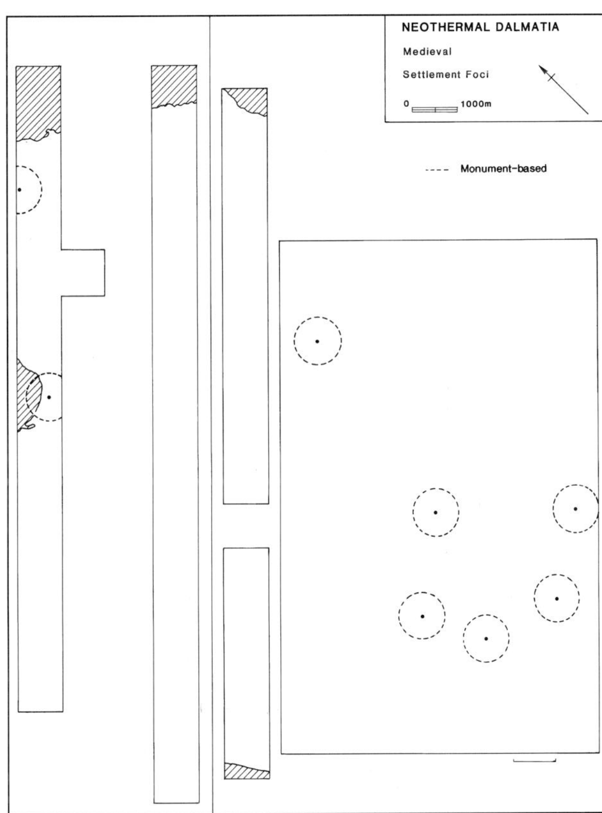

58. Medieval settlement foci in the Survey Area

59. Jovići deserted medieval village, from north-west

60. Lišane Tinjske medieval chapel, from south-west

61. Lišane Tinjske deserted medieval village, from south

Post-medieval and modern pottery (AD 1750–1990: figs. 62–3)

By R. Carlton

> Survey results: 22 findspots and 23 single finds, scattered evenly across survey area, with one concentration at Polača-Prtenjača-Jagodnja.

The early modern period is characterized by a widespread distribution of hand-wheel pottery industries in the former Yugoslavia (fig. 62). The distribution of such pottery in the survey area indicates widespread discard on Arable and non-Arable land (fig. 63). Typological study of this pottery, which was made in and near the study region (Carlton 1988a), indicates the existence of three main groups: (1) glazed wares (imported into the Ravni Kotari from Italy, Spain, Bulgaria, Lika and north-east Yugoslavia); (2) non-glazed fine wares (imported from similar sources as (1), but mostly from Lika); and (3) coarse wares (6 sub-types: most common sub-type is a calcite-tempered red-orange ware, made on the island of Iž from at least the mid-eighteenth century until today).

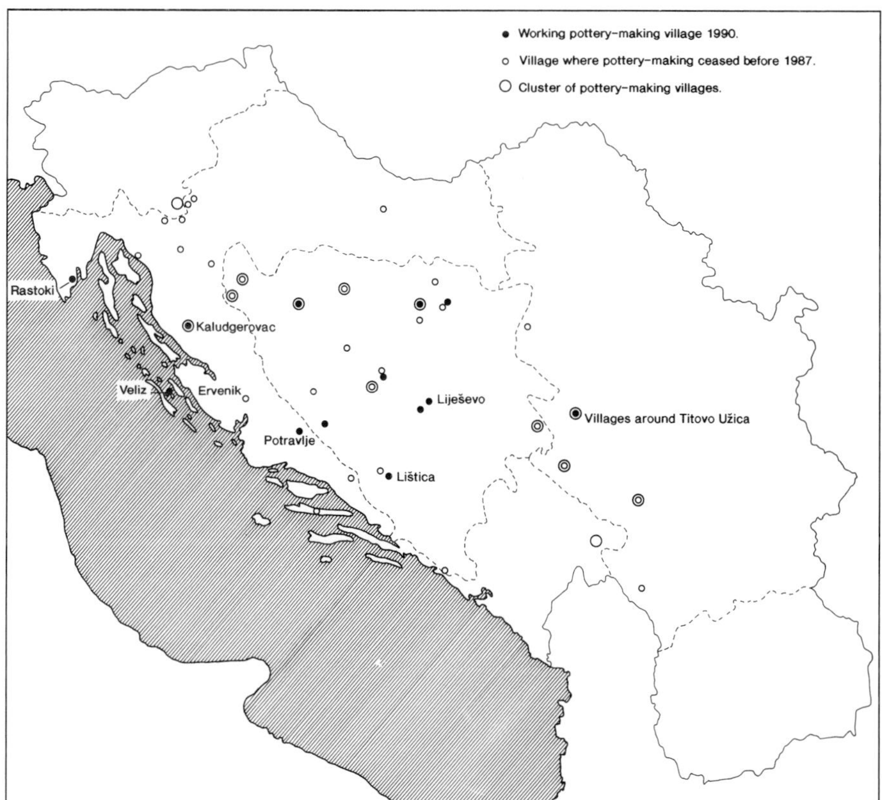

62. Distribution map of hand-wheel pottery industries in the former Yugoslavia

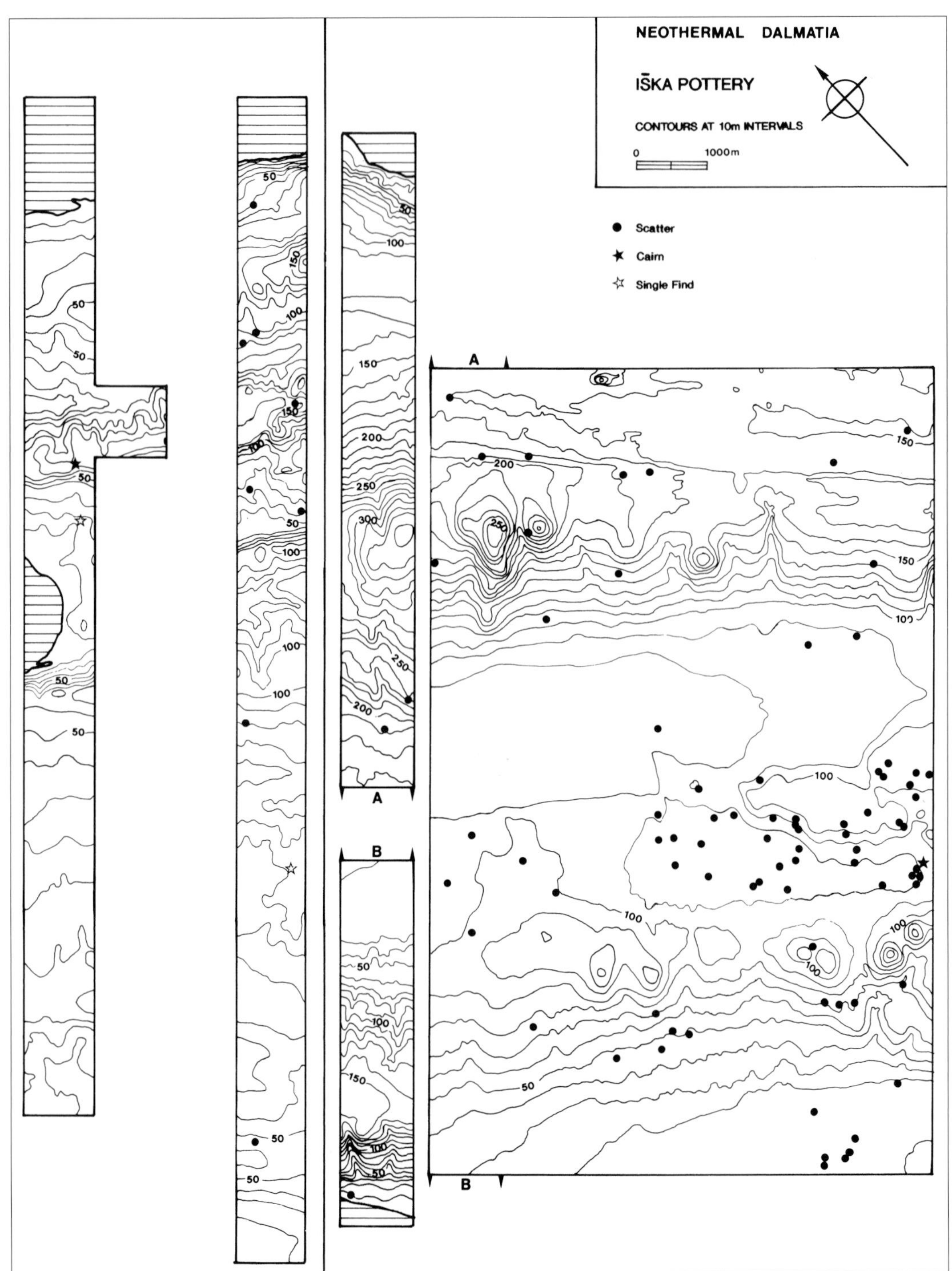

63. Iška pottery remains in the Survey Area

Undated remains

Cairns (figs. 64–5)

820 cairns found, the most common monument in the survey area; moderately dispersed, with occasional clusters in large cairnfields. Most cairns found within 1km of (presumably contemporary) settlement foci. Volumetric analysis indicates possible differences in degree of monumentality and display functions, especially for larger cairns within hill-forts or enclosures. Potential dual function as both stone clearance from fields and burial sites.

Linear features (fig. 66)

77 found, mostly in the survey block; length ranges from 10m to 1.23km; drystone wall construction unlike modern style of drystone wall. Associated with cairns (n = 13) but associated with only one hill-fort (Kutlovica). Mostly found within 1km of settlement foci dated to Bronze Age or Roman, consistent with the agricultural expansion noted in these periods.

Later chipped stone (figs. 67–8)

255 findspots of later (post-Palaeolithic) chipped stone 'associated' with datable pottery (204 on Mataci-Stojici Ridge, mostly with Bronze Age pottery). Outside the Mataci- Stojici Ridge, 11 LCS with Neolithic or Copper Age, 12 with Bronze Age, one with Roman, 11 with medieval, 13 with Iška pottery and 3 with both medieval and Iška.

The study of surface lithics in north Dalmatia has produced two major and very different patterns of lithic exploitation. First, the presence of local pebble flint on the Mataci-Stojići Ridge led to the concentration of knapping in a large number of activity areas mostly dating to the Bronze Age. The second pattern is a lower-density discard of mostly retouched, with some unretouched, pieces made of pebble, and other, flint and chert; this relates to consumption of lithics introduced from other local areas but including the final reduction stages.

Other settlement remains (fig. 69)

7 classes of remains were found, none of which has been generally recorded in Dalmatian surveys: (a) 6 drystone-walled enclosures, (b) 2 drystone-walled settlements, (c) 5 platform sites (Roman–post-medieval), (d) isolated buildings, in drystone, stone or wattle-and-daub, (e) 3 cropmarks (one cropmark may indicate a Roman villa), (f) 2 exposures of ridge-and-furrow cultivation, and (g) 5 lime-pits. With the exception of c–d, all categories are likely to be dated to the post-medieval or modern period.

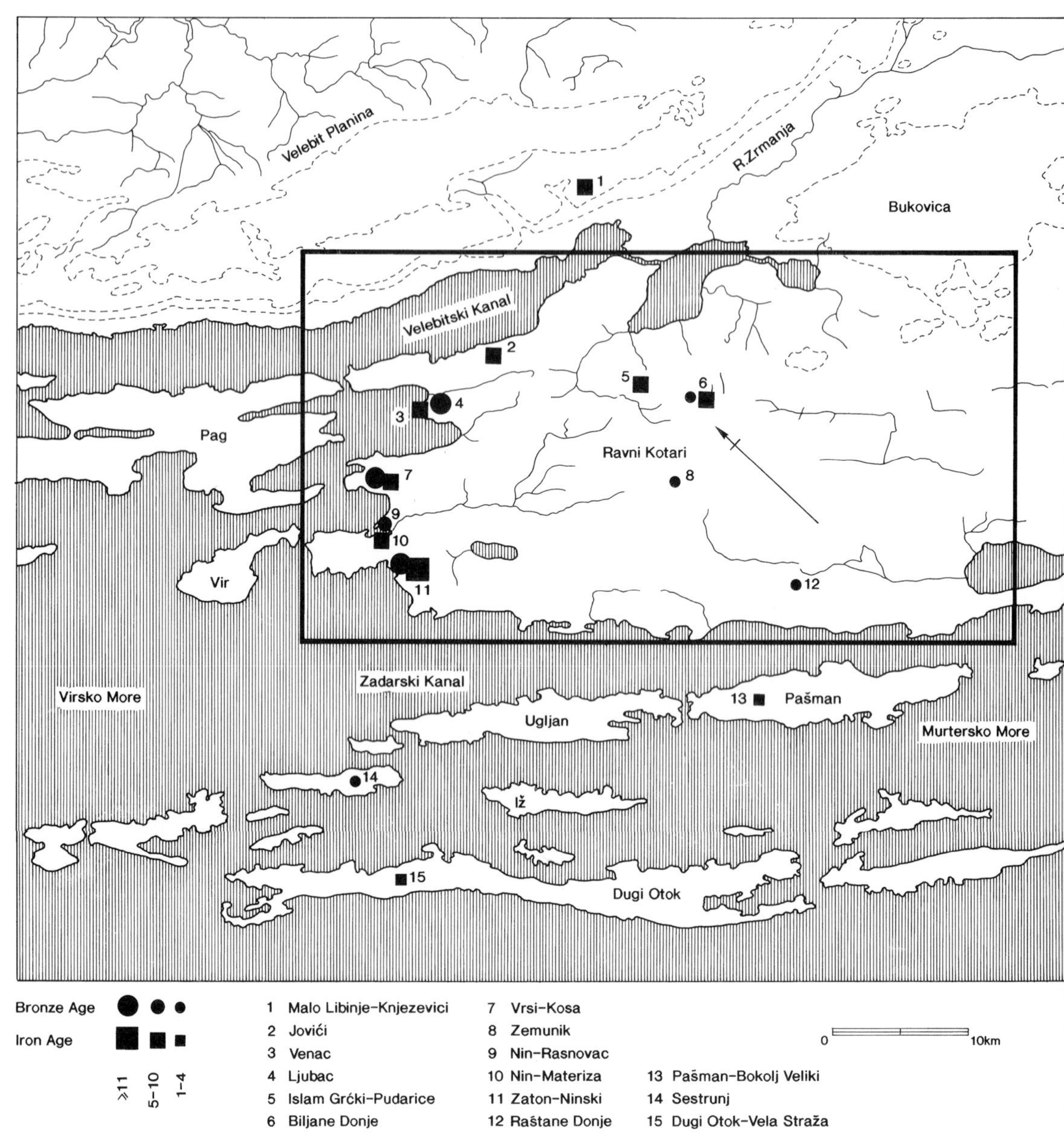

64. Previously known cairns in the Study Region

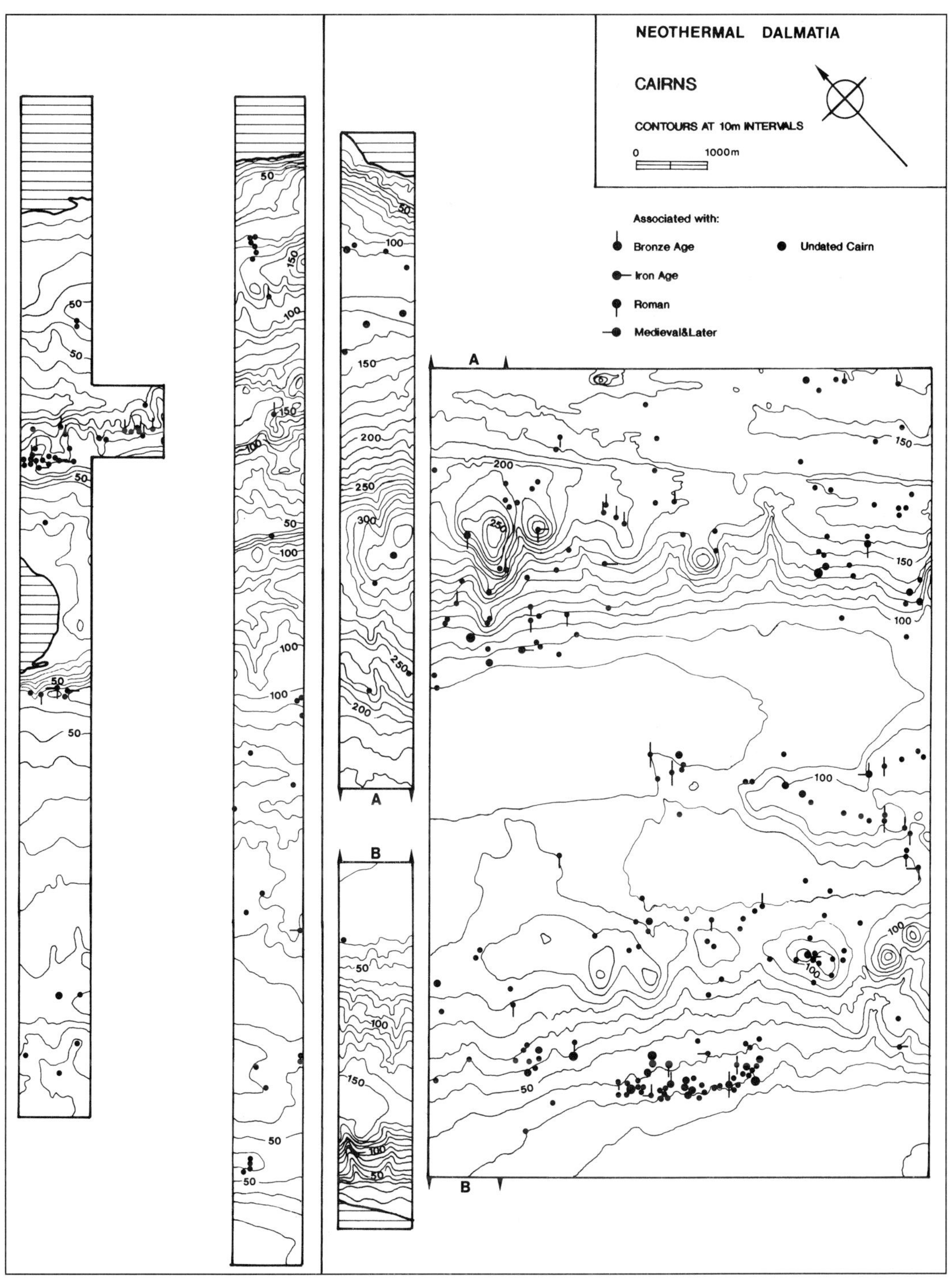

65. Cairns in the Survey Area

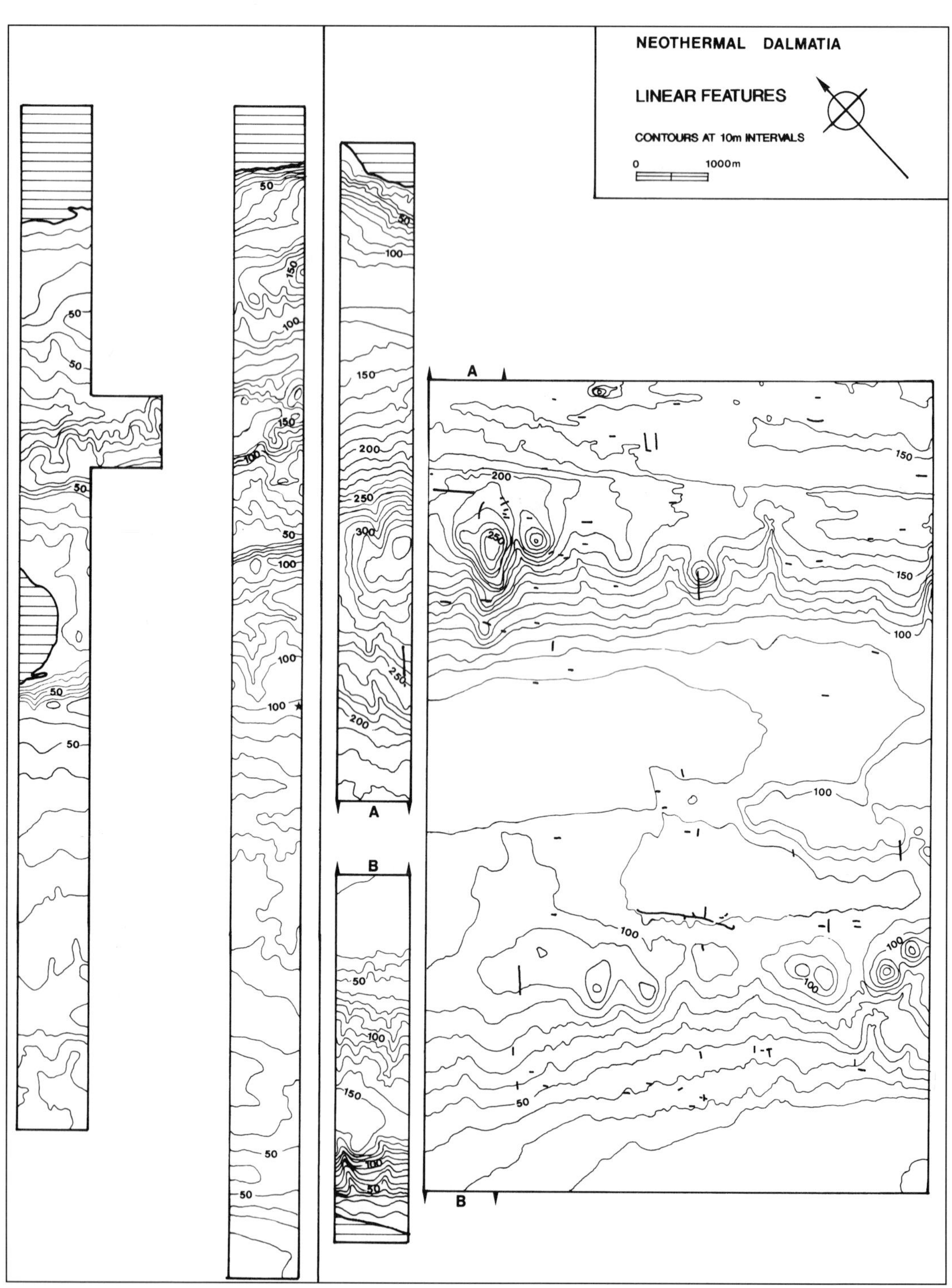

66. Linear features in the Survey Area

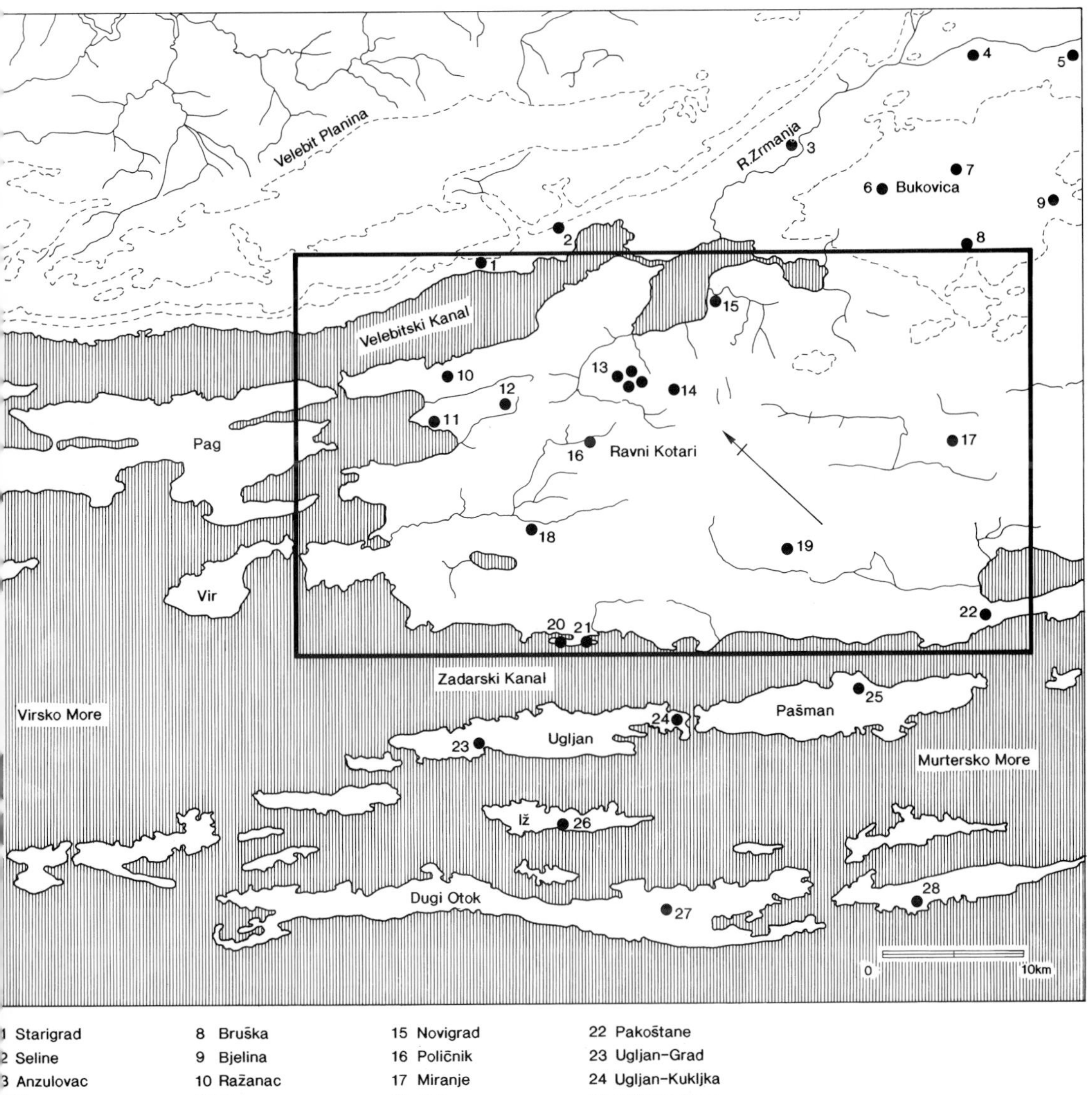

67. Previously known later chipped stone in the Study Region

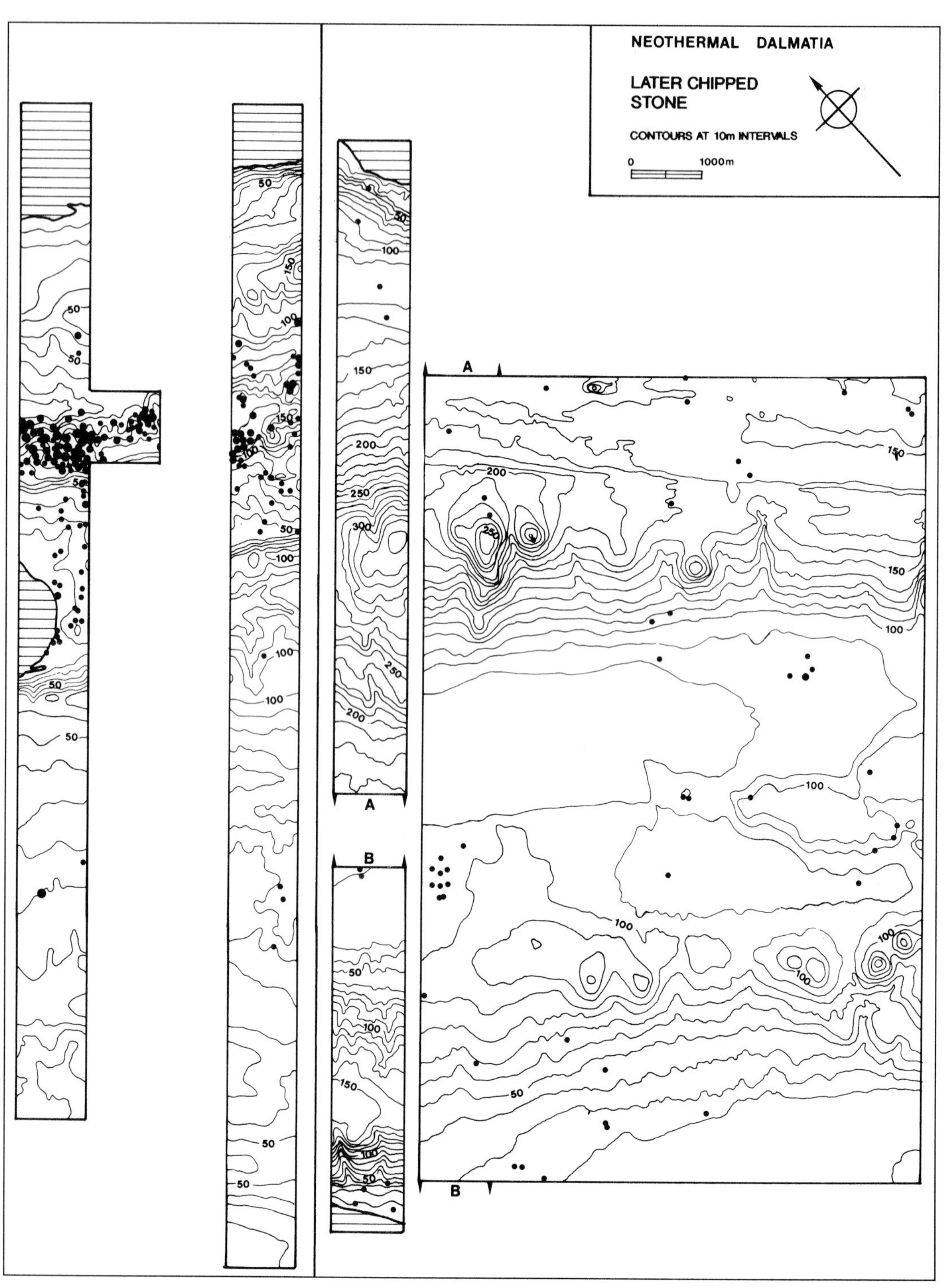

68. Later chipped stone in the Survey Area

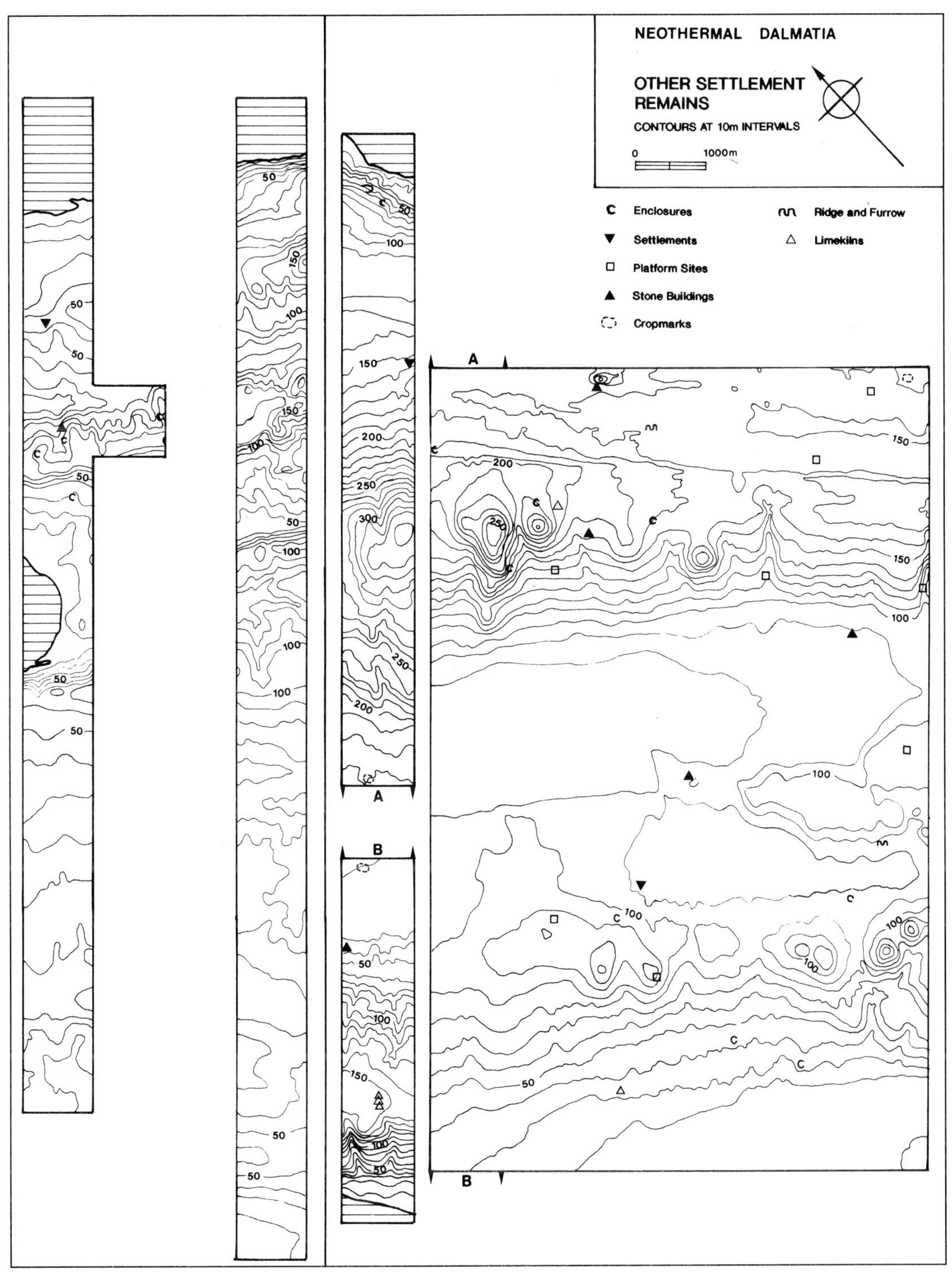

69. Other settlement remains in the Survey Area

Modern settlement (fig. 70)

The modern settlement pattern in the Ravni Kotari consists of a four-tier settlement structure, with the regional capital of Zadar at the apex, market towns such as Benkovac at the second level, villages such as Biljane Donje at the third level and small aggregations of a few farmsteads, such as Nadin, at the lowest level. In the survey area, only settlements of the third and fourth levels were encountered.

Settlement pattern analysis

Introduction

We may now turn to the third and fourth basic questions to which survey can provide at least partial answers, as defined by Cherry, Gamble and Shennan (1978): the relationship between archaeological sites and environmental variables, and the inter-relationships between archaeological sites. Two data sets were prepared for the settlement analysis:- all the datable survey findspots (n = 557: henceforth 'AllFinds') and all the settlement foci (n = 122: henceforth 'SettFoci'). Comparison of the analyses from both data sets can provide insights into the relative balance of intensive and extensive land use by period.

Information on seven environmental variables was systematically collected during fieldwork, as follows:

1. *Altitude*: total variation in the survey area 0–332masl: altitude divided into seven 50m ranges.
2. *Geology*: five general categories based on 1890s geological maps: alluvium; Quaternary sands and loams; Eocene marls and sands; Tertiary limestones; and Cretaceous limestones.
3. *Topography*: more general division into three categories: hills, hillslopes and valleys; more specific categorization into eight classes: hilltops and ridgetops; gorges, hillslopes and base of slope; terraces, valley bottoms and coastal plains.
4. *Slope/Erosion*: both categories divided, during fieldwork, into four categories: none, limited, moderate and extensive.
5. *Vegetation*: divided, during fieldwork, into eight categories: šibljak, maquis, scattered trees, heathland, orchard, vineyard, pasture, cropping.

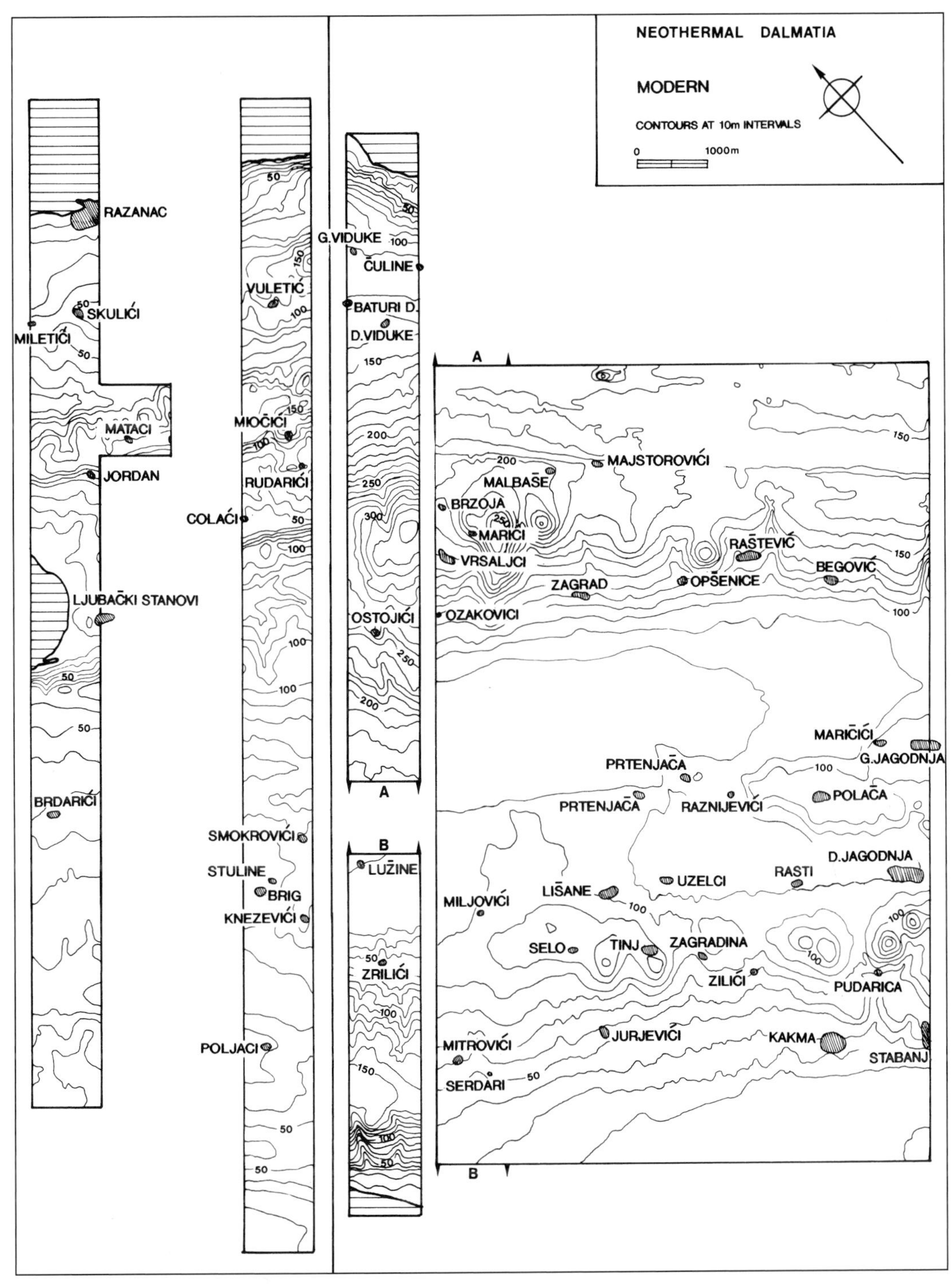

70. Distribution of modern villages in the Survey Area

6. *Modern Land Use Classes*: five classes (for definitions, see p. 24): Arable, Stony, Terrace, Karst and Bottomland.

7. *Past Land Use Classes*: the same classes are used as for modern LUCs, but the distribution of past LUCs varies from the present pattern for two categories (Karst has expanded at the expense of Stony in most areas of human land management). (Shiel and Chapman 1988; Chapman and Shiel 1993)

Three series of statistical analysis were attempted. Univariate and bivariate analyses were based on the SPSSX statistical package release 3.0 (Norusis 1983), using the Crosstabs and Frequencies routines. Territorial analysis of sites and monuments in the main survey block was based on the percentage representation of the five LUCs (Past and Modern) in land within both 0.5km and 1km radius of a given site or monument. The small sizes of the site territories reflected the predominantly dispersed nature of settlement pattern. These data were analysed multivariately, using the SAS version of Principal Components Analysis (SAS Inc. 1990).

The results

The analytical results provide an array of settlement and environmental data enabling a better understanding of the context of the settlement pattern and its many changes. A summary of the most significant characteristics of each period's settlement structure follows, together with an assessment of the changes over time (table 14). It should be noted that, in case of a divergence, conclusions based on

Table 14 Land use class preferences in the survey area by period

Date	
Palaeolithic	Scatters on valley sites on alluvial sediments, with flat Arable land and little erosion; scatters on flat ridgetop sites on Eocene marls with Stony land and moderate erosion
Neolithic/ Copper Age	Scatters on low-level, flat valley sites on alluvial sediments with Arable land and Bottomland and no erosion
Bronze Age	Unenclosed sites on low-level, flat valley sites on alluvial sediments with Arable land and Bottomland and little erosion; enclosed sites on medium-level hillslopes on Cretaceous limestones with Karst and Stony land and moderate erosion
Iron Age	Hill-forts and some open sites on ridgetops and hilltop sites on Tertiary or Cretaceous limestones with Karst land or balanced mix of LUCs
Roman	Full altitudinal range; other rural settlements on alluvial sediments with Arable land and Bottomland; hill-forts and farms on hillslopes and ridgetops on Cretaceous limestones with Karst land and moderate erosion
Medieval	Scatters on level valley sites on Eocene sediments with Arable land; villages and hill-forts on hillslopes on alluvial sediments and Tertiary limestones with Stony and Terrace land
Modern	Arable-dominated villages with greater emphasis on Arable and Stony land; pastoral-dominated villages with greater emphasis on Karst and Bottomland

past LUCs are given greater weight than those based on modern LUCs. It will be seen how closely certain environmental parameters are related in the changing configurations of settlement.

The Palaeolithic

The Middle Palaeolithic settlement of north Dalmatia is based on the exploitation of two niches within the lower altitudinal range of the region. In the lower niche, at 0–49masl, discard is concentrated on the Quaternary sediments of the valley topographical unit, more especially the coastal plain. The discard sites are generally flat, suffering from little erosion and are generally associated with Arable LUC as well as some Stony, Karst and Terrace land, often with cropping.

The higher niche lies at 100–149masl, on the Eocene marls and sands of the Mataci-Stojići Ridge. The topographical preference is therefore for ridgetops rather than hilltops and the ridge discard sites are flat, with moderate erosion. The predominant LUC is Stony, often covered in šibljak. No multivariate analysis of Land Use Classes was possible, owing to the absence of Palaeolithic remains in the main survey block.

The Neolithic and Copper Age

The main foci of Neolithic and Copper Age settlement lie within a narrow altitudinal band, at 50–99masl, with occasional discard and one focus on higher slopes. The foci are mostly on alluvial sediments, in valleys rather more than on hillslopes, but on locally flat sites with no erosion. The sites are strongly associated with Arable LUC and cropping vegetation. The higher scatters lie on Cretaceous limestone, with Stony, Karst and Terrace LUCs.

In each of the multivariate analyses of land use classes where all periods were considered together (henceforth 'AllPeriod' analyses), Neolithic and Copper Age settlements showed a strong preference for Arable LUC, either singly or in conjunction with the Bottomland LUC (fig. 71). This specific preference broke down in the multivariate analyses of each separate period (henceforth 'Separate analyses'), where a hitherto unsuspected variation in territorial LUCs was demonstrated (fig. 72). In this sense, Neolithic and Copper Age populations as a group can be clearly differentiated from groups of later date in respect of choice of LUCs but also reveal a wide range of different preferences within their period.

The Bronze Age

Within the wider altitudinal range used in this period, Bronze Age foci were concentrated on two low-lying niches: 50–99masl and 100–149 masl. In addition to

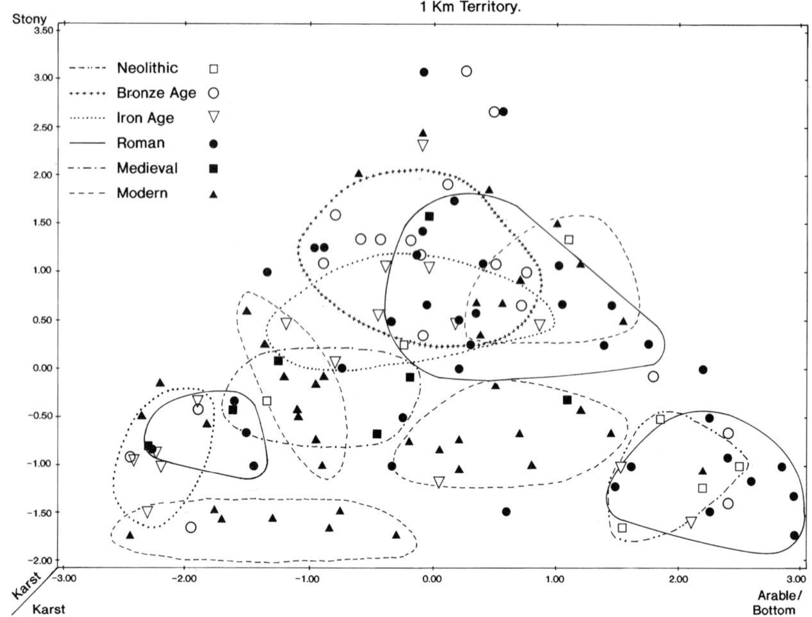

71. Principal Components Analysis (Similarity Co-efficients) of Past LUCs within 1.0km territories for all periods

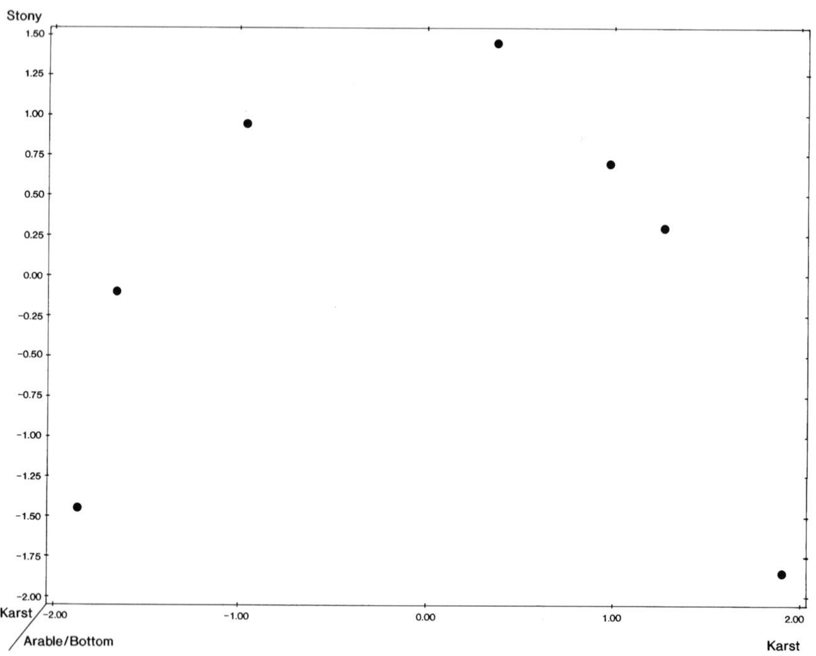

72. Principal Components Analysis (Similarity Co-efficients) of Past LUCs within 0.5km territories: Neolithic/ Copper Age

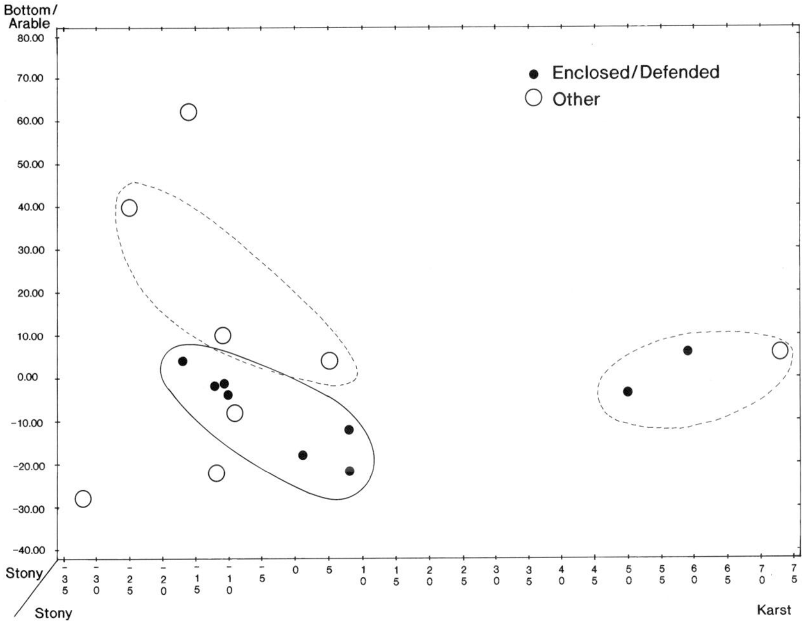

73. Principal Components Analysis (Similarity Co-efficients) of Past LUCs within 0.5km territories: Bronze Age

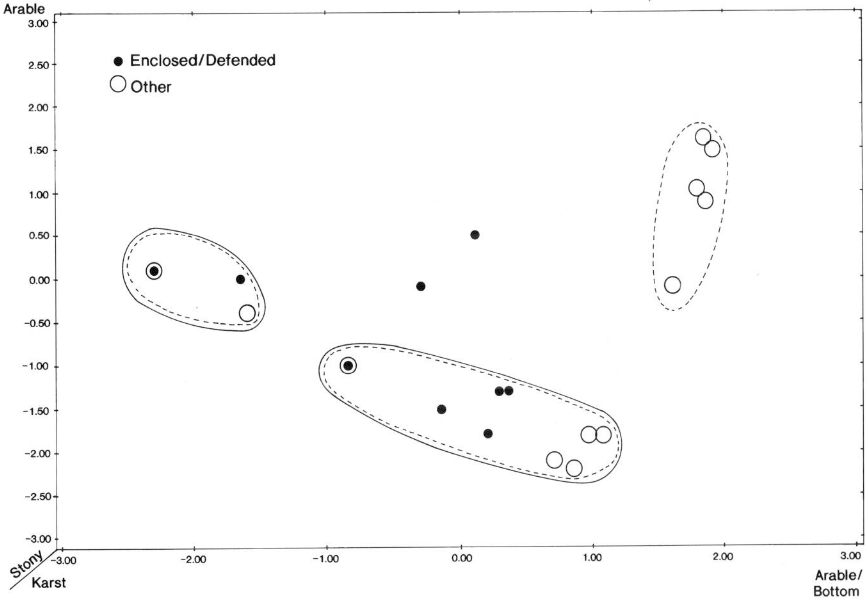

74. Principal Components Analysis (Similarity Co-efficients) of Past LUCs within 1.0km territories: Bronze Age

the settlement foci in this period, extremely high discard occurred on the Mataci-Stojići Ridge, which is therefore treated as a separate unit of analysis. In the lower niche, scatters and scatter-based SettFoci were common on alluvial sediments located in valley units and especially on terraces. Low-lying limestones were also important and often weathered to Arable LUC. On the alluvial deposits, Stony and Arable LUCs predominated and the vegetational cover was typically šibljak.

In the higher niche, SettFoci occur both on and off the Mataci Ridge. In the case of the latter, foci were mostly on Cretaceous limestones on hills and especially ridgetops. These locations had a mixture of Karst and Stony LUCs and were often covered in maquis. Enclosed/defended settlements, cairn-based and scatter-based foci were typically found in this niche.

On the Mataci-Stojići Ridge, discard and all the three foci occurred on Eocene marls and sands, on hillslope locations with limited to moderate slope and limited to moderate erosion. The LUCs were more often Stony than Karst and the vegetational cover tended to be šibljak.

In the AllPeriods multivariate analyses, the preference for especially Arable, but also Stony and Karst LUCs in the 0.5km territories becomes weaker at the 1km territorial size, where a more balanced suite of LUCs is chosen. Site differentiation between enclosed and unenclosed sites is rare; insofar as it is present, the unenclosed settlements show a stronger preference for Arable or Arable plus Bottomland.

In the Separate analyses, differences in land use potential between site classes are stronger for smaller rather than larger territorial sizes, perhaps a reflection of sensitivity to cropping potential. Separate clusters of enclosed sites show preferences for Karst and Arable LUCs, as well as Terrace and Stony land, whereas unenclosed settlement clusters show a consistent preference for Bottomland and Arable LUCs, with some selection of Stony land (fig. 73). The blurring of this possible site differentiation in the 1km territories (fig. 74) is partly a reflection of the mosaic effect of LUCs, but also may signify the absence of strong site differentiation at this period.

In comparison with the Neolithic/Copper Age territorial preferences, there is continuity in the Bronze Age interest in Arable and Bottomland. What is a new departure is the Bronze Age selection of Karst, Stony and Terrace LUCs, with preference for Stony in both enclosed and unenclosed sites and choice of Terrace and Karst units by enclosed settlements only.

The Iron Age

Iron Age discard occurs over the full altitudinal range available in the Ravni Kotari. The foci cluster around two ranges: 50–99masl and 100–149masl. In the lower niche, discard occurs on alluvial and Eocene sediments and on some low-lying limestones. These valley locations are typically on terraces, with more karst than stony than Arable LUCs and šibljak vegetation.

In the higher niche, enclosed/defended settlements occur together with cairn-based foci and linear-feature-based foci. The foci characteristically occupy Tertiary or Cretaceous limestone hills and hillslopes, with ridgetops preferred to hilltops. These locations typically have a limited slope, with limited to moderate erosion. The principal LUC is Karst and vegetation is divided between šibljak and maquis.

The results of all multivariate analyses indicate strong preferences for either the Karst LUC or a balanced mix of LUCs; there is only one instance of selection of an Arable LUC. In AllPeriod analyses, there is little site differentiation between hill-forts and unenclosed sites. By contrast, in the Separate analyses, there is a tendency for hill-fort populations to select certain suites of LUCs which are avoided by those in the unenclosed settlements, who select a wide variety of LUCs (fig. 75). In these analyses, hill-fort populations tend to prefer the Karst LUC, but Terrace, Arable and balanced mixes of LUCs are also selected. The balanced range of LUCs may form the basis for long-term choice of territorial potential. It should be noted, however, that even the low-lying hill-forts and some unenclosed settlements often

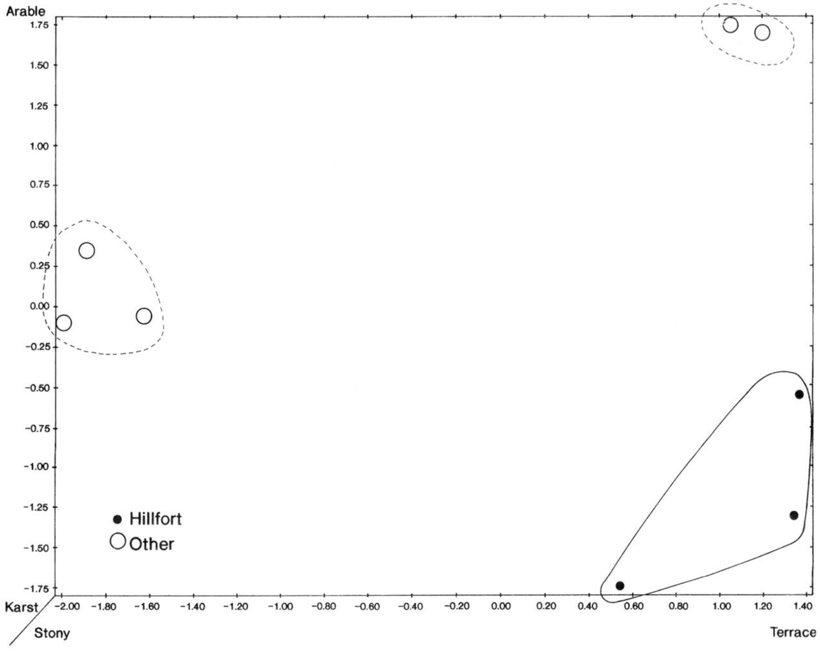

75. Principal Components Analysis (Similarity Co-efficients) of Past LUCs within 1.0km territories: Iron Age

maintain a strong preference for what is now, and was most probably then, the Karst LUC.

The evident continuity between Bronze Age and Iron Age territorial choices reflects the continued occupation of many of the same hilltop sites. What is different is the neglect of Arable and Bottomland in the Iron Age and, consequently, a lack of territorial differentiation between hill-forts and unenclosed sites.

The Roman period

Roman discard and settlement occurs over the full altitudinal range but with marked concentrations below 200masl. In the lowest altitudinal niche (50–99masl), Alluvial sediments are more frequent than low-level limestones in the valley locations, where terraces are the preferred topographical unit. The settlements here enjoy limited or no slope and erosion. Farms are characteristic forms of settlement, as are scatter-based, linear feature-based and cairn-based foci. These settlement foci are found mostly on Stony and Karst land, with cropping more common than šibljak.

At higher altitudes, enclosed sites occur with cairn-based and linear feature based foci. These locations are principally on Cretaceous limestones, on hillslopes more than ridgetops yet with limited slope and confined to moderate erosion. The LUCs are predominantly Karst more than Stony and Terrace, but high-level Arable land is also found. The modern vegetation is sibljak more frequently than maquis.

The principal characteristic of the Roman territorial strategy is a diversification of land use preferences for Arable and Karst LUCs, as well as a balanced mix of LUCs. A preference for Arable and Karst LUCs is found in all multivariate analyses, while the balanced suite of LUCs is preferred in the AllPeriods analysis only (fig. 76).

A complex picture of LUC selection according to site type is highlighted by the Separate analyses. When hill-forts occur in separate clusters, the preference is for the Karst LUC. When hill-fort and farm clusters overlap, yet are differentiated from other rural sites, Terrace as well as Karst LUCs are selected. By contrast, clusters containing only, or even predominantly, the other rural sites show a strong preference for Arable and Bottomland LUCs. To generalize, there is a distinction between hill-forts and farms, which tend to neglect the Arable and Bottomland, and other rural settlements, which tend to favour these resources.

In comparison with the Iron Age, the Roman rural populations continue to favour both the Karst LUC and a balanced mix of all LUCs; there is also a continuation of preference for the Terrace LUC by hill-fort groups. The Roman strategy differs from that of the Iron Age in its emphasis on Arable and Bottomland, as in the Bronze Age, and a clear differentiation between unenclosed and higher-order settlements.

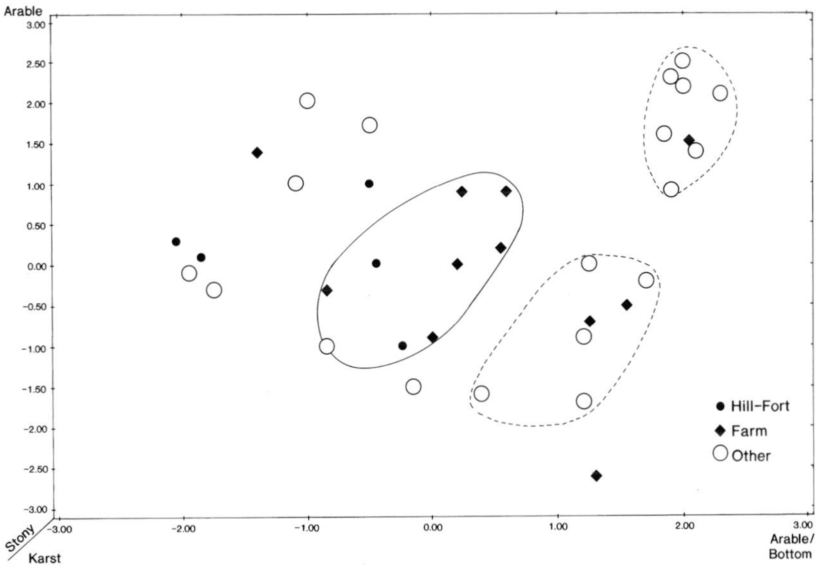

76. Principal Components Analysis (Similarity Co-efficients) of Past LUCs within 0.5km territories for all periods: Roman highlighted

The medieval period

The medieval settlement foci show a marked preference for lower altitudes, from sea level to 150masl. In the lowest range, Eocene sediments in valleys are preferred, especially on terraces rather than coastal plains. These scatter-based foci are on flat locations with no erosion and preference is shown for Arable LUC. The modern vegetation is typically cropping rather than šibljak.

At higher altitudes, foci are located more on alluvial sediments than Tertiary limestones, although discard on Eocene and Cretaceous deposits is known. The hillslopes are generally preferred to the hilltops and sites with limited slope and erosion are characteristic. Stony land is the norm and modern vegetation is equally divided between šibljak and maquis. A wider range of settlement forms occurs in the higher niche – Deserted Medieval Villages, defended settlements and linear feature-based foci as well as scatter-based foci.

Medieval groups continue to prefer two of the three LUC strategies selected by Roman populations: the Karst and the balanced mix of LUCs. In the AllPeriods multivariate analyses, site differentiation is documented between the hill-forts, with their choice of Karst, and the villages, with their preference for the balanced mix. In the Separate analyses, this clear-cut site differentiation is supported, but with varying LUC preferences (fig. 77). Hill-fort choice varies between Terrace and

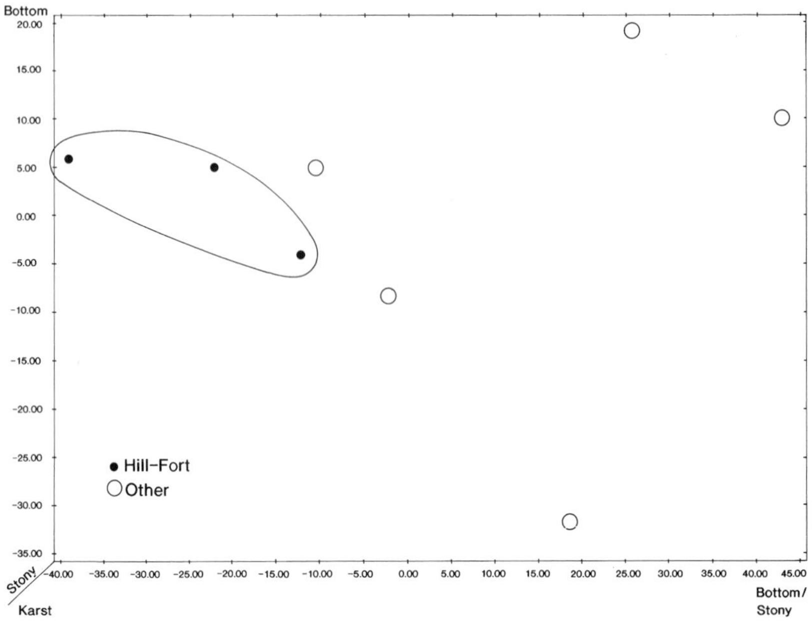

77. Principal Components Analysis (Similarity Co-efficients) of Past LUCs within 1.0km territories, medieval

Bottomland plus Karst LUCs; village groups favour either Stony or Arable plus Terrace LUCs. These results indicate a growing importance of the Terrace LUC. The overall LUC preferences resemble the Roman mix, with the main contrast being the LUC selections of medieval villages, which differ from those of both Roman farms and other rural settlements.

Modern

The territorial preferences of modern villages are clearly for the Karst LUC and for balanced mixes of all LUCs; selection of the Arable LUC is less commonly found. In the majority of analyses, villages whose subsistence practices are dominated by cropping are differentiated from those with a stronger pastoral component (fig. 78). The problem is that the axes on which this differentiation is based are variable. A summary of these axes indicates that cropping-dominated villages place slightly greater emphasis on Arable and Stony LUCs, while pastoral-dominated villages show a slight preference for Karst and Bottomland LUCs. The mosaic effect of the land use distribution should, however, not be ignored, for the greater distances which pastoral groups move in the Ravni Kotari also places a limitation on this kind of local territorial analysis.

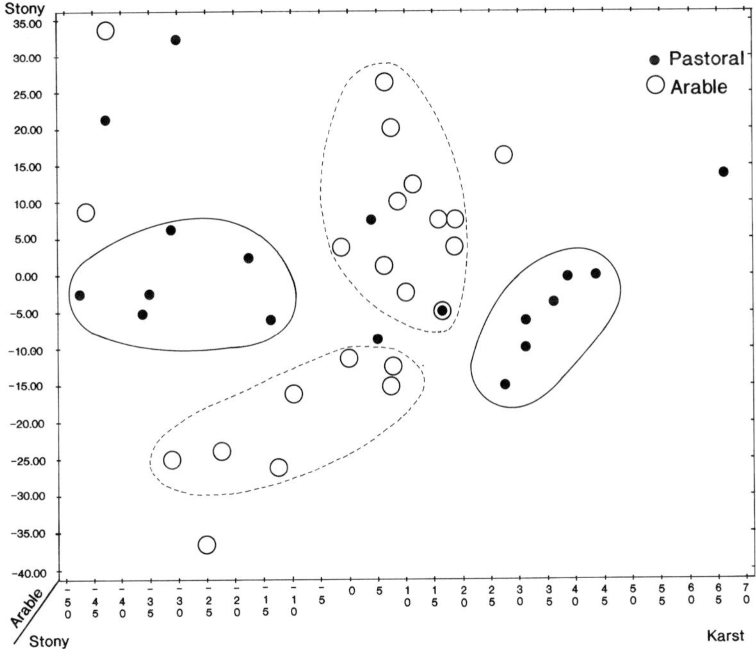

78. Principal Components Analysis (Similarity Co-efficients) of modern LUCs within 1.0km territories, modern villages

Summary

The wide range of analyses – univariate, bivariate and multivariate – attempted for settlement pattern data from the NDP survey has led to the discovery of significant patterning in changing settlement locations over the last 40,000 years in north Dalmatia. It has been found that the social groups in each chronological period have impressed their individual signatures on the landscape through exerting their preference for specific settlement locations in a complex, mosaic environment. Through multivariate analyses, we have defined a range of territorial potentialities, which changed subtly from period to period. There is a general locational trend from specialized to generalized, which appears to be balanced by an inverse trend in land use. This notion can be explored only through the collection of subsistence data from excavations. We return to this theme in a later chapter.

4 Analytical field survey

Aims

Analytical field survey has been characterized as the detailed ground survey of all adequately preserved remains, done with a view to answering carefully formulated questions and providing plans that can be relied upon in all ways (RCHME 1978, 10). In this chapter, the results of analytical field survey in the Ravni Kotari will be presented. The aims of this phase of fieldwork are fourfold:

1. The production of a complete and accurate record of surviving upstanding features and surface scatters.
2. The definition of site chronology (construction sequence), function and land use in the surrounding area.
3. Analysis of inter-site and inter-regional similarities and differences in order to investigate regional architectural styles.
4. The provision of a cartographic basis for future sites and monuments protection.

The selection of monuments for inclusion within the analytical survey programme depended upon knowledge of the distribution of monuments at the start of the project and the discovery of new monuments during field survey.

The database for detailed plans of stone-walled monuments prior to 1982 was concerned almost entirely with hill-forts. Plans of hill-forts appear in Wilkes (1969), Suić (1974), Batović (1975, 1977) and Benac (1985). With the exception of the South-West Bosnian hill-fort survey (Benac 1985), the frequently schematic nature of the plans limits their value for these aims.

According to the hill-fort database, a total of ninety-three hill-forts fell within the boundaries of the NDP study region (see above, fig. 43). Apart from several large 'single' hill-forts, many of the sites fell into distinct clusters (Batović 1977, Carte 1). Two of these groups fell within the survey transects and blocks – the Nadin group and the Jagodnja group. It was decided to concentrate attention on these groups in an attempt to integrate analytical survey data with the more extensive data gathered from field and soil survey. In addition, two extra single sites were included on account of their discovery during the survey – the Mataci enclosure and the Pridraga cairnfield.

Summary data and plans of thirteen sites are presented below, as follows: (1) the Mataci enclosure, (2) the Pridraga cairnfield,(3) the Nadin group (Nadin-

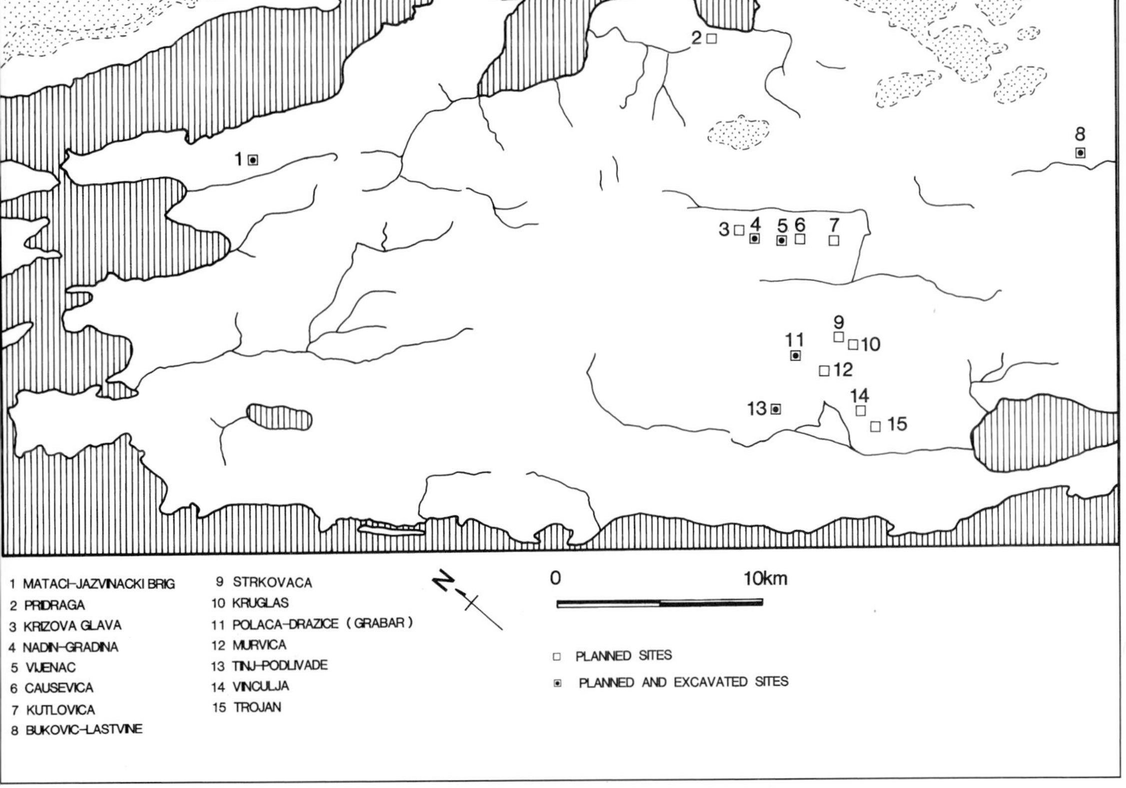

79. Distribution of monuments discussed in Chapter 4

Gradina, Krizova Glava hill-fort, Vijenac hill-fort, the Čauševica field system and Kutlovica hill-fort), (4) the Jagodnja group (Mutvica hill-fort, Strkovača hill-fort, Kruglas hill-fort, the Polača field system, Vinculja hill-fort and Trojan hill-fort). The locations of all studied sites are presented above (fig. 79).

Site results

Mataci-Jazvinački Brijeg: Bronze Age enclosure (figs. 80–1)

History of investigations

Discovered by NDP in 1982; excavations in 1983. Part of a complex, partially preserved Bronze Age landscape. The only previously known component of the Bronze Age remains on the Mataci-Stojići ridge was a group of cairns thought to be part of the linear tumulus cemetery associated with the Iron Age hill-forts of Venac and Ljubljana.

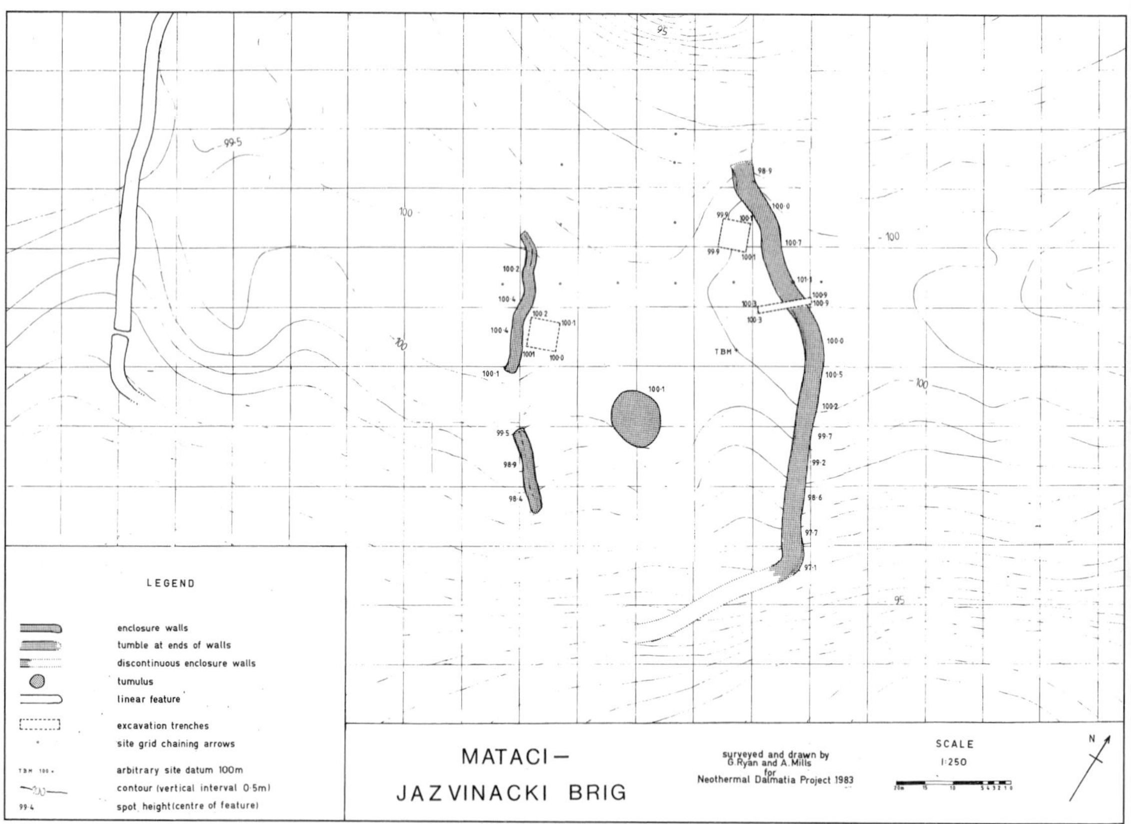

80. The Mataci-Jazvinački Brijeg enclosure

Environment

Site lies at *c.* 100masl, on limestone ridge rising to 146masl; parts of ridge capped with extensive if low-quality source of pebble flint; freshwater springs are located on the south-west side of the ridge; modern soil cover on the Mataci-Stojići ridge includes moist and acidic Ridge land class (p. 212), with a very variable group of other land resources (Stony, Terrace, Arable); uniquely in this otherwise calcareous area heathland vegetation is found, with dwarf Mediterranean oaks and other luxuriant vegetation; four classes of environmental change are found: karstification, vegetation, soil erosion and soil deposition (for details, see Excavation report, Chapter 6).

Field survey

Later Bronze Age pottery and lithics scatters common on the Mataci ridge; little pottery found inside enclosure, but much pottery eroded down the south-west slope from the enclosure.

81. Mataci-Jazvinački Brijeg: main rampart, south-east side

Analytical survey
Single enclosing drystone wall, severely eroded (fig. 81). South-west gate with butt end, 9m in width. Only surviving internal surface feature is a large cairn (height 0.5m; 10 × 8.5m), located opposite the gateway. Some 65m south-west of the south-west rampart, a surviving fragment of earthen bank was built on the same axis as the south-west rampart.

Interpretation
Stock enclosure with possible attached field(s).

Pridraga: Bronze Age cairnfield (figs. 82–3)

History of investigations
Discovered by NDP in 1983; further work in 1984 and 1986.

Environment
Pridraga lies on north-east facing lower slopes above the inland sea of Karinsko More, at 20–110masl. The site is in an ecotone location, at the junction of the predominantly pastoral Bukovica and the more agricultural Ravni Kotari. The site hillslope has alternate limestone outcrops and natural, level grassy terraces. There is a permanent spring on the shores of the sea at Vrulje, some 0.5km from the

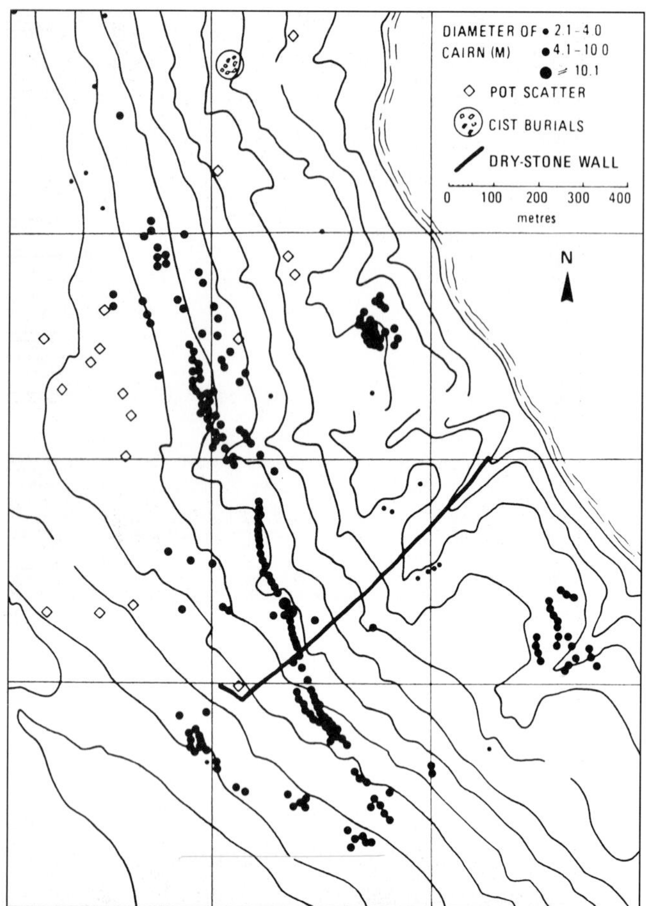

82. The Pridraga cairnfield

cairnfield. Most of the site soils are a terra rossa over limestone, which would have been Stony LUC, changing to Karst when vertically and horizontally eroded. Closer to Karinsko More are easily eroded, better quality brown forest soils. Evergreen oaklands dominate the site wherever there is no arable cultivation. Environmental change can be documented in the erosion after initial cultivation and land improvement measures to deal with this problem.

Field survey

Fifteen pot scatters were found within or on the edge of the cairnfield, twelve of which contained only Later Bronze Age pottery. Pottery on cairns was exclusively Bronze Age and two cairns with surface pottery were built over the drystone wall.

Analytical field survey

Cairnfield of 245 cairns distributed over an area of 12 sq km, with a drystone wall (fig. 83) bisecting the cairnfield, a total of fifteen scatters of Bronze Age pottery

83. The Pridraga cairnfield: drystone wall, mid-slope

within the cairnfield and a group of six cists on the north edge of the site. The cist graves are made of limestone slabs, up to 1.5m long and 0.5m wide. Some 850m in length, the wall was rarely preserved to more than 0.4m in height and was consistently 1.5–2m wide. The wall was constructed using medium-sized, unworked limestone boulders in a haphazard style. The most significant part of the site is the group of cairns themselves. The vast majority of cairns (82 per cent) are smaller than 6m in diameter. The larger cairns (greater than 8m in diameter) are restricted to the upper and intermediate slopes. Fourteen groups of cairns can be defined, whether linear (along terraces) or clustered (across terraces). In ten out of fourteen groups, the largest cairn was located at the end of the line. There is an inverse relationship between size and frequency of cairns per group.

Interpretation

A prolonged occupation of the site is hypothesized, with the likelihood of two phases of agricultural activity – a less intensive phase of initial cultivation of the grassy terraces, which encouraged soil erosion, followed by a more intensive episode, during which increasing stone clearance led to the construction of clearance cairns. The location of Bronze Age domestic occupation may be indicated by the pottery scatters. The construction of a drystone wall in the earlier part of the site's occupation is best regarded as a territorial boundary of the settlement area, which went out of use with the expansion of the settlement in the second phase. The implications of Pridraga for Dalmatian later prehistory are that the reinterpretation of cairns in terms of markers of cultivation as well as burial activity opens up new opportunities for the identification of hitherto almost unrecognized Bronze Age domestic sites. Far from maintaining the traditional assumption of pastoralism dominating the Bronze Age economy, the likelihood of widespread areas of cultivation in limestone areas provokes a re-examination of land use and settlement.

The Nadin group

Nadin-Gradina: multi-period hill-fort with extra-mural settlement (figs. 84–95)

History of investigations

Six periods of use can be defined for the Gradina site: (1) a Late Bronze Age surface find (Batović 1953); (2) Iron Age occupation within and perhaps outside an impressive rampart built of 'megalithic' blocks of limestone (Batović 1977, 1987); (3) the creation of a *municipium* called *Nedinum* in the Roman period, with the development of monumental buildings on the hilltop and extra-mural settlement; (4) after abandonment in late Antiquity, reoccupation in the high medieval period (as attested by documentary evidence: Klaić and Petricioli 1976); (5) occupation of a restricted part of the hilltop as a fortress in the Turkish period; and (6) military occupation by the JNA in AD 1990–4.

Environment

At 265masl, the site lies on the top and slopes of the dominant limestone summit of the third limestone ridge inland from the Adriatic Sea (see figs. 47–8). To the south-west lies Nadinsko Blato (fig. 15), a crucial summer grazing resource for all the surrounding villages. There are no springs on the Gradina hill and no evidence for a Roman aqueduct. The modern Nadin territory consists of a high percentage of what is now Karst land (90 per cent within 500m radius; 70 per cent within 1km radius), with large areas of Terrace land within a 1km territory. Maquis communities dominated by evergreen oak (*Quercus coccifera*) are thriving on the Nadin ridge. Environmental changes relate to soil degradation following deforestation of the ridge, land management (construction of terracing) and the drainage of Nadinsko Blato.

Field survey

Iron Age, Roman and medieval sherds were found in 95 per cent of the site area, although mostly in secondary contexts.

Analytical survey

Nadin-Gradina covers a total area of *c.* 32.6ha (fig. 84), of which some 7.1ha lies within the main stone rampart crowning the Nadin hill (fig. 85). The remains on the slopes of the hill cover an arc of 320 degrees, being absent only on the west side,

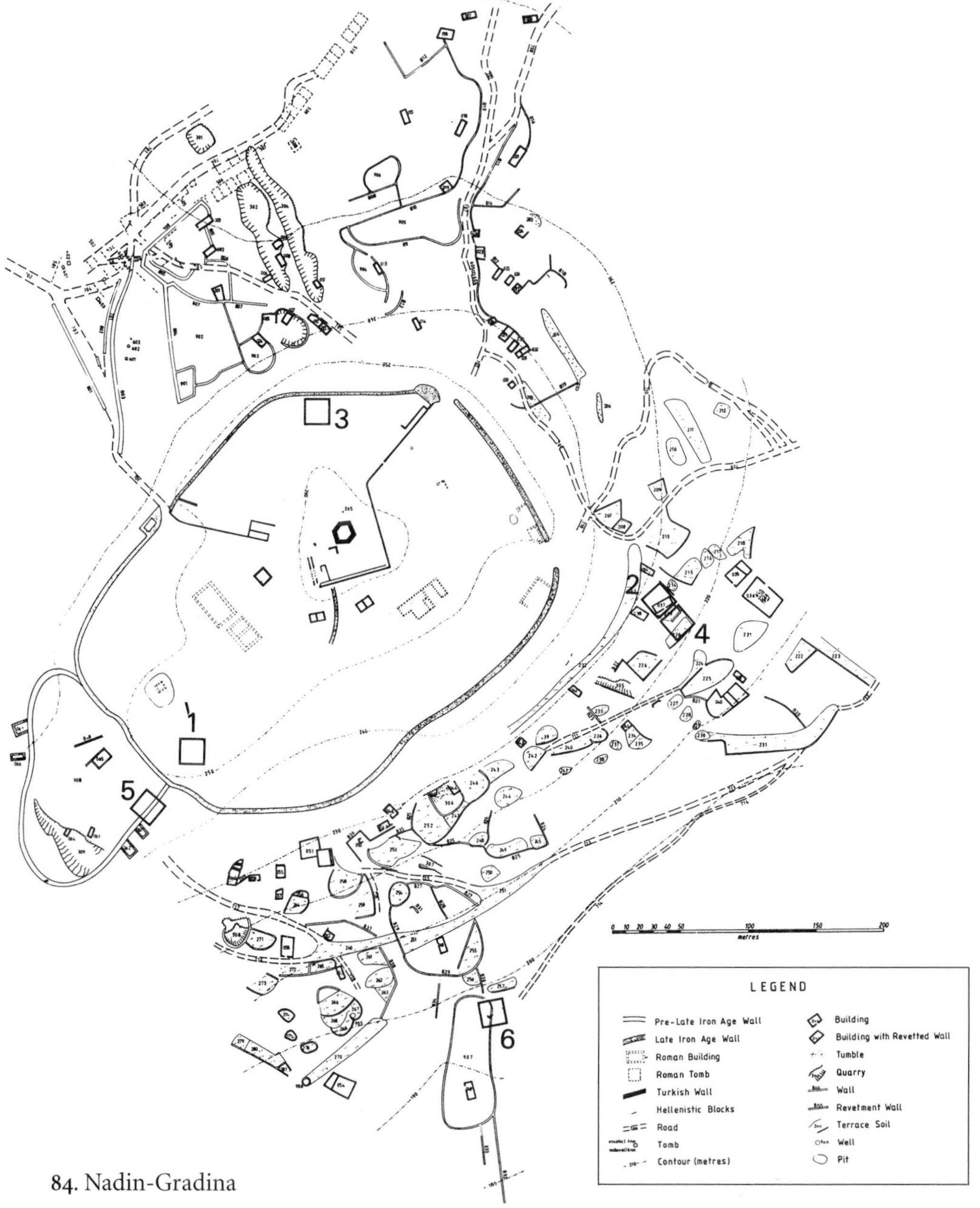

84. Nadin-Gradina

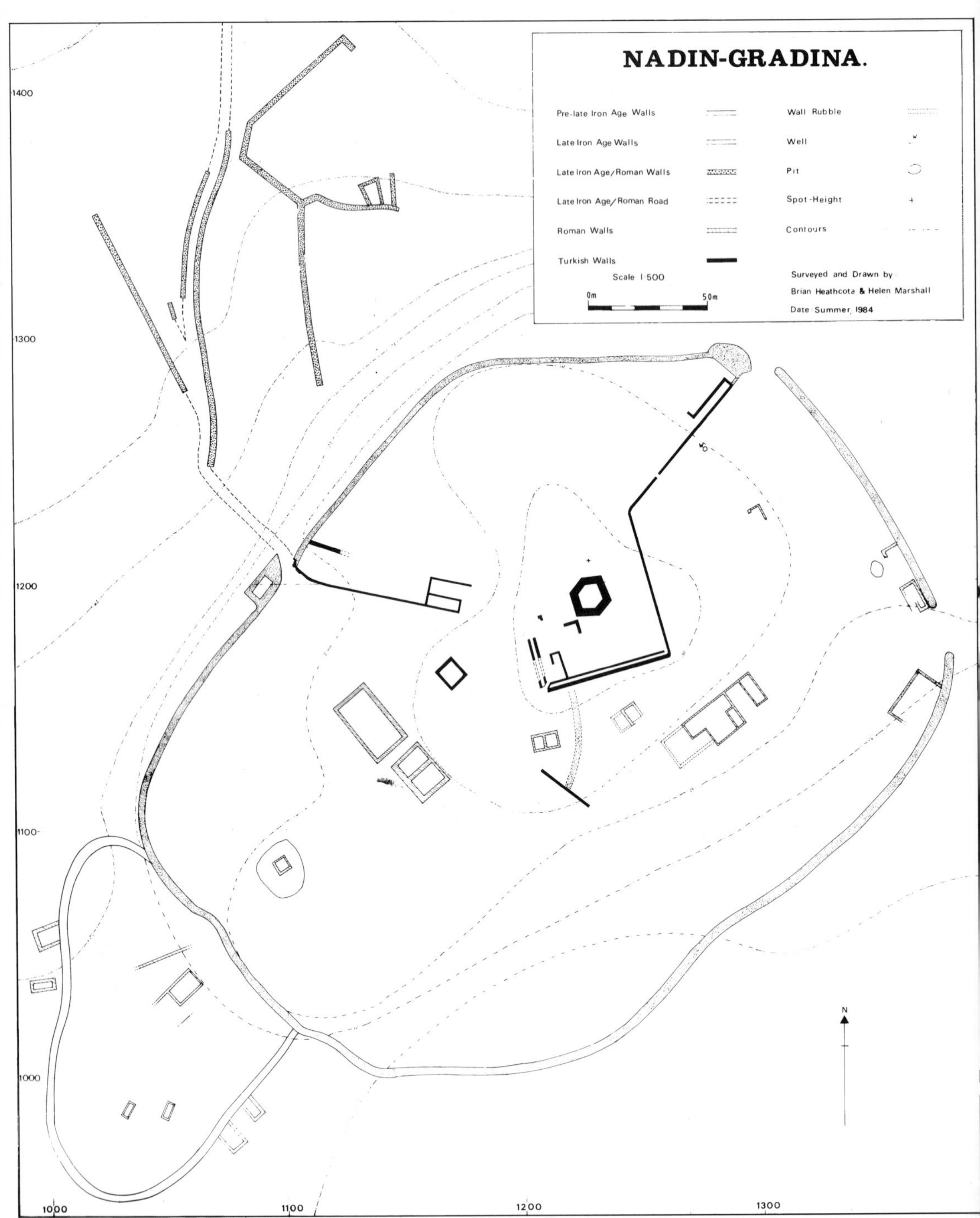

85. Intra-mural area, Nadin-Gradina

86. Nadin-Gradina: quarry 306, from east

with its modern hamlet. There are seven constituents of the site plan: the main rampart, the buildings, the quarries, the terraces, the enclosures and dividing walls, the graves and the roads. Unless otherwise stated, all features are Roman in date.

Quarries: At least fifteen are known, on the north, east and south-east slopes below the ramparts (fig. 86). Each rampart sector was built of the stone from the nearest quarry. All the ancient quarries exploited outcrops of Senonian limestone; the most heavily exploited quarries were those on the south side of the hill. The buildings inside the hill-fort were constructed using stone from quarries on the north side of the hill. The builders of the Turkish tower used calcareous sandstone from flysch deposits on the edge of the Benkovac trough, 3km away. Fragments of Brački kamen from the islands of Hvar or Brač, some 180km distant, were found in destroyed buildings in the interior of the hill-fort. Grindstones were made of local quartzitic sandstones and conglomerates, as well as from a non-local basalt perhaps imported from Italy (pers. comm. D. Cerina, 1986).

Ramparts: Main 'megalithic' rampart, of length 962m, width from 4.2–6.6m (fig. 87), stone blocks up to 500 × 300mm but mostly 400 × 200mm (fig. 88), 3 gateways (east: butt-end; north-west: butt and mound; west: butt and sub-rectangular block). Turkish rampart: mortared, over 3.5m high (fig. 89), surrounding polygonal tower (or kula), 16 × 14m.

87. Nadin-Gradina: cross-section of south rampart, from south-east (recorded from an illicit excavation of 1987)

88. Nadin-Gradina: exterior of Iron Age megalithic blocks, east rampart

89. Nadin-Gradina: Turkish wall, near north-west gate, from east

90. Nadin-Gradina: double drystone wall technique, Building 48, north wall, from west

91. Nadin-Gradina: House-and-garden complex

92. Nadin-Gradina: Terrace 201, from west

93. Nadin-Gradina: Roman road 710, from north

Buildings: Eighty-four buildings preserved, mostly extramurally. Built in double drystone wall technique with rubble fill (fig. 90), except for finer stone in large intramural buildings (largest, 47 × 16m). Two size classes: <100 sq m and >100 sq m. House compounds (house plus garden: fig. 91) found in South district.

Terraces: Eighty-one found, mostly on south-east slopes; most with drystone revetment walls, oval or sub-rectangular shape; most frequent size: 100–200 sq m (fig. 92).

Enclosures: Fourteen found, mostly in north-east district; drystone walls, oval or sub-rectangular; two size classes: 200–500 sq m and 1,000–10,000 sq m; twelve out of fourteen enclosures associated with small buildings.

Roads: Eighteen roads form an integrated network (fig. 93), perhaps based on Iron Age trackways; road lengths range from 35m–325 m; vertical-set paving stones in three cases.

Burials: Seven Hellenistic cist burials (Batović 1987); ten rectangular Roman grave parcels; three medieval cist graves.

Interpretation by S. Ellis

In the Iron Age, there is a strong probability that occupation was limited to the intramural sector, with cultivation and pasture on the hillslopes. Here, the basic principle underlying settlement form was a bounded totality defined by the rampart. In the Roman period, a new, open-ended principle of settlement form took over. Three distinctive extra-mural districts emerge (fig. 94). The south district is characterized by small enclosures and terraces, each of which contains a relatively large building. The north-west district is characterized by the presence of tombs and quarries. The north-east district consists of some large enclosures, and a few small buildings. Each district of Nadin may have had a particular role to play in the community. The north-west district was heavy with the atmosphere of the past, with tombs of those famous citizens whose shades protected their ancestral home. The north-east district resembles a trading district selling to visitors, and people who came to the local market. The south district was the main agricultural area, close to the citadel so as to be in easy reach, and yet sheltered from visitors for protection. The principle of bounded space regains the upper hand in the medieval period, especially during the Turkish military occupation, concentrated on the highest part of the hilltop, within a strongly defended area of 1.75–2 ha (fig. 95). Population estimates based on floor area and built-to-unbuilt space ratios indicate an Iron Age population of probably fewer than 400 people, with a possible doubling of that figure in the Roman period.

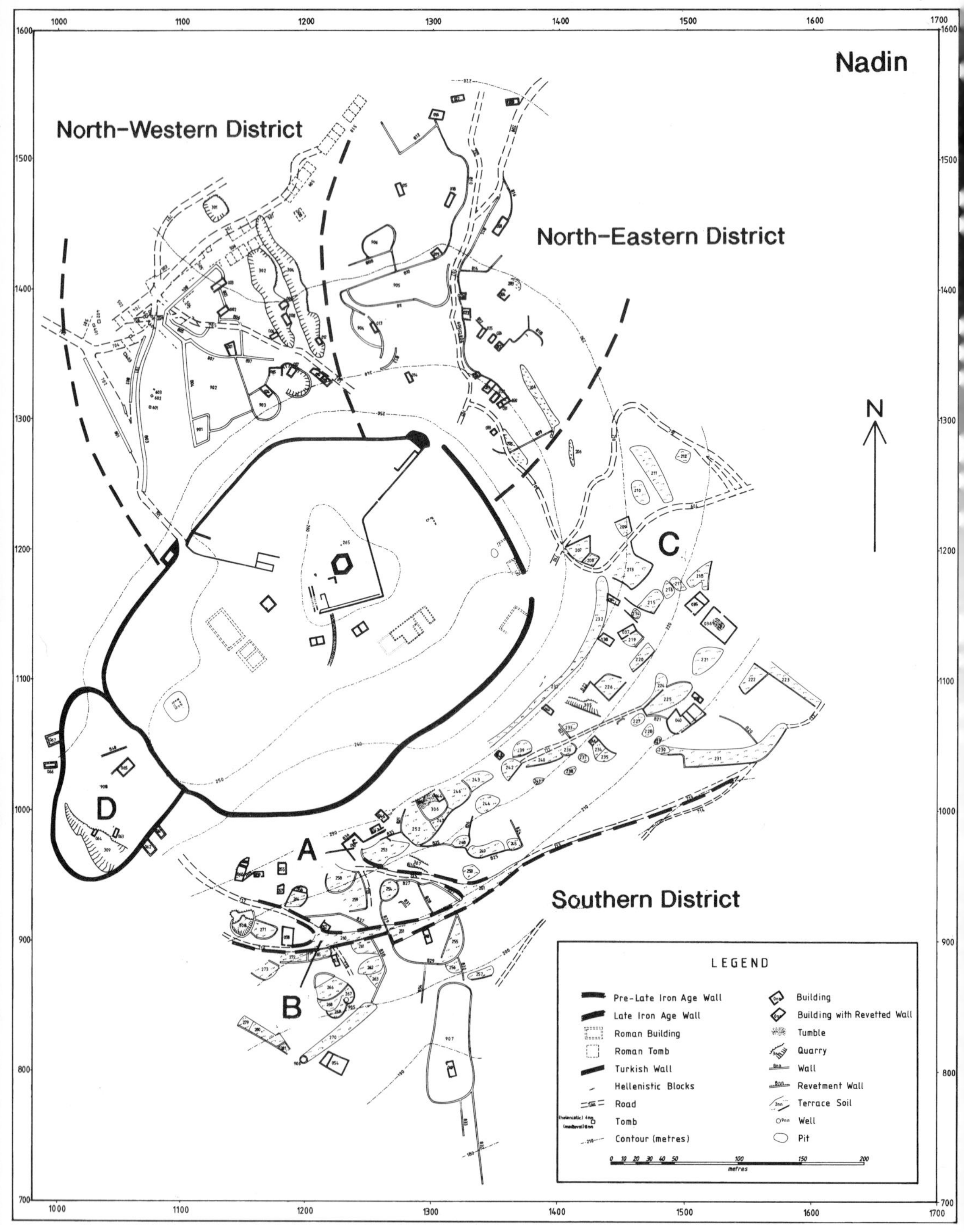

94. Zonation of extra-mural settlement, Nadin-Gradina (*S. Ellis*)

95. Nadin-Gradina in Turkish times, from a print discovered in Nadin hamlet

Krizova Glava: undated hill-fort (fig. 96)

History of investigations
Found by NDP in 1983; analytical survey in 1986.

Environment
Site near Nadin, on a lower (235masl) summit of the Nadin ridge. There is little or no surface water on the Nadin ridge near Krizova Glava; located close to the junction of four land classes (Terrace, Stony, Arable, and the dominant Karst type).

Field Survey
No surface pottery within enclosure; Iron Age and Roman sherds on col between the site and Nadin.

Analytical survey
Single drystone rampart, badly damaged by JNA, survives on north-east, north-west and south-west sides, enclosing area of 1.9ha; horned gateway on north-west side; quarry on south-west side, with one building (13 × 5.5m); two medieval cist graves in south sector; subsidiary, and smaller, enclosure to south of main rampart.

96. Krizova Glava

Interpretation
Subsidiary stock enclosure to Nadin-Gradina, reused for medieval burial.

Vijenac: Bronze and Iron Age hill-fort (figs. 97–100)

History of investigations
Not listed in Batović (1977); first surveyed by NDP (1984 and 1986).

Environment
Site on second highest hilltop (240masl) of Nadin Ridge, separated from Nadin by deep valley (fig. 98); within a 0.5 and 1km radius, the soils are dominated by Karst (80 per cent), with 15 per cent Terrace and 5 per cent Stony. *Karstrillen* analysis, a technique which enables the estimation of soil erosion through measurement of

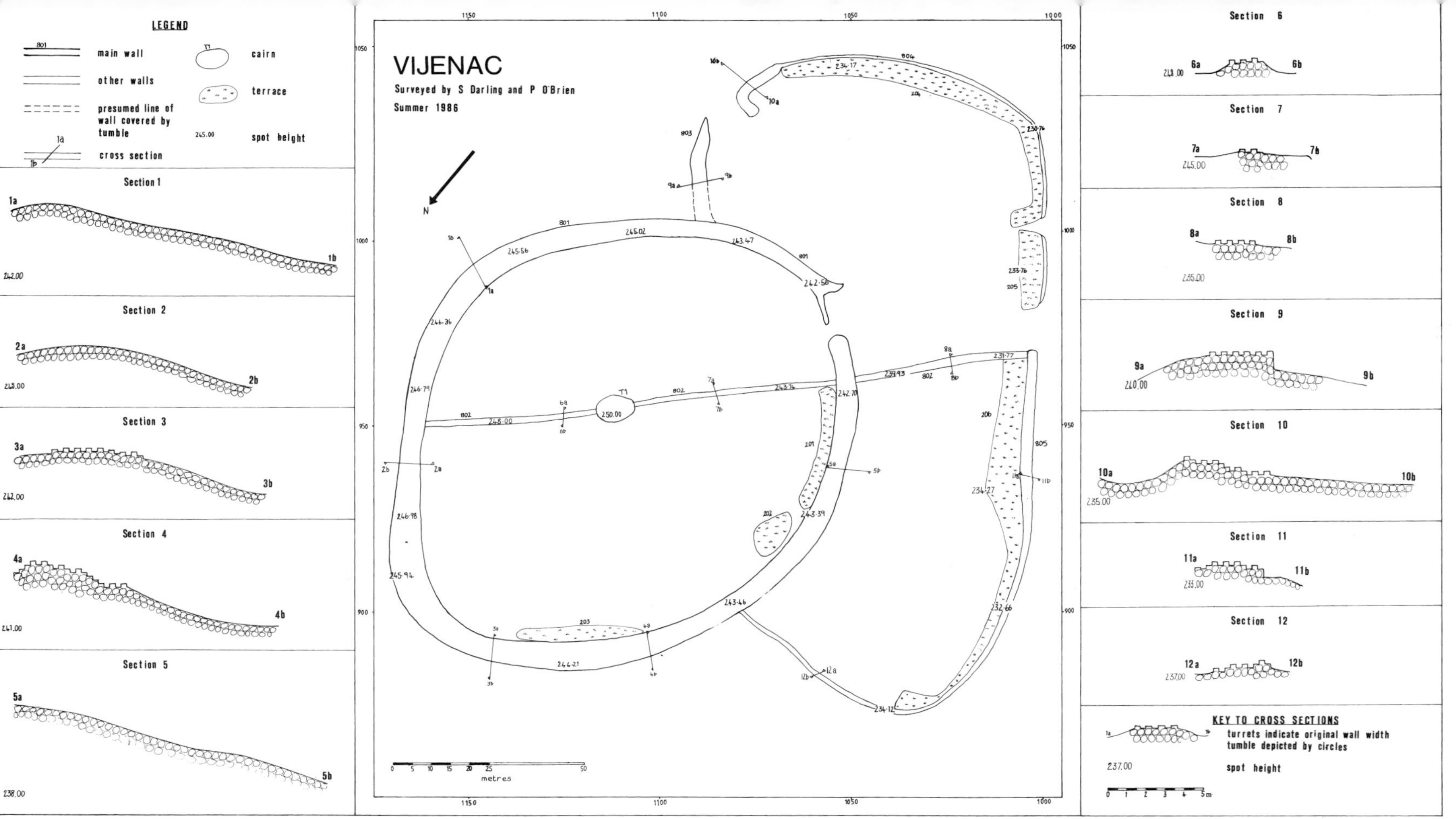
LEGEND
main wall
other walls
presumed line of wall covered by tumble
cross section
cairn
terrace
spot height
Section 1
Section 2
Section 3
Section 4
Section 5
VIJENAC
Surveyed by S Darling and P O'Brien
Summer 1986
N
metres
Section 6
Section 7
Section 8
Section 9
Section 10
Section 11
Section 12
KEY TO CROSS SECTIONS
turrets indicate original wall width
tumble depicted by circles
spot height

97. Vijenac

98. Vijenac, from Nadin-Gradina, from north-west

the gap between modern land surface and the bottom of rills in *in situ* limestone rocks and boulders, indicates the loss of between 0.1 and 0.2m of soil from within the hill-fort.

Field survey

Bronze and Iron Age sherds were found within the main enclosure; Iron Age sherds were found on the south-west terraces; a small quantity of Roman material was found around the cairn in the main enclosure.

Analytical survey

There are three main constituents of the site (fig. 97): the main enclosure, the subsidiary enclosure and the terraces (not plotted). Excluding the terraces, the site encloses a total area of 2.2ha.

Main enclosure: Primary site feature, with drystone rampart (fig. 99) enclosing 1.2ha; central to enclosure is a large cairn (10 × 7.3m); enclosure divided into two by internal cross wall; rampart 5m wide, with one horned gateway on south side (once 12m wide, later 3m with blocking-wall). Three perimeter terraces.

99. Vijenac: north-west rampart, from south-east

100. Vijenac: terrace of outer fort, from north

101. Čauševica: Enclosure 3, west rampart

Subsidiary enclosure: Rampart enclosing 1.06ha, built in at least five segments of differing wall width; three hillslope terraces (fig. 100).

Interpretation

The hill-fort of Vijenac is a two-phase construction with occupation dating to the Bronze Age and Iron Age (*c.* 1700 – 100 Cal. BC). In the first phase, an oval rampart of 1.2ha was built on the hilltop; a greater depth of soil existed then, presumably permitting some cultivation. At some time after enclosure, erosion removed some soil cover to the foot of the ramparts, where perimeter terraces developed. The primary function of the subsidiary enclosure may have been the extension of the fort's cultivation area. At a time of relative peace, lower terraces were built on the south-west slope of Vijenac hill. These terraces are similar in size and shape to those at Nadin-Gradina.

Čauševica: Bronze Age enclosed farmstead (figs. 101–2)

History of investigations

Found by NDP in 1984: soil map and trial excavations in 1985: analytical survey in 1985–6.

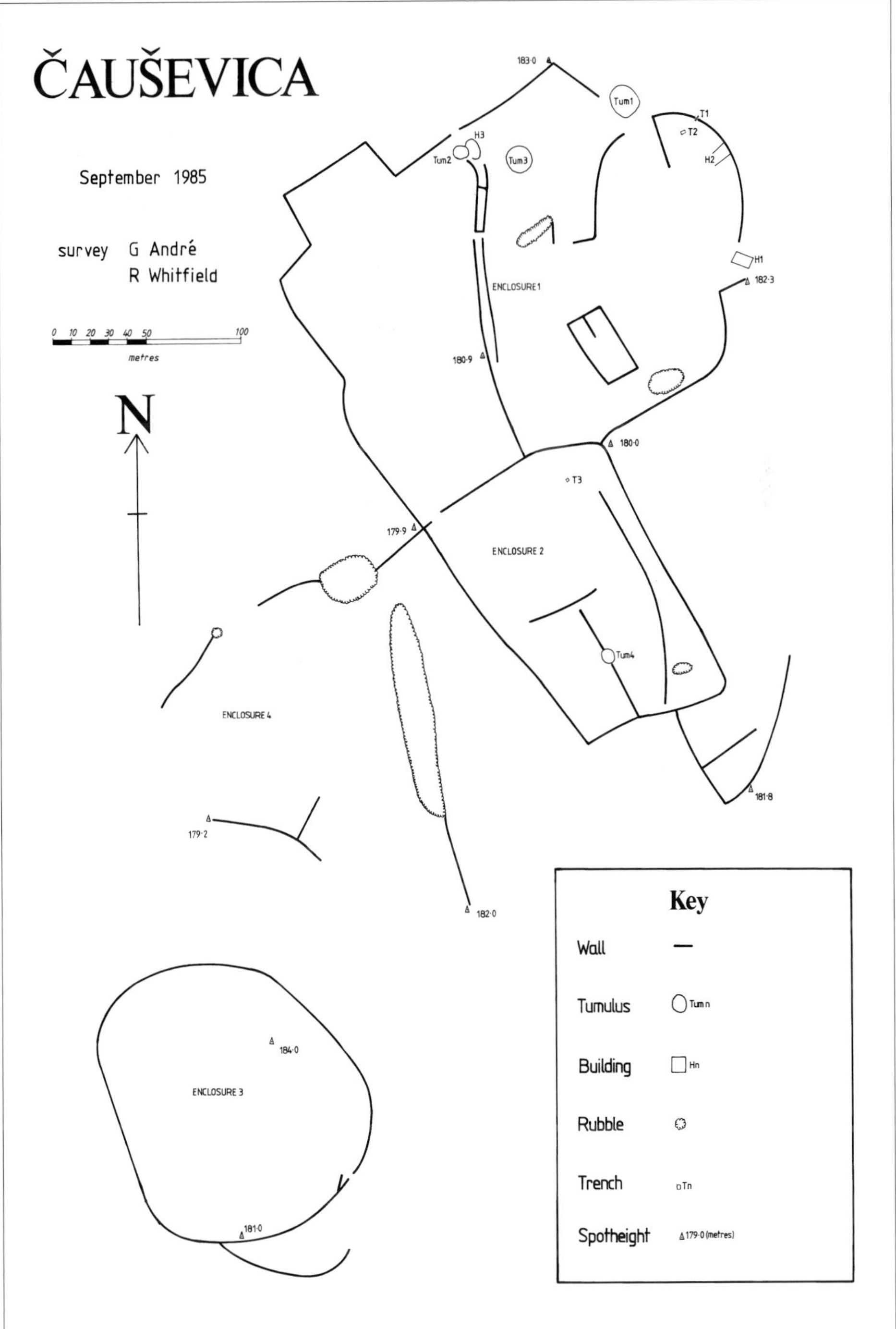
ČAUŠEVICA
September 1985
survey G André
R Whitfield
0 10 20 30 40 50 100
metres
N
183·0
Tum1
T1
T2
H3
Tum2
Tum3
H2
H1
182·3
ENCLOSURE 1
180·9
180·0
T3
179·9
ENCLOSURE 2
Tum4
ENCLOSURE 4
181·8
179·2
182·0
184·0
ENCLOSURE 3
181·0
Key
Wall
Tumulus
Tum n
Building
Hn
Rubble
Trench
Tn
Spotheight
179·0 (metres)

102. Čauševica

Environment

Site on the lowest summit (179–184masl) of the Nadin Ridge, a sub-triangular knoll with widespread limestone outcropping and no surface water. Land resources dominated by Karst. *Karstrillen* analysis indicates a soil loss of 0.2–0.3m within Enclosure 1 since construction.

Field survey

Later Bronze Age sherds occur in fifteen out of nineteen quadrats, with small quantities of Roman pottery and even less Iron Age material.

Analytical survey

A complex drystone walled site, with four main enclosures and related structures (party walls, buildings, cairns, rubble mounds, trackways, lime heap). The site had a multi-period occupation, and the plan of the walls is incomplete.

Enclosures: Surface areas have been calculated for all the four main enclosures and inner subdivisions of Enclosures 1–3 (fig. 102). Most of the linear features and enclosure walls of the Čauševica complex are drystone walls of the standard double-wall, rubble-filled type (fig. 101).

The buildings: Three buildings have been found which correspond to the size of Bronze Age houses (10 × 6m, 7 × 4.6m, 10 × 6m). In addition, there is a large structure in the south sector of Enclosure 1 (37 × 20m).

Cairns: Four cairns have been found, all but one in Enclosure 1 (15.5 × 14.8m; 7.6m diameter; 14m in diameter; 6.8m in diameter).

Rubble mounds: Seven discovered, the largest of which (23m in length, 7.1–7.6m in width) forms the boundaries of Enclosure 4.

Trackways: Three trackways were found, two at the junction of enclosures and one within an enclosure.

Lime heap: Large mound (18m in length, 17.7m in width and 3m in height) used in the preparation for the slaking of lime.

Interpretation

The 10ha site of Čauševica is the first Bronze Age field system to be recorded in Dalmatia. The initial construction of a small internally sub-divided enclosure (2) at the outset, was followed by expansion of enclosed space both to the north

(Enclosure 1) and the south (Enclosures 3 and 4). A later phase of more intensive stone clearance led to the construction of massive stone banks (east wall of Enclosure 4), rubble heaps and cairns. The site has all the main elements of a prehistoric farmstead. The deepest, most fertile soils were found in Enclosure 2, on the proposed periodization the earliest nucleus of occupation. The stone clearance in the later phase of occupation is linked to local soil erosion.

Kutlovica: Bronze and Iron Age hill-fort (figs. 103–4)

History of investigations

Recorded in Batović' list of Liburnian hill-forts (1977, Carte 1, no. 155). Investigated by NDP in 1985–6.

Environment

The site was built on the fifth, most south-easterly summit of the Nadin ridge of Cretaceous limestone (194masl) (fig. 49). There is little or no surface water on the Nadin ridge. Modern land in the Kutlovica area is dominated by Karst, with a large block of Terrace in the 1km territory. *Karstrillen* analysis indicates local soil erosion of 150–200mm from within the enclosed area.

Field survey

Surface sherds dated predominantly to the Iron Age, with Bronze Age pottery concentrated around scoops in the interior slope.

Analytical survey

A single, oval rampart enclosing an area of 2.3ha, including much limestone outcrop (fig. 103). Single rampart of double drystone wall with rubble infill, widths ranging from 3.8–4.7m. No obvious gateway.

Houses: Natural scoops along the inner edges of the perimeter terraces, two with building remains (14 × 7m in size; 24 × 6.5m).

Terraces: Four perimeter terraces are found, the largest 275 × 13–18m (fig. 104).

Interpretation

A Bronze Age occupation in buildings constructed on house terraces, either prior to, or coeval with, a major phase of rampart construction. The Iron Age occupation was much more widespread, with considerable densities of surface pottery over all the site.

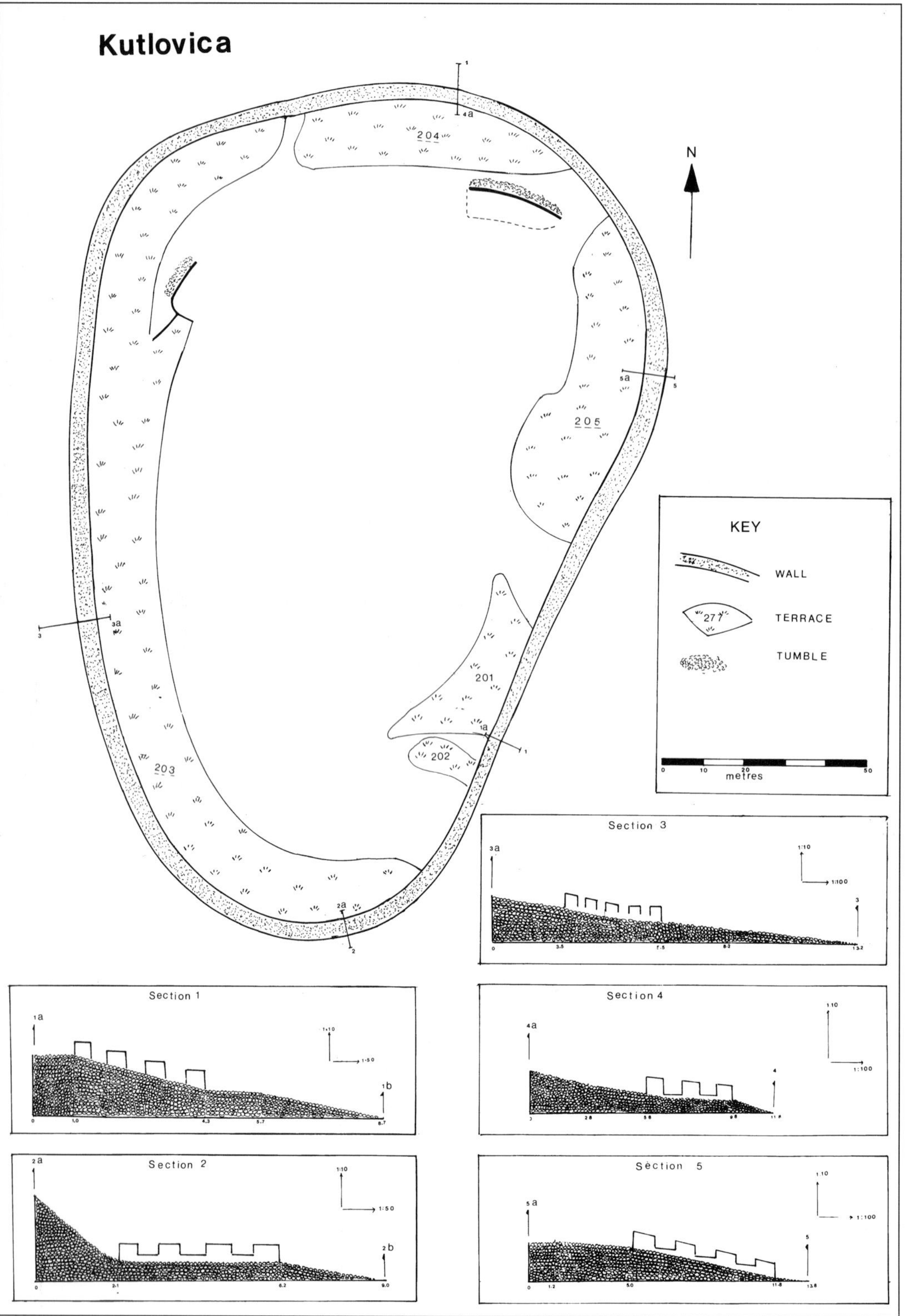

103. Kutlovica

104. Kutlovica: Terrace 205, from south-east

The Jagodnja group

Mutvica: Bronze Age enclosure (fig. 105)

History of investigations
Discovered by NDP in 1985 and surveyed in 1986.

Environment
Site on a small summit (134masl) on the subsidiary limestone ridge between the Nadinsko Blato depression and the Polača basin (fig. 42). The ridge is narrow enough to allow good access to the fertile Arable land in both adjacent lowlands. The site lies close to two well-watered alluvial areas. In a 1km radius, the mosaic of all five land classes (Stony, Terrace, Arable, Bottomland and Karst) provides the land use potential for a varied economy.

Field survey
Concentrations of Later Bronze Age pottery were found within the enclosure.

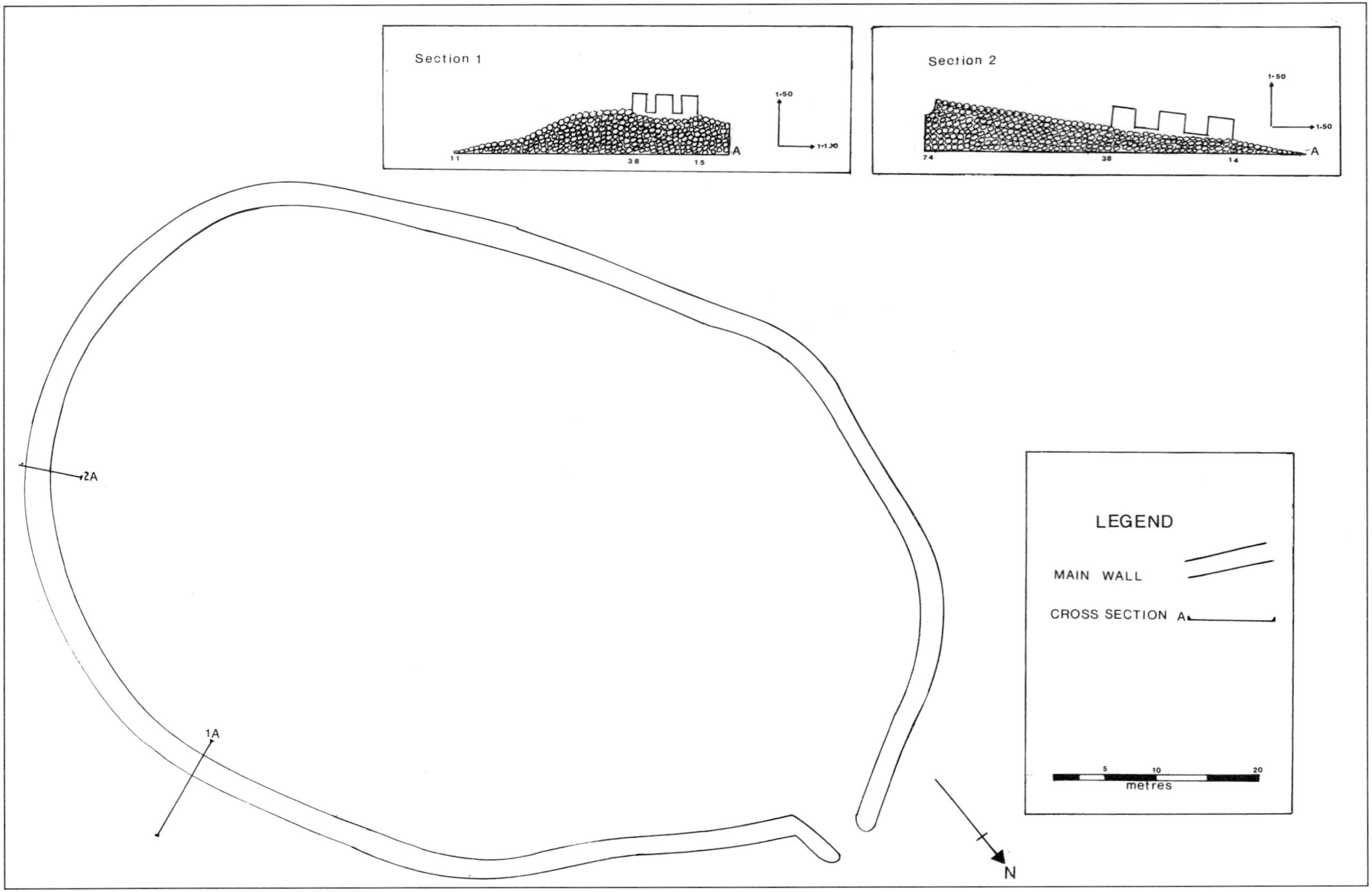

Section 1
1·50
11
38
15
A
Section 2
1·50
1·50
74
38
14
A
2A
1A
LEGEND
MAIN WALL
CROSS SECTION A
5
10
20
metres
N

105. Mutvica

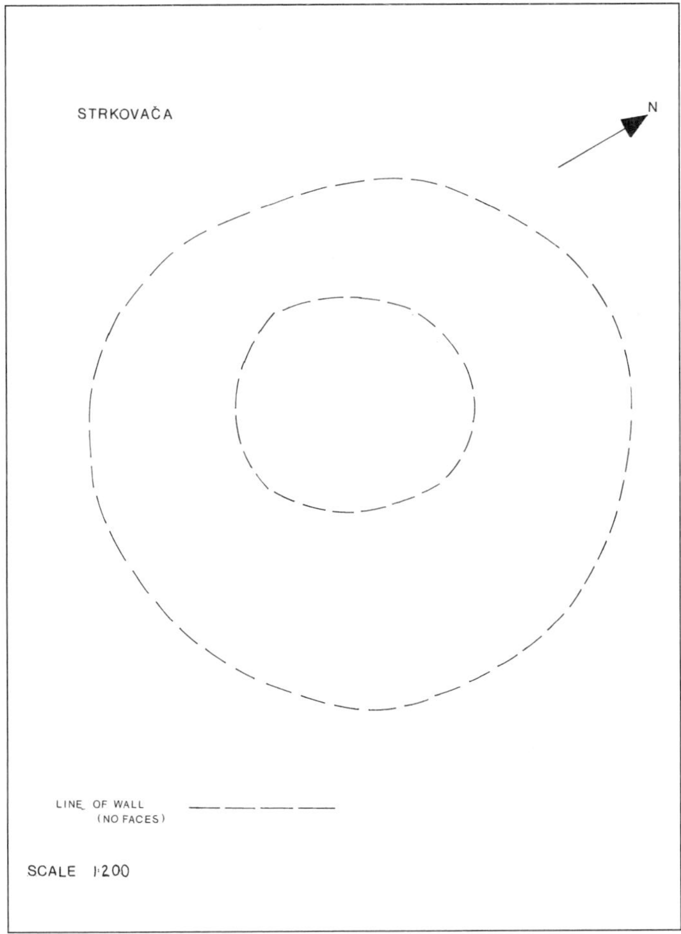

106. Strkovača

107. Strkovača, from Kruglas, from south-east

Analytical survey
A single, oval drystone rampart (2.3–2.4m wide) enclosing an area of 0.46ha (fig. 105) butt-end gateway on north-west side. No evidence of internal structures.

Interpretation
This site exemplifies the simple single-walled stock enclosure of the Bronze Age, a site type that may well be regarded as the precursor of the more heavily defended hill-forts.

Strkovača: Bronze Age hill-fort (figs. 106–7)

History of investigations
Recorded in Batović' list of hill-forts (1977, Carte 1, no. 110). First surveyed in 1986 by NDP.

Environment
Site on a small but steep summit (157masl) on the Prtenjača limestone ridge (figs. 42, 107). The closest well-watered area lies to the south-west. A typical soil mosaic characterizes the 1km radius including all LUCs. Severe erosion has led to the partial collapse of the drystone ramparts originally set up on the summit of the steep hill.

Field survey
Several scatters of Bronze Age pottery were found on the slopes of the hill some distance from the rampart, in secondary position.

Analytical survey
Erosion on the summit of Strkovača has been so great that no wall faces survive from what appears to be a double line of concentric drystone walls (fig. 106). The inner wall encloses a surface area of 0.035ha, the outer an area of 0.2ha. Large central cairn on the top of the hill.

Interpretation
Poorly defined Later Bronze Age hilltop enclosure. The possibility of a look-out function cannot be excluded.

Kruglas: Bronze Age, Iron Age and Roman hill-fort (figs. 108–10)

History of investigations
Recorded in Batovic' list of hill-forts (1977, Carte 1, no. 111); first systematically explored in 1986 by NDP.

Environment
Site built on one of the small, steep summits (141masl) of the Prtenjača limestone ridge. On the north-east side, there is a small closed basin at the foot of the hill, with very fertile soils. On the south-west side, the hill slopes to the Polača basin. Well-watered areas are found nearby, to the north-west and the south-east. Karst land dominates the territory, with some Terrace, Arable and Stony.

Field survey
High densities of surface Bronze Age and Roman pottery, with less Iron Age material, was discovered in the hill-fort and on the south-west slopes, indicating a long-term preference for this site.

Analytical survey
Kruglas hill-fort encloses an area of 0.48ha with a single oval drystone wall, 1.5–1.6m wide, with a possible tower on the north-west side and a single horned gateway on the south-west side (fig. 108). Leading to the gateway is a rock-cut track which connects the fort to the Polača basin. The area enclosed is relatively steep, with a large limestone outcrop on the summit, near the north-east side. One perimeter terrace and two internal hillslope terraces provide small flat areas for horticulture. Two buildings have also been found in the enclosed area (1-roomed, 19.4 × 5.8m; 1-roomed, 10 × 8m). The gateway is approached from the south-west by a track which covers a length of over 30m, rock-cut for the last 10m and 2.5m wide (figs. 109–10). The cutting of the track represents a minor engineering feat for the Kruglas inhabitants and is hitherto unparalleled in the Ravni Kotari.

Interpretation
The hill-fort of Kruglas was occupied from the Bronze Age into the Roman period. There is no reason why the tower, the gateway and the track cannot be regarded as an integrated plan of a Bronze Age site selected for long-term occupation because of the high land use potential of its economic territory.

Polača-Dražice or Grabar: Bronze Age wall and field system (figs. 111–12)

History of investigations
Discovered by NDP in 1985; analytical survey, trial excavation and soil study conducted in 1986.

Environment
The site lies on the gentle north-east slopes of the Tinj ridge, at 80–85masl (fig. 112), and above the Bičine marsh. The closest surface water available to the inhabitants

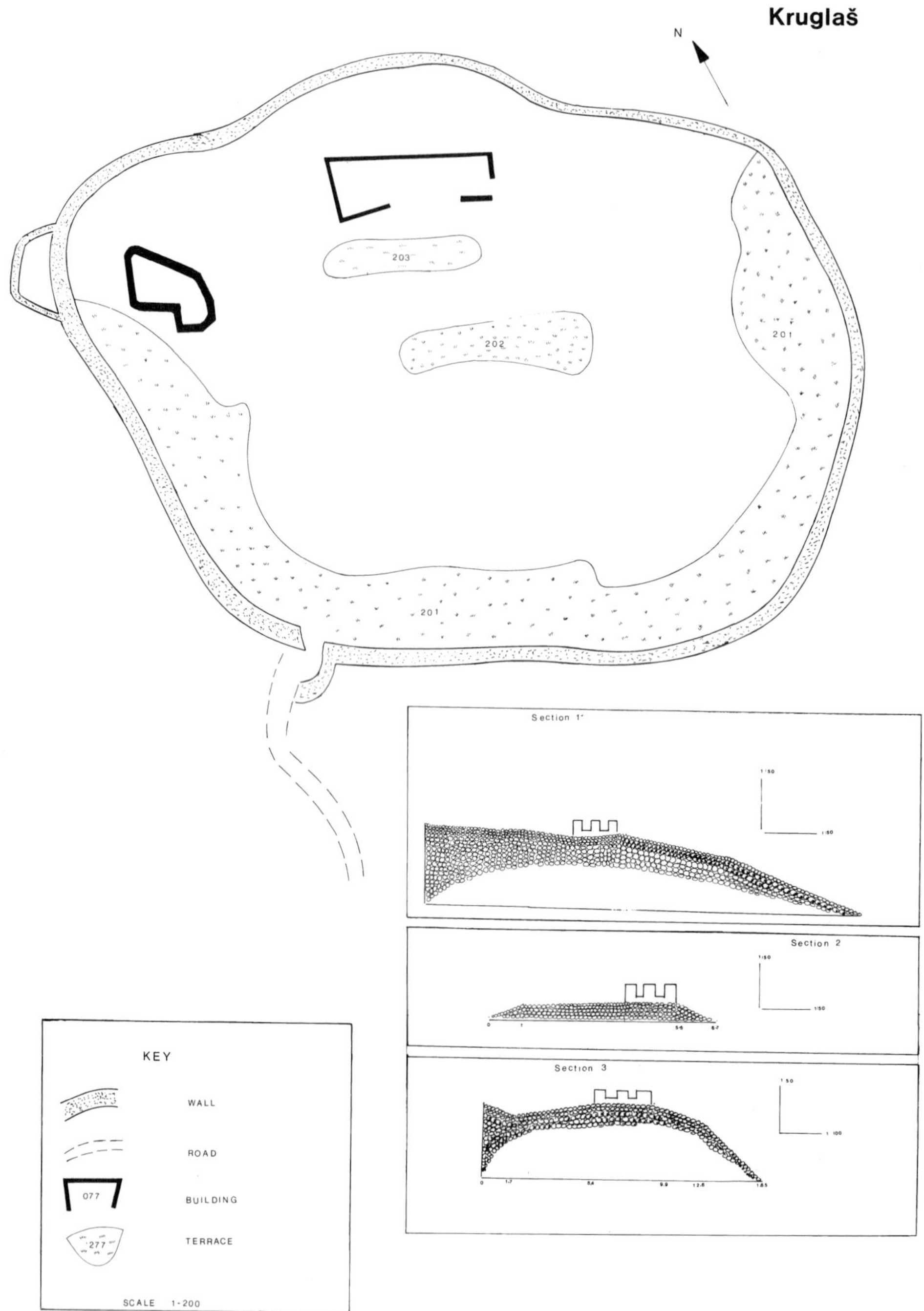
Kruglaš
N
203
202
201
201
Section 1
Section 2
Section 3
KEY
WALL
ROAD
077
BUILDING
277
TERRACE
SCALE 1-200

108. Kruglas

109. Kruglas: rock-cut approach track from north

110. Kruglas: lower part of rock-cut road, from north

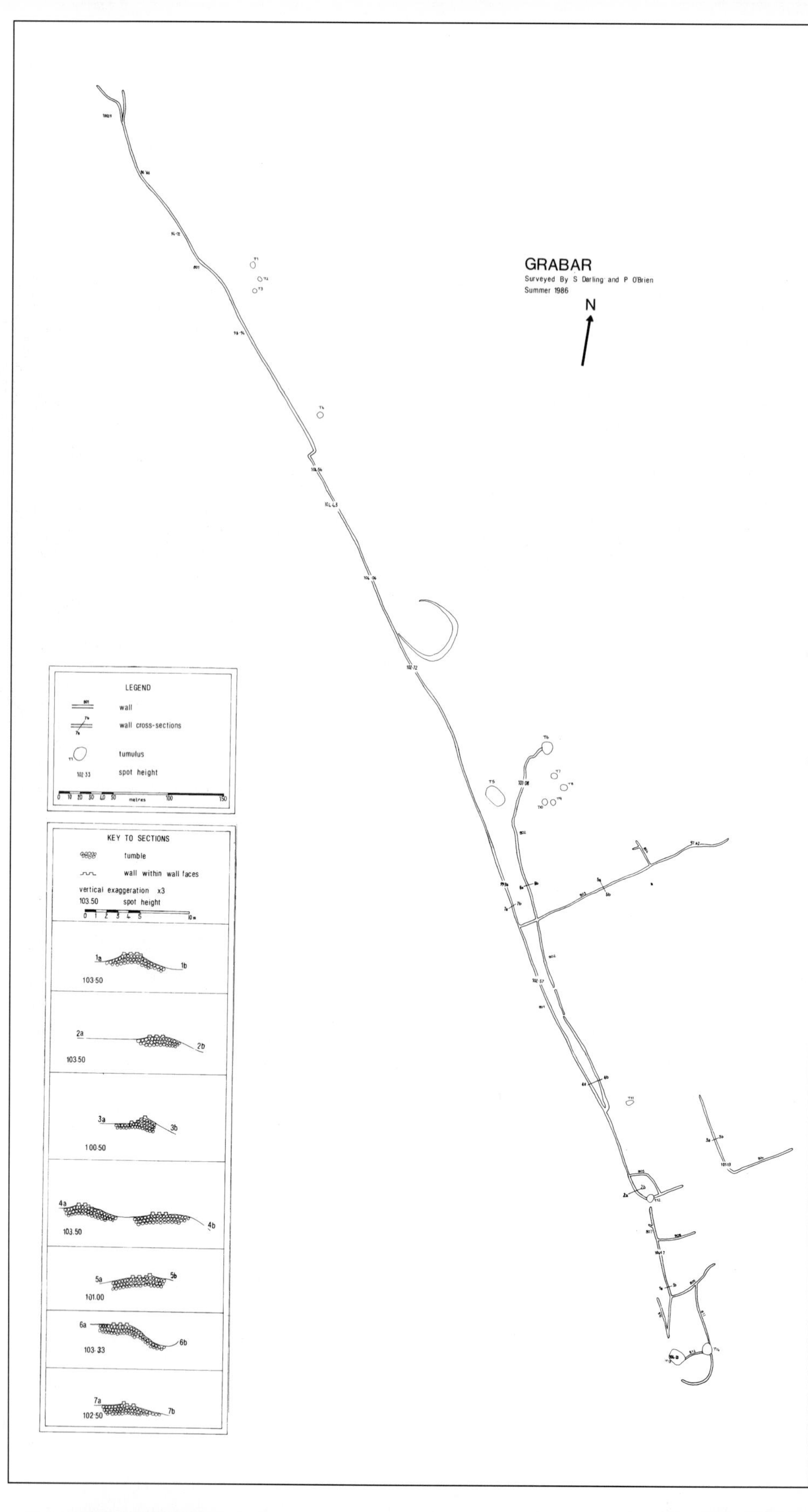
GRABAR
Surveyed By S Darling and P O'Brien
Summer 1986
N
LEGEND
wall
wall cross-sections
tumulus
102·33
spot height
metres
KEY TO SECTIONS
tumble
wall within wall faces
vertical exaggeration x3
103.50
spot height
1a
1b
103·50
2a
2b
103·50
3a
3b
100·50
4a
4b
103.50
5a
5b
101.00
6a
6b
103·33
7a
7b
102·50

112. Polača-Dražice (Grabar), from south-east
111. *opposite* Polača-Dražice (Grabar)

of Dražice would be the Bičine marsh. The immediate environs of Polača are dominated by Karst land but, within the 1km or 2km territories, all the remaining Land Use Classes are present in a varied mix. The rich summer grazing of Nadinsko Blato lies 1.5km to the north-west. *Karstrillen* analysis indicated soil loss of between 0.08 and 0.18m. The land management changes are constituted by the construction of the Polača wall and the associated enclosures and linear features. Recent drainage of Nadinsko Blato and the Bičine marsh have reduced the diversity of both flora and fauna in the Bottomlands.

Field survey

The drystone wall at Polača was initially thought to be 700m in length, predominantly associated with Later Bronze Age pottery. During analytical field survey, it was realized that the wall extended even further, to a length of 1.23km. Sporadic Iron Age and Roman sherds were also found in the central part of the site.

Analytical survey

Polača-Dražice represents a new kind of site type in the Dalmatian Bronze Age – a field system with a long boundary wall running parallel with the contours of the Grabar hill (fig. 111). The system has only been partially preserved owing to building work and cultivation. There are three main components of the Polača monument – drystone walls (twelve examples), cairns (fourteen examples) and fields and enclosures (seven, possibly eight examples). The main function of the wall appears to be largely to separate the 'bad' lands to the south-west from the 'good' lands to the north-east; all the other features of the complex are located south-east of the wall, on the 'good' land. The Polača system can be sub-divided into three main zones: (1) north-north-west zone – the main wall with a few cairns and one enclosure, (2) central zone – the main wall with offset walls, a double wall and clearance cairns, and (3) south-south-east zone – the main wall with a field system. The major feature associated with the main wall in this zone is a field system comprising clearance cairns and five small fields (25 × 20m; 30 × 40m; 55 × 34m; 32 × 25m); a sixth is located *c.* 85m from the main wall to the north-east. The clearance cairns are later than the linear features and fields.

Interpretation

As a combination of long linear feature, clearance cairns and fields, the Polača-Dražice site is so far unique in the Dalmatian Bronze Age. The fields and clearance cairns indicate small-scale farming, but the double wall may well be a special stock control feature, perhaps for sheep-shearing. Thus the wall may best be regarded as a device to separate the cultivated land of the local farmers from grazing on the Karst land of the upper part of the Grabar hill, which was used by visiting shepherds during sheep-shearing time.

Vinculja: Bronze Age, Iron Age and medieval hill-fort (figs. 113–14)

History of investigations

Recorded in Batović' list of Liburnian hill-forts (1977, Carte 1, no. 109); field and analytical survey by NDP in 1986.

Environment

Built on the south-west summit of a pair of hills (133masl) on a limestone ridge dominated by Petrim (253masl). On the north-east side, the fertile Polača depression lies nearby, with the summer pastures of the Vrana bottomland to the south-west. No surface water sources are known on the Tinj–Petrim ridge. The territory is dominated by Karst land, with equal areas of Terrace, Arable and Stony land.

SECTION 1

SECTION 2

SECTION 3

SECTION 4

Vinculja

SEPT 1986

n

LEGEND

MAIN WALL

SECONDARY WALL

BUILDING

RUBBLE

SECTION

SCALE 1:250

113. Vinculja

114. Vinculja: south-west rampart, from west

Field survey
Bronze Age, Iron Age and medieval pottery were found within the main rampart, while only medieval pottery occurred between the secondary wall and the rampart.

Analytical survey
A single, oval rampart of drystone rubble walling, which encloses a moderately flat area of 1ha, with a secondary wall outside the west section of rampart (fig. 113). The main rampart is of rubble-filled double drystone walls, varying in width from 2.5m to 4.2m (fig. 114). There are two gateways in the north and west sectors, both with simple butt ends and widths of 6m. On the south and west sides, nine buildings

which abut the inner face of the rampart have been constructed on the terraces (size range: 4.2 × 3.6m–11.4 × 8.3m). Below the west rampart, a winding, narrow (0.90m) wall was built, in secondary relationship to the primary rampart. The discovery of medieval pottery in the enclosure suggests a medieval date for this feature.

Interpretation
The main period of hill-fort occupation was in the Later Bronze Age and Iron Age (*c.* 1700–100 Cal. BC), during which the oval rampart was constructed together with drystone wall buildings on the perimeter terraces. A less intensive, perhaps pastoralist, reoccupation occurred in the medieval period.

Trojan: Iron Age hill-fort and Roman farm complex (figs. 115–19)

History of investigations
Described by Batović (1971, 1987) and recorded in his list of hill-forts (1977, Carte 1, no. 108; cf. Čače 1985, T. IV). Analytical survey by NDP in 1986.

Environment
Trojan lies on a tongue of land (65–67masl) on the Tinj–Petrim limestone ridge (fig. 50), overlooking the Vrana depression and with a large permanent well at the foot of the hill. The south-west part of the 1km territory is dominated by potentially fertile Bottomland, the site itself lies on Stony land, with a band of Karst to the north-east.

Field survey
Dense distributions of both Iron Age and Roman finds all over the site.

Analytical survey
Area of 3.2ha (fig. 115) enclosed by a drystone wall rampart, part of which is built on a huge earthen bank (fig. 116). Site components include three rampart gates, a long approach road, two quarries, perimeter and hillside terraces and a mass of interior structural remains (fig. 117).

Rampart: Two styles of construction are used in the rampart: a simple drystone rampart and megalithic blocks (near the south gate). Three gateways have been identified, all with butt ends; the west gate may be a Roman breach of an Iron Age wall.

Quarries: Two found on the north side of the site (fig. 118), one with Senonian limestone.

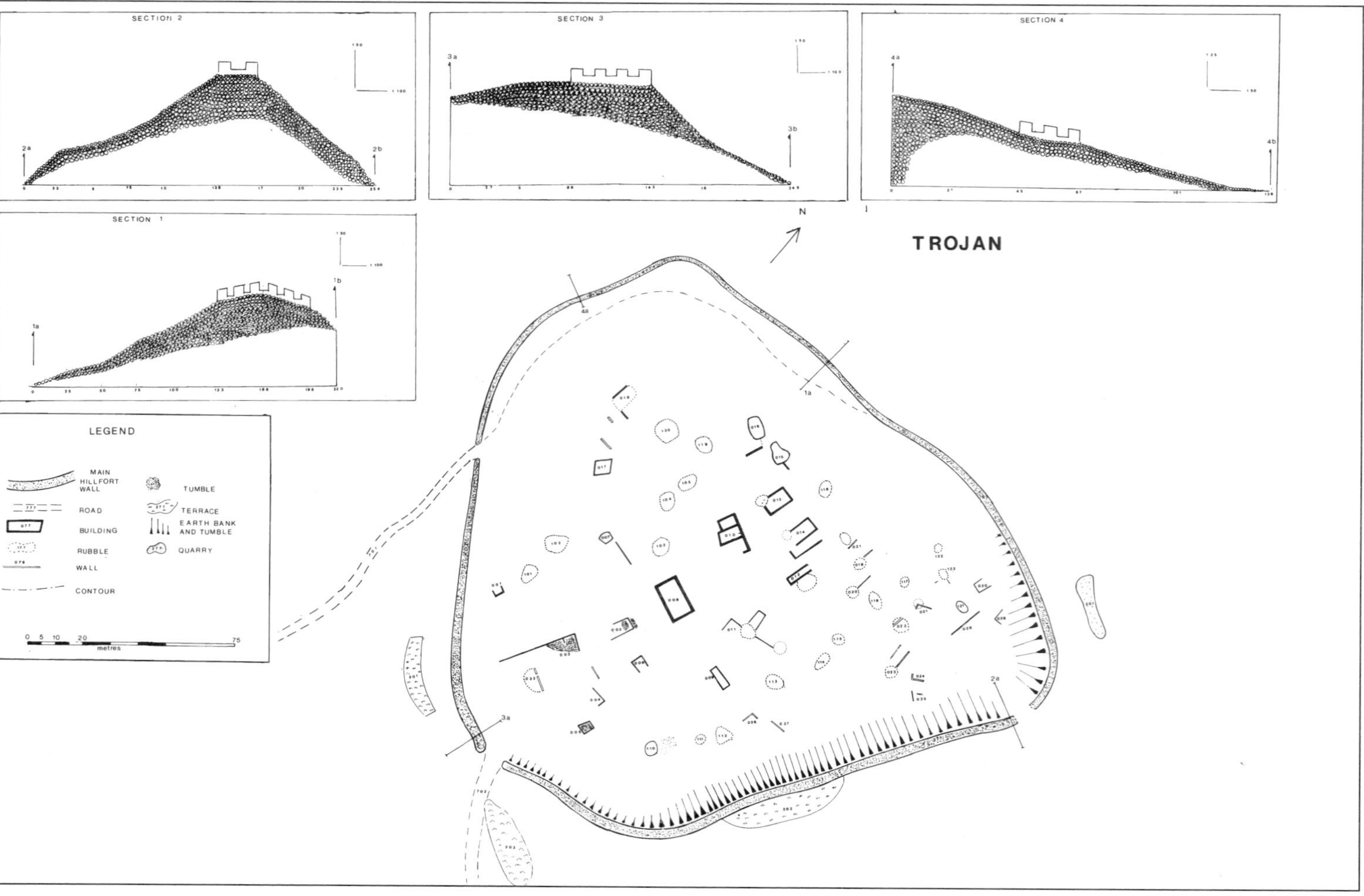
TROJAN
SECTION 2
2a
2b
SECTION 3
3a
3b
SECTION 4
4a
4b
SECTION 1
1a
1b
N
LEGEND
MAIN HILLFORT WALL
ROAD
BUILDING
RUBBLE
WALL
CONTOUR
TUMBLE
TERRACE
EARTH BANK AND TUMBLE
QUARRY
0 5 10 20 75
metres

115. Trojan

116. Trojan: earthen bank from interior of site

117. Trojan: site interior from earthen bank

118. Trojan: quarry on north-east side, from south-west

119. Trojan: main road up to west gate, from north-east

Roads: Two roads were identified on the south approaches: a short (50m) length and a longer (300m) length starting from the foot of the hill (fig. 119).

Terraces: Two long perimeter terraces, and three hillslope terraces on the south side.

Buildings: The remains of fifty-four stone buildings, mostly Roman in date, have been found; the size range is 5 × 3m–15 × 9m (2-roomed), comparable to the smaller buildings at Nadin.

Interpretation

The earlier occupation consists of an Iron Age hill-fort presumably associated with Iron Age structures now buried. The later phase consists of a group of Romanized farm cottages – perhaps a cluster of farms nucleated on one site – with small-scale rural industries in some of the buildings. The crucial resource for the farmers was the rich summer pastures of the Vrana Bottomland.

Regional patterning

The drystone walled structures described above comprise a wide range of monument types present not only in North Dalmatia but also in other limestone areas of Yugoslavia and Italy. Initial construction of cairnfields in the survey area can be dated to the Earlier Bronze Age (2300–1700 Cal. BC). The earliest drystone walled enclosures date to the Later Bronze Age (1700–900 Cal. BC). On current evidence, field systems such as Polača and Čauševica are datable solely to the Later Bronze Age, as are the small hill-forts of Strkovača and Mutvica, the Pridraga cairnfield and the enclosure at Mataci. Other hill-forts, such as Vijenac/upper enclosure, Kutlovica, Vinculja and Kruglas, were first occupied in the Later Bronze Age and reoccupied in the Iron Age. The two larger hill-forts of Nadin and Trojan were first occupied in the Iron Age. Roman finds have been made on Vijenac and Kruglas, although site use in this period is unlikely to have been intensive. Major Roman occupations are attested at Nadin and Trojan. Medieval reoccupation is witnessed only at Nadin and Vinculja.

The following characteristics of the Ravni Kotari monuments serve to define a regional style of both layout and construction:

1. The size range for field systems (9.4–11.1 ha) is larger than that of hill-forts (0.2–7.1 ha).
2. There is an overlap in the basal widths of drystone walls in the field systems (0.9–3.3m) and that found in the ramparts of the hill-forts (1.5–6.6m). The

majority of hill-fort ramparts are of a width exceeding 3m, with a concomitantly greater height.

3. The characteristic material for field walls and defences is undressed limestone boulders, from 0.3 to 1.0m in diameter, built into double drystone walls with rubble infilling. In rare cases, the drystone wall is built on an earthen bank. It is only in the Late Iron Age that quarried and dressed limestone blocks come into use, through the apparent diffusion of the Hellenistic style of military architecture (Faber 1976; Lawrence 1979).
4. The number of formal entrances to fields and hill-forts varies from one to three; half of the sites have one entrance, while 25 per cent have respectively two and three gates.
5. With the exception of Nadin, there are two standard forms of hill-fort entrances – the butt end and the horned gateway. Since butt end entrances are ubiquitous in the field systems, they may be the source for hill-fort gates. Single-horned gateways occur as early as the Later Bronze Age at Mutvica. The only double-horn gateway known in the study area is the undated example at Krizova Glava. At Nadin, the east gateway is built between two large earth bastions which carry the wall up to the gate.
6. Two forms of terrace are known on a minority of the Dalmatian sites: hillslope terraces are rare and occur at only three sites (Roman Nadin, Trojan and Vijenac), while perimeter terraces are more common (five sites – Trojan, Vijenac, Vinculja, Kutlovica and Kruglas).
7. A major difference between the hill-forts and the field systems is the rarity of cairns associated with the former. Only at Mataci and Vijenac is a cairn found within a enclosure. By contrast, cairns are integral to the field systems at both Polača and Čauševica, while an agricultural function has been proposed for at least some of the Pridraga cairns.
8. The majority of hill-forts comprises stone defences enclosing a single, undivided interior space. In the case of the field systems, internal partitioning of space is common by definition. The hill-fort exceptions are Strkovača and Vijenac. At the former, two concentric walls are found. At the latter, a single drystone wall divides both enclosures into two more or less equal parts. At Trojan, the natural feature of an upper plateau divides the site into two unequal parts. At Nadin, extramural partitioning of space is basic to a differentiated town plan.
9. In a minority of cases, approach roads are constructed to fields and hill-forts. The simplest trackways are those at Čauševica, bounded on each side by a low wall or bank. The approach track to Kruglas necessitated cutting through 1m-

thick limestone outcrops. The Trojan road surmounted an earthen bank and was of excellent quality. The most complete road network can be found at Nadin. While the Čauševica trackways date to the Later Bronze Age, there is no evidence to suggest that any of the true roads are pre-Roman in date.

The dating of the site plans and their structures is in harmony less with a unilinear development of increasingly elaborate constructional features than with a piecemeal adoption of the same techniques at different times and places. Many of the details used extensively in the Late Iron Age were also used before in a simpler form at Čauševica or Polača. Increases in rampart size and magnificence are the principal innovations of the Late Liburnian period in north Dalmatia; otherwise, the canon of drystone walled structures displays continuity from the earliest period (Early Bronze Age) into the Roman period.

Inter-regional comparisons

Enclosed and/or defended sites are a defining characteristic of the last two millennia of European prehistory in the Mediterranean limestone lands and adjoining areas. In this concluding section, the north Dalmatian monuments are placed in a broader geographical context of land division, defence and monumentality. These comparative studies will proceed thematically, dealing with dating, form, function and size

Dating

The main phase of monument building in the central Ravni Kotari took place in the Later Bronze Age, a period for which there is evidence of use on ten out of twelve datable sites. Subsequent extension or remodelling of existing cairnfields and hill-forts took place in the Iron Age, together with the construction of major new hill-forts in central places. This dating evidence is in contradiction to Batović' (1977) claim that occupation of most Liburnian hill-forts began in the Iron Age. The period of most intense hill-fort construction varies by region in the coastal and Dinaric zones. In Istria, hill-forts are first built in the Middle Bronze Age and construction continues on into the Early Iron Age (Gabrovec and Mihovilić 1987). Amongst the Japodes of central Croatia and the Delmatae of south-west Bosnia, most hill-forts are built in the Late Bronze Age (Drechsler-Bižić 1987; Benac 1985; cf. Čović 1987 for central Dalmatia). An exception is west Hercegovina, where Oreć claims more Early than Middle Bronze Age constructions (Oreć 1978). The earliest hill-forts known in Yugoslavia are the Late Copper Age hill-forts of central Bosnia, dated to the third millennium Cal. BC (Čović 1983b).

Defended hilltop sites in several areas of Italy (Apennines, north Italy, the Veneto uplands, Sardinia) tend also to date from the second half of the second millennium Cal. BC, as in north Dalmatia. This supports the view that the most intensive phase of hill-fort construction in the central Mediterranean is contemporary with the Urnfield phenomena in Central Europe (Müller-Karper 1959; Coles and Harding 1979).

Form

Various authors have identified a tendency for increased differentiation of hill-fort form through time (Benac 1985; Drechsler-Bižić 1987). The north Dalmatian monuments do not readily fit into this unilinear model of progressive elaboration. The notion of regional styles can, however, be tested by comparison of the incidence of those architectural characteristics identified for the Ravni Kotari group outside that area.

The Ravni Kotari hill-forts are positively defined by their single, undivided inner space and negatively defined by a rarity of associated cairns, terraces, acropoleis, approach roads and earth banks (Batović 1977; Čače 1982). The Ravni Kotari group is comparable to other hill-forts in the broader Liburnian group which covers the whole of north Dalmatia. By contrast, in Istria, a far higher percentage of hill-forts exhibit complex internal subdivisions of space (Marchesetti 1903/1981). In the Japodean group east of the Velebit, a minority of hill-forts include features such as perimeter and hillslope terraces, acropoleis and internal subdivision of space. A more common feature linking the Japodean group with those of the Delmatae is the use of 'protection cairns' dominating the main entrance to the fort. This feature is rare in Liburnian hill-forts.

The intensive research of Benac and his group has made south-west Bosnia the best-known area for hill-fort studies in the Dinaric zone (Benac 1977; 1985; Govedarica 1982). Five differences from the Dalmatian monuments can be recognized: (1) the rarity of complete ramparts, (2) the use of drystone rubble piles and cairns rather than formal drystone walling, (3) the rarity of formal gateways, (4) the extreme rarity of elaborated gateways, and (5) the common use of blocking cairns in almost a third of the Bosnian forts. The Bosnian region is the only area outside Dalmatia where hill-fort terraces have been excavated and dated (Benac 1985). Each of the three excavated terraces falls within the Iron Age.

Thus, Drechsler-Bižić's hypothesis of regional differences in building styles appears to be borne out by the comparative analysis. While some of the characteristics of north Dalmatian hill-forts are found in other areas (terraces, cairns), the sites of the Ravni Kotari group are closer to other Liburnian hill-forts than to those of other regional groups. In this sense, it is possible to speak of a specifically north Dalmatian tradition of architectural features.

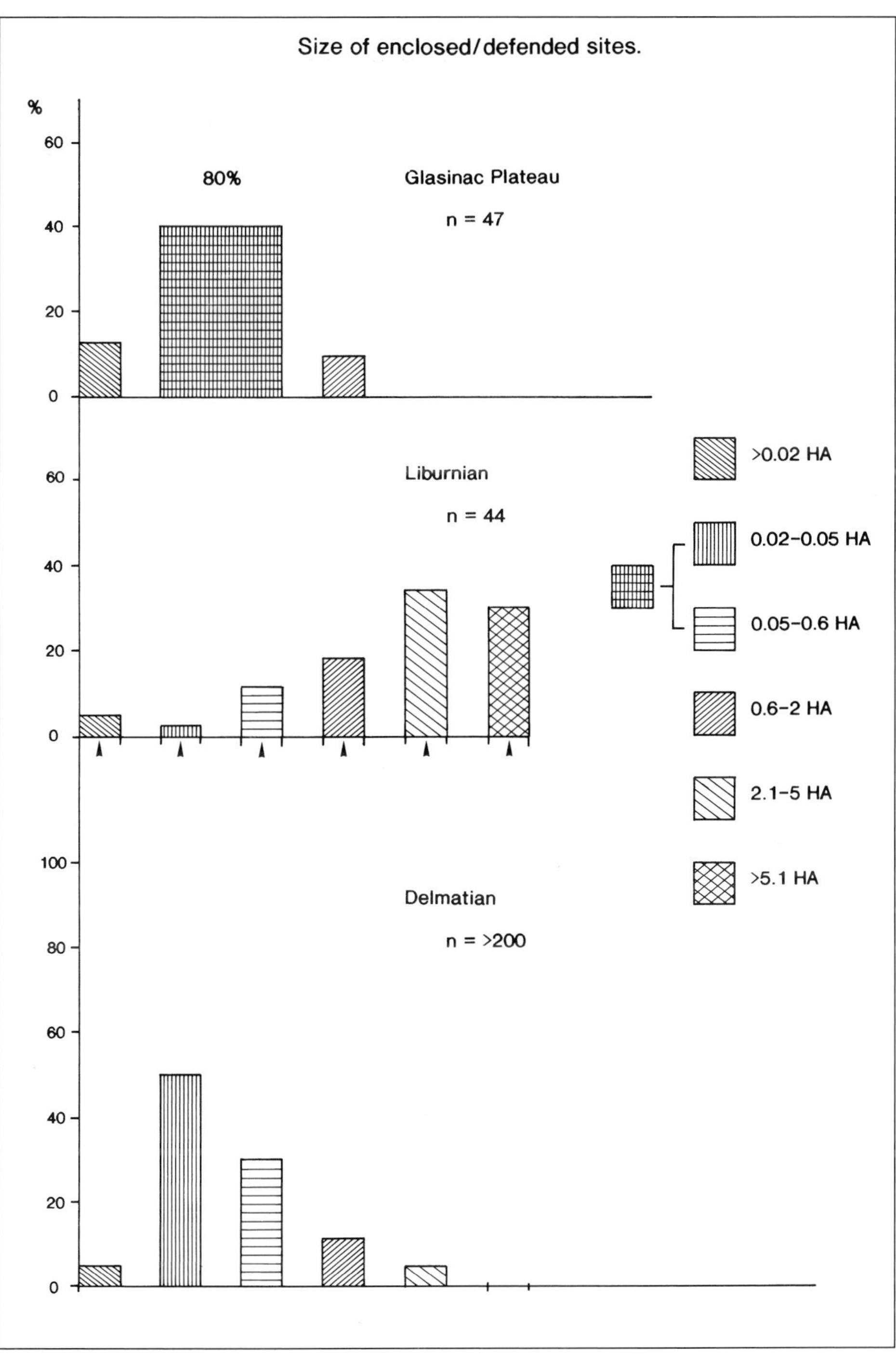

120. Hill-fort dimensions in North Dalmatia, Glasinac plateau and the Delmatae DR

Function

There are several possible alternatives for the function of the drystone walled enclosures and hill-forts under study. Hill-forts can be used as refuges, as acropoleis, as ritual places, as stock enclosures, as permanent living areas or as a combination of any of the former. In north Dalmatia, there is evidence for human occupation on a regular if not long-term basis at Polača, Čauševica, Pridraga, Vijenac, Trojan and Nadin (cf. the occupational debris found at each excavated south-west Bosnian hill-fort: Govedarica 1982). In addition, there is a likelihood that Mataci was used as a stock enclosure. Of the other sites, no clear-cut interpretation of function can be made.

Site size

The size of hill-forts and field systems can be computed in three areas in the Dinaric and coastal zones – north Dalmatia, the Glasinac plateau and the Delmatean zone (fig. 120). If the three samples are directly comparable, this figure would indicate a considerably higher degree of settlement nucleation amongst the Liburnians than in the interior areas. The fact that the Delmatean and Glasinac size distributions are based on all known hill-forts in the respective areas and that this is not the case with the Liburnian sites means that there is undoubted bias towards representation of larger sites in Dalmatian data. Nevertheless, the absence of any hill-forts larger than 1.7ha in the Glasinac area and larger than 5ha in the Delmatean sample corroborates this view of a consistently larger set of sites in and around the Ravni Kotari. The north Dalmatian site sizes are broadly comparable to the south Etrurian site clusters in the late second millennium Cal. BC, with site sizes rarely exceeding 2ha, with rather larger sites (up to 5ha) in the succeeding Final Bronze Age (Barker 1981). However, far larger sizes are known from the terramare settlements of the Po plain of North Italy (up to 20ha, with average size of 6–12ha) in the Late Bronze Age, while massive site nucleation took place off the plain after the collapse of the terramare system in the Final Bronze Age (Coles and Harding 1979).

Conclusions

The comparative study of field systems and hill-forts reveals patterning in the morphology and size ranges of monuments built by neighbouring groups. The rarity of internal subdivision in the Dalmatian sites differentiates the group from the hill-forts of Istria, while the absence of cairns incorporated into ramparts in the Ravni Kotari stands in marked contrast to the hill-forts of the Japodes and the Delmatae. Terracing was more common in Bosnia than in north Dalmatia. Finally, the tendency towards site nucleation was much more advanced in north Dalmatia than amongst the Delmatae or on the Glasinac plateau. Thus most small Bosnian hill-forts can be interpreted as dispersed, defended farms rather than the nucleated villages in the Ravni Kotari. It should be noted that Benac (1985) identifies a growth in Bosnian hill-fort sizes in the sixth–fifth centuries Cal. BC and links this trend to the growing power of local aristocracies. If this is the case in Bosnia with a relatively small number of large sites, there is considerable potential in exploring the idea of aristocratic influence in the evolution of Liburnian society in the first millennium Cal. BC.

5 The work study

Introduction

As a result of wider research interests on the archaeological agenda since the 1960s, archaeologists have become interested in the labour costs of building communal monuments. Work studies characteristically involve the identification of the relevant construction techniques, an estimate of the quantity of raw materials used and a further estimate of the time and labour used in such building. The principle underlying work studies is that the study of modern comparanda can illuminate past techniques and methods of construction (Childe and Thorneycroft 1938; Jewell 1963; Hobley 1971; Coles 1973, 1979; Orme 1981; Startin and Bradley 1981; Ralston 1986).

The number of work studies which are devoted to drystone walled structures is strictly limited, for three reasons: the majority of drystone walled structures are poorly preserved; later reuse or robbing hinders estimation of the original quantity of stone; and lack of well-preserved comparanda for such structures inhibits further study. However, these are not objections in principle but can be overcome by the discovery of appropriate comparanda. It is on the basis of the comparative approach that a work study was initiated on the drystone walled enclosures and hill-forts of north Dalmatia.

Methodology

Following extensive consultation with drystone walling specialists and stonemasons (especially Mr Richard Tufnell), a nine-stage procedure was evolved for the estimation of the time and labour needed to build drystone walled monuments in the NDP study area. These stages are all based on the uniformitarian principle that drystone wall building in particular stone (in this case, limestone) has remained similar for long periods of time. In particular, three areas of similarity can be identified:

1. The qualities of the rocks in the limestone range used are the same.
2. Similar solutions to structural problems of building in limestone are likely to have evolved over periods of time.
3. A similar range of simple drystone walling tools was used in both the past and the present (notably, the shovel, the sledge, the wooden frame, a heavy stone-splitting hammer and a metal crowbar).

The nine stages of the work study are as follows:

1. Calculation of the basal wall area (BA) from the wall lengths (L) for given basal wall widths (BW) from tacheometrically surveyed site plans with complete cross-sections of walls.
2. Estimation of a range of potential wall heights (WH) from regression data and ratio data drawn from two comparative data sets.
3. Estimation of the top width (TW) of the walls using the estimated degree of batter on walls, as derived from the same data sets.
4. Calculation of three areas of trapezoidal section (TS) through each wall, based on the three different wall height (WH) estimates.
5. Calculation of three volumetric (V) estimates of stone content in each wall.
6. Estimated haulage time (H) for a given volume of stone.
7. Estimated construction time (C) for a given volume of stone.
8. Estimated construction time (use of scaffolding and lifting) (SL) for high walls.
9. Estimation of the total labour-time (T) necessary for construction.

A detailed description follows for each stage in the work study, which makes the additional assumption that most wallers worked in pairs. It is estimated that the grouping of wallers in pairs may increase productivity by 10–15 per cent (pers. comm. R. Tufnell, 1988).

Stage 1: wall length and width

The length of walling (L) in the drystone monument was taken from the plan using a standard map measurer. If only one complete cross-section could be found, the wall width recorded was taken as representative of the entire circuit. If two or more cross-sections were recorded, the length of the wall was divided proportionally between the different widths. Where two cross-sections of greatly differing widths were recorded for the same sector of wall, the wall length was divided midway between the two cross-sections. The basal area (BA) of the wall was calculated as follows:

$$[BA = (L_1 \times BW_1) + (L_2 \times BW_2) + (L_3 \times BW_3)]$$

Stage 2: estimated height

The choice of comparanda is critical to any successful estimation of drystone structural dimensions. In this case, two classes of comparative data are required:

limestone drystone walling in monuments of a size range of 0.5–10 ha, with linear dimensions of up to 3km and megalithic drystone walling of 'random rubble built to course' or 'coursed rubble' (*pace* Davey 1961, figs. 9 and 13), of similar dimensions. Very few drystone monuments have survived in good preservation, except for the monument classes based on towers (duns, brochs, nuraghi, torri, etc.), which must be excluded because of their structural specificity. The only data sets which remain are modern drystone walls in Britain, and the proto-historic Irish forts or cashels of the early medieval period. The obvious comparanda for megalithic walls are Hellenistic city walls in the Mediterranean and the Near East, which provided the model for Dalmatian Iron Age builders (Faber 1976). However, metrical data on such walls are too limited to be of use in the work study.

The British drystone walls (Scottish 'drystane dykes') have the advantage of being numerous and relatively well-studied. Many are well enough preserved to take accurate measurements for basal width (BW), top width (TW) and wall height (WH). The disadvantage is that most of these walls are relatively narrow in comparison with the Dalmatian walls. With the exception of the Aberdeenshire 'consumption' dykes, built to consume stone (Glentworth and Muir 1963), it is rare to find a drystone wall wider than 1.7m (5ft). Consequently, the WH of the drystone walls is unlikely to be comparable to those in Dalmatia. Nevertheless, valuable metrical data are plentiful (Stephens 1908; Rainsford-Hanney 1972; British Trust for Conservation Volunteers 1977; Hart 1980; Callander 1982). Measurements from seventeen styles of drystone walling have been used to enable the calculation of BW:WH regression lines and WH:BW ratios.

The best data set for broader drystone walls come from the proto-historic period in Ireland. From a total of over 5,000 forts, a sample of fourteen sites remains whose walls have either survived to a respectable height or which have been carefully restored, using all surviving surface rubble, in the nineteenth century (Westropp 1901, 1910; O'Riordain 1942; Evens 1966; Harbison 1971; for a recent work study on Irish forts, see Conroy 1992). Most of the forts have defensive walls which enclose areas of 20–50m in diameter; the exceptions are the long curtain walls of sites such as Dun Aengus (Harbison 1971). The walls range in BW from 2.5 to 6m, in WH from 2.5 to 7.2m.

The estimates of WH from existing BW of Dalmatian monuments are thus derived from regression data and ratios based on the British drystone walls and the Irish forts. The regression data are presented in the form of a graph (fig. 121), in which three curves are represented: a median curve summarizing the variations of all data points, and two outer curves denoting extreme values. The extreme values were checked for consistency with the WH:BW ratio measures. Since the pattern is for a lower ratio with increased BW, these ratios are consistent with the extreme values taken from the regression data. Three estimated readings for WH are taken from the regression curve: the lower, the median and the upper.

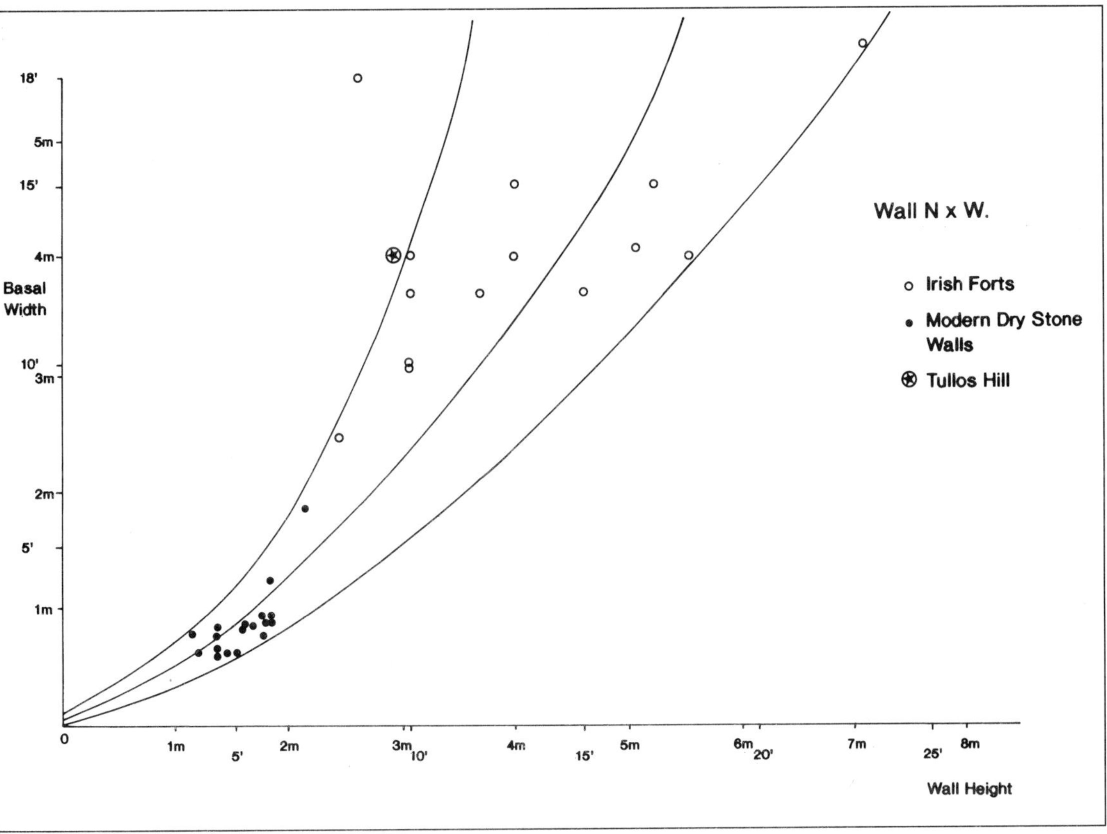

121. Regression analysis of Wall Height versus Basal Width of drystone walls

Stage 3: estimation of top widths

An almost ubiquitous feature of drystone walling is the progressive thinning of the wall with increasing height. Known as a batter, this feature enhances structural stability. In the majority of drystone walls, the batter is regular, with a unit decrease in width per unit increase in height. Thus the sectional area of a wall is not a rectangle but a trapezium. It is therefore important to estimate the top width (TW) of each drystone wall.

Data on the TW of Irish forts are almost non-existent, so the only data set for this estimation are the British drystone field walls. Eight varieties of limestone field wall were examined and the total range of batter is from 1in per foot to 4in per foot (25–102mm per 305mm). Allowing for the greater structural stability of the thicker Dalmatian walls, it is proposed to use the highest value for batter – a value of 0.33m per metre increase in height.

Stage 4: sectional area

Using the three estimates for wall height derived from Stage 2 above, three calculations of sectional area (TS) were made, using the following formula:

$$\left[TS = \frac{(TW + BW) \times WH]}{2}\right]$$

Stage 5: volumetric calculations

Three volumetric totals, based on the three respective WH values, are calculated for each wall by the following formula:

$$[V = (TS_1 \times L_1) + (TS_2 \times L_2) + (TS_n \times L_n)...]$$

Stage 6: work rate (haulage)

On all the Dalmatian sites in question, limestone rubble is readily available within 100m of the walling site. Thus there is no shortage of hand-picked stone for use in drystone ramparts and field walls. At Nadin and Trojan, quarries have been identified on site within 100m of the walls. Hence local availability of stone presents no difficulties; the problem is whether or not wheeled transport was used for hauling the stone the short distance to the construction site. It is instructive to compare the haulage costs for wheeled vehicles and hand carriage.

In a study of the construction of the Mayan ceremonial centre at Uxmal, Erasmus (1965) provides data on the quantity of stone carried by hand in a five-hour working day over a given distance. With a correction for an eight-hour working day, the weight of stone carried for a distance of 250m was between 0.75 and 1.0 metric tonnes. By comparison, a horse and cart could carry 4.4 metric tonnes to the site from a radius of 1.5km (pers. comm., R. Tufnell, 1988). Hand and wheeled carriage differs by a factor of 30–35 times – a clear demonstration of the efficiency of wheeled transport for large volumes of materials, once the initial outlay of cart and road construction has been made. In order to take both modes of haulage into account, two estimates have been provided for each volumetric total:

1. A low-efficiency haulage estimate (HL), based on Erasmus' data, where 0.75 cu m of stone are carried per day by hand (170 trips over 100m in an eight-hour day, carrying a mean weight of 28kg per trip).
2. A high-efficiency haulage estimate (HH), based on Tufnell's data, where 2.5 cu m of stone are transported by horse and cart per day.

In the case of Nadin and Trojan, two additional labour costs are the quarrying and shaping of the stone. According to Erasmus' (1965) data, 0.8 cu m of limestone could be quarried in an eight-hour day. At Nadin, the rectangular blocks measure on average 400 × 300 × 250mm; given that the width of the wall varies from 4.2m to 6.6m, a 10m length with a height of 6m would require anything between 8,000 and 13,000 such blocks, laid in alternate rows at right-angles to each other. The estimated total haulage time at Nadin is derived from the sum of the time estimated for quarrying, shaping and haulage.

At Trojan, only five rectangular blocks were discovered extant on the site; it is problematic whether only part of the rampart was megalithic or whether the majority of these blocks have been removed at a later date. The haulage estimates for Trojan assume a complete circuit of megalithic limestone blocks; this may well be an overestimate of haulage time.

Stage 7: work rate (building)

The estimates for the actual construction of drystone walls draws on four data sets, some modern and some experimental. The total range of built stone is 2.4–5.1 cu m per person-day. This variable depends on many factors, not least the skills of the building team, the requisite standard of the finished wall and the quality and size of available building stone. On this basis, two estimates are provided for building labour: a low-efficiency, high-quality estimate (CL) of 2.5 cu m per day and a high-efficiency, lower-quality estimate (CH) of 5 cu m per day.

Two experimental building projects are relevant to stone constructions – the Uxmal centre and the Pictish vitrified fort of Tullos Hill. In the Uxmal experiment, Erasmus records that 1 cu m of mortared wall took four people-days to build. This is an indication of the extra labour required in the use of mortar. At Tullos Hill, a stretch of 9.4m of timber-laced wall was reconstructed using Deeside gabbros in twenty-five people-days. Given the volume of the wall at 54 cu m, and ignoring the time taken for timber insertion, the construction rate per person-day was 2.1 cu m per person/day (Ralston 1986).

The results of these experiments are consistent with the high labour costs of building in stone. The vitrified fort results are comparable to the Dalmatian monuments and confirm the validity of extrapolation from drystone field walls.

Stage 8: work rate (scaffolding)

R. Tufnell (pers. comm., 1988) has pointed out that the construction of walls higher than *c.* 2m would require scaffolding and considerable extra labour in lifting the stones onto increasingly lofty walls. There are no obvious comparanda for such labour calculations and Tufnell has suggested a figure equal to that of the haulage of 2.5 tonne for a 6m high wall. From this basic estimate, it is possible to estimate the labour costs of lifting stones for lower walls, as follows (table 15).

Table 15 Estimated labour costs for lifting stones

Wall height	Volume lifted per person-day (cu. m)
6	2.5
5	3.0
4	5.0
3	10.0
2	no extra labour/scaffolding

Earthen bank construction

At the Trojan hill-fort, part of the rampart was built on top of a massive earthen and stone bank. Of the experimental work on earthen banks summarized by Coles (1973, 1979), the most valuable comparandum is the experimental earthwork of Overton Down, since the bank is a mixture of earth and chalk. The Overton Down earthwork involved the excavation of the bank material from a corresponding ditch, of a volume of 115 cu m. The labour necessary for excavating the ditch and building the bank was estimated at 145 people-days, exclusive of supervision time. The volume of the Trojan bank (V) was calculated using an equation which makes two uniformitarian assumptions: the mean height of the bank was one-sixth of its basal width; and the shape of the bank could be adequately modelled as a triangular solid whose vertex lay $\frac{2}{5}$ along its baseline. The equation (pers. comm. T. Cox, 1988) is as follows:

$$[V = (b_1 + 2b_1 + ... + 2b_n + b_n) d + (b_1 b_2 + ... + b_n b_n) d]$$

where b_1 is the height of the first triangle, b_2 the height of the next triangle, b_n the height of the last triangle, and d is the distance between triangles (d = 10m).

Application of the equation to the dimensions of the Trojan earthwork led to the estimation of the bank volume at 5,895 cu m. Using the Overton Down labour estimates, the Trojan bank could have been constructed in 7,500 people-days. The possibility that the bank was set on already sloping terrain, rather than the flat surface assumed for the equation, means that a lower estimate of 3,750 people-days has been allowed for this construction.

Stage 9: total labour costs

The calculation of the total labour cost for each monument involves the addition of three separate labour estimates: haulage (H), building (B) and lifting (CL) (plus the earthen bank construction at Trojan), as follows:

$$\begin{bmatrix} T_{lowest} = (VL \times HL) + (VL \times CL) + (VL \times SL) \\ T_{highest} = (VH \times HH) + (VH \times CH) + (VH \times SL) \end{bmatrix}$$

These calculations provide two values for each of three height estimates, low- and high-efficiency values for low, medium and high wall heights. The calculation of several values reflects the potential error factor in the nine-stage calculations. The final labour costs are expressed in terms of people-years (henceforth PYs: *viz.*, T/365). These figures are subdivided into the labour inputs of specialist builders (construction time only) and less skilled haulers (haulage and lifting).

The results

Ten sites with surveyed ground plans have sufficient data for work study estimates. These sites are: Nadin, Vijenac, Trojan, Kutlovica, Mataci, Mutvica, Vinculja, Kruglas, Čauševica and Polača. Separate estimates for the whole site and its constituent parts are presented for both Vijenac and Čauševica. The Mataci results assume a complete, rather than the currently surviving interrupted, rampart circuit. The extra row of figures for Trojan represents the cost of building the earthen bank on the E and S sides of the site.

The results are presented below (tables 16–17).

Discussion of results

There is a wide range of variation in the amount of labour invested in the construction of Dalmatian stone-built monuments (fig. 122). The labour estimates for the monuments vary from fewer than 10 PYs (Kruglas) to a median value of over 188 PYs and a maximum value of over 320 PYs (Nadin).The median values for labour estimates will be used unless otherwise stated.

The labour estimates would appear to form a continuous series of gradually more ambitious building activities, with a sole exception. The labour requirements for the largest monument are more than double those of the next largest and almost four times more than those of the third largest rampart. This result corroborates the belief that Nadin was the most important Iron Age hill-fort in the central part of the Ravni Kotari.

In terms of morphology, three classes of site are represented: field systems (Polača, Čauševica), drystone walled hill-forts (Vijenac, Kutlovica, Vinculja, Mataci, Mutvica, Kruglas) and hill-forts with 'megalithic' walls (Nadin, Trojan). The range of labour requirements for these categories is as follows:

1. Field systems; 6.7–26 PYs (including the individual enclosures at Čauševica and the complete site)
2. Drystone walled hill-forts: 3.3–56 PYs (including the whole of Vijenac)
3. 'Megalithic' hill-forts: 83–188 PYs

Table 16 Labour estimates for drystone walled monuments (people-hours)

Site	Wall height	Volume	Quarrying	Haulage Low	Haulage High	Building Low	Building High	Lifting	Total Low	Total High
Nadin	1	16130	20162	21747	6524	6524	3262	6524	54975	36472
	2	23246	29056	30995	9298	9298	4649	9298	78647	52301
	3	28860	36075	38480	11144	11144	5572	11144	96843	63935
Vijenac/ Upper	1	5165	–	6887	2066	2066	1033	1721	10674	4820
	2	7116	–	9488	2846	2846	1423	2372	14706	6641
	3	8577	–	11436	3431	3431	1716	2859	17726	8006
Vijenac/ Lower	1	3170	–	4267	1268	1268	634	634	6169	2536
	2	4257	–	5676	1703	1703	852	851	8230	3406
	3	5130	–	6840	2052	2052	1026	1026	9918	4104
Vijenac/ Total	1	8622	–	11496	3449	3449	1725	2355	17300	7529
	2	11743	–	15657	4697	4697	2349	3223	23577	10269
	3	14143	–	18857	5657	5657	2829	3885	28399	12371
Trojan	1	5599	6999	7465	2240	2240	1120	1120	17824	11479
	2	7448	9310	9931	2979	2979	1490	1490	23710	15268
	3	9028	11285	12037	3611	3611	1806	1806	28739	18507
	Z			7500	3750					
Kutlovica	1	5615	–	7487	7487	2246	1123	1123	10856	9733
	2	7955	–	10607	10607	3182	1591	1591	15380	13789
	3	9518	–	12691	12691	3808	1904	1904	18403	16499
Mataci	1	1000	–	1333	400	400	200	13	1716	613
	2	1391	–	1855	556	556	278	52	2463	886
	3	1785	–	2380	714	714	357	137	3231	1208
Mutvica	1	1141	–	1521	456	456	228	114	2091	1026
	2	1408	–	1877	563	563	282	141	2581	1267
	3	2048	–	2731	819	819	410	205	3755	1843
Vinculja	1	2566	–	3421	3421	1026	513	513	4960	4447
	2	3544	–	4725	4725	1418	709	709	6852	6143
	3	4052	–	5403	5403	1620	810	810	7833	7023
Kruglas	1	754	–	1005	1005	302	151	–	1307	1156
	2	914	–	1219	1219	366	183	–	1585	1402
	3	1083	–	1444	1443	433	216	–	1877	1660
Polača	1	4586	–	6115	1834	1834	917	–	7949	2751
	2	5400	–	7200	2160	2160	1080	–	9360	3240
	3	6688	–	8917	2675	2675	1338	–	11592	4013
Čauševica/II	1	1464	–	1952	586	586	293	–	2538	879
	2	1755	–	2340	702	702	351	–	3042	1053
	3	2064	–	2752	826	826	413	–	3578	1239
Čauševica/I	1	1969	–	2625	788	788	394	–	3413	1182
	2	2354	–	3139	942	942	471	–	4081	1413
	3	2779	–	3705	1112	1112	556	–	4817	1668
Čauševica/III	1	1899	–	2532	760	760	380	190	3482	1330
	2	2411	–	3215	960	960	480	240	4415	1680
	3	2855	–	3807	1140	1140	570	285	5232	1995
Čauševica/ total	1	5332	–			2134	1067	190	9433	3391
	2	6520	–			2604	1302	240	11538	4146
	3	7698	–			3078	1039	285	13627	4902

There are considerable overlaps between the first two site classes, suggesting that size and function are not closely related. However, the 'megalithic' hill-forts appear to stand out in a size class of their own.

An alternative categorization is chronological. Three broad periods can be established: sites with only Later Bronze Age pottery, sites with only Iron Age

Table 17 Labour estimates for drystone walled monuments (people-years)

Site	Wall height	Total Low	Total High	Haulers Low	Haulers High	Builders Low	Builders High
Nadin	1	183	121	94	43	89	78
	2	262	174	134	62	128	112
	3	323	213	166	74	157	139
Vijenac/Upper	1	36	16	23	13	7	3
	2	49	22	40	17	9	5
	3	59	27	48	21	11	6
Vijenac/Lower	1	20	8	16	6	4	2
	2	27	11	21	8	6	3
	3	33	14	22	11	11	3
Vijenac/Total	1	58	25	47	19	11	6
	2	78	34	62	26	16	8
	3	94	41	75	32	19	9
Trojan	1	84	51	54	24	30	27
	2	104	63	63	27	41	36
	3	120	74	70	31	50	43
Kutlovica	1	36	32	29	29	7	3
	2	51	46	40	41	11	5
	3	61	55	48	49	13	6
Mataci	1	5.8	2	4.5	1.3	1.3	0.7
	2	8.2	3	6.4	2.1	1.8	0.9
	3	11	4	8.6	2.8	2.4	1.2
Mutvica	1	7	3	5.5	2.3	1.5	0.7
	2	8	4	6	3	2	1
	3	12	6	9.3	4.6	2.7	1.4
Vinculja	1	16.5	15	13.1	13.1	3.4	1.9
	2	23	20.4	18.3	18.1	4.7	2.3
	3	26	23.4	20.6	20.7	5.4	2.7
Kruglas	1	4.3	3.8	3.3	3.3	1	0.5
	2	5.3	4.7	4.1	4.1	1.2	0.6
	3	6.2	5.5	4.8	4.8	1.4	0.7
Polača	1	26.5	9	20.5	6	6	3
	2	31	11	24	6.4	7	3.6
	3	39	13	30	8.6	9	4.4
Čauševica/II	1	8	3	6	2	2	1
	2	10	3.5	7.7	2.3	2.3	1.2
	3	12	4	9.3	2.6	2.7	1.4
Čauševica/I	1	11	4	8.4	2.7	2.6	1.3
	2	13.6	4.7	10.5	3.1	3.1	1.6
	3	16	5.5	12.3	3.7	3.7	1.8
Čauševica/III	1	11.6	4.4	9.1	3.1	2.5	1.3
	2	14.7	5.6	11.5	4	3.2	1.6
	3	17.4	6.6	13.6	4.7	3.8	1.9
Čauševica/Total	1	31	11	24	7.5	7	3.5
	2	38	14	29.3	9.7	8.7	4.3
	3	45	16	35	11	10	5

pottery and sites with both types of pottery. Median labour estimates for each period range from 6–26 PYs (Bronze Age), 3.3–94 PYs (Bronze and Iron Ages) and 83–188 PYs (Iron Age).

Owing to lack of excavation, it is difficult to date rampart construction at any of the Bronze or Iron Age sites. However, on the basis of the ceramic dating from

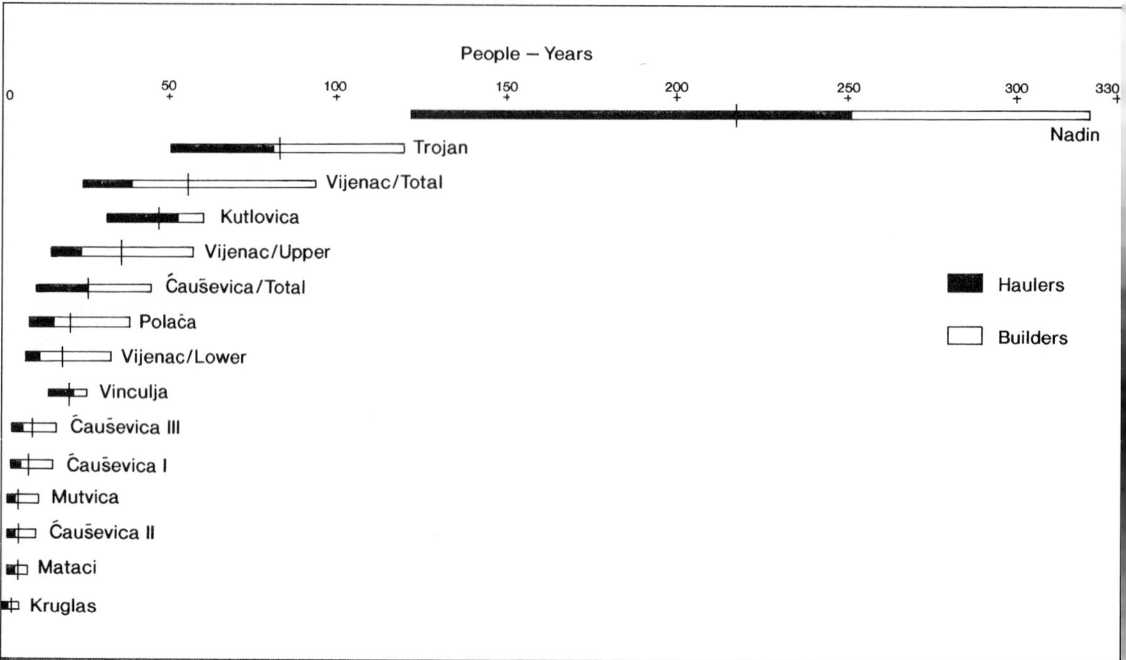

122. Estimated construction times (people-years) of drystone walled monuments

surface collections, there appears to be a major increase in labour inputs in Iron Age sites compared to the earlier period. This increase becomes greater if only ramparts are included in the comparison, for the Bronze Age sites with 21 and 26 PYs are both field systems. On this basis, it would seem unlikely that the Kruglas hill-fort, at 3.3 PYs, was built in the Iron Age but was constructed earlier and occupied in the first millennium Cal. BC as well.

Another important question concerns the degree to which the labour estimates refer to multi-period structures. Three of the monuments are evidently multi-period, although the time which elapsed between building periods is unknown. These sites are Čauševica (labour estimate for total site: 26 PYs), Polača (21 PYs) and Vijenac (56 PYs). If indeed these sites were built in several distinct operations, the contrast between Bronze Age and Iron Age labour inputs would be heightened (Bronze Age: 6–10.1 PYs; Iron Age: 83–188 PYs) and the gap between the megalithic hill-forts and the rest commensurately widened (hill-forts: 83–121 PYs; next largest: 35 PYs).

In summary, there is some chronological trend in the size variation of Dalmatian monuments but this observation does nothing to explain how this trend came about. In the remainder of this section, an attempt will be made to account for this variability.

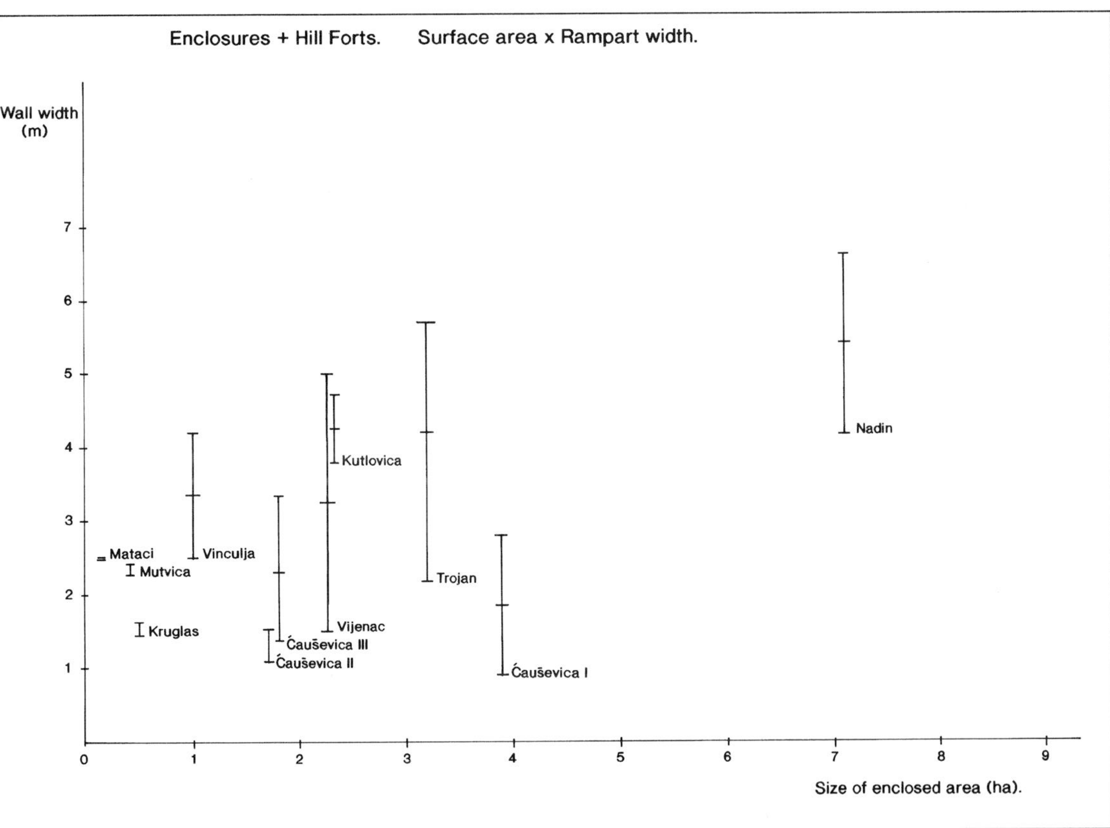

123. Enclosed area versus rampart width, drystone walled monuments

Explanations of variability

A useful starting point for explanations of variability is an examination of the covariation of labour expenditure and other variables. One interesting negative point is that there appears to be very little relationship between the range of wall basal widths and the surface area which the walls enclose (fig. 123). This is the only case in which there is no sign of a chronological trend separating Bronze Age from Iron Age sites. There is perhaps an unstated assumption that site size and wall thickness are positively correlated, based on the belief that larger sites require concomitantly stronger defences. This assumption does not appear to be warranted in the Dalmatian case.

A clearer pattern emerges in the relationship between labour expenditure and size of enclosed area (fig. 124). Here, there is a functional and a chronological distinction between sites with only Bronze Age pottery and others: in the former, the amount of labour grows far more slowly with increasing site size. This is partly

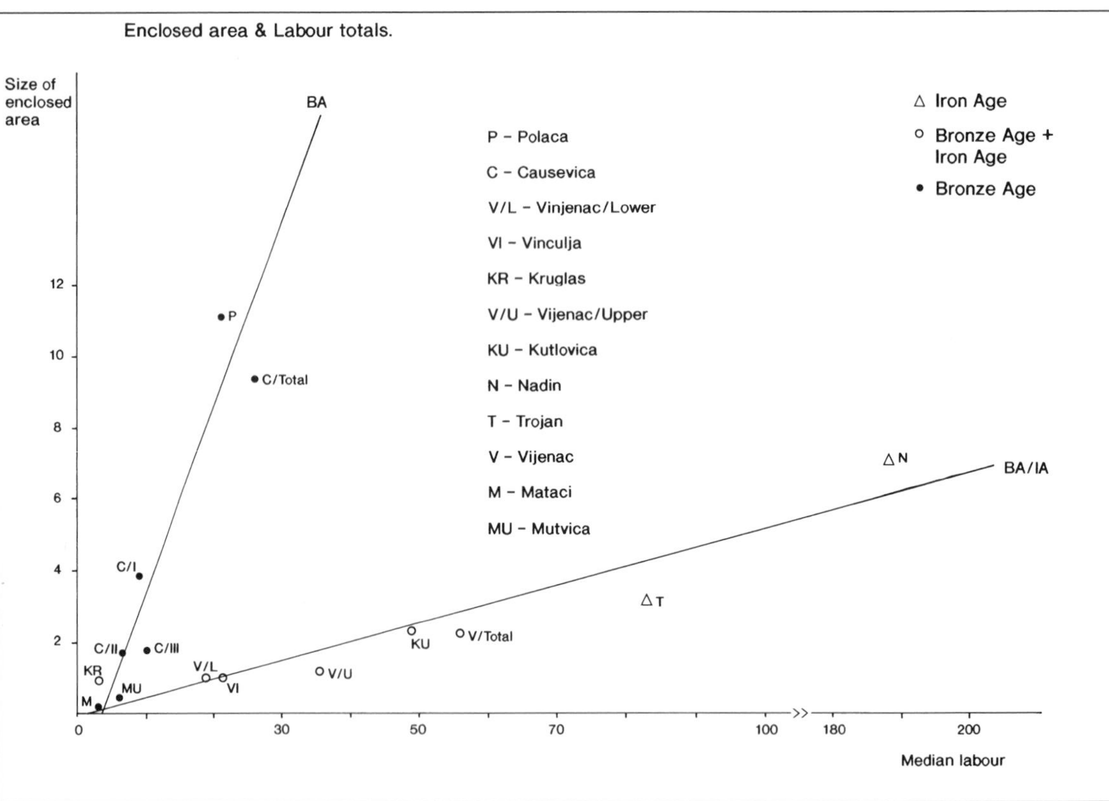

124. Labour total for drystone walled monuments

explained by the fact that most of the Bronze Age sites are field systems and not hill-forts. Hence, there appears to be a fairly high correlation between labour expenditure and hill-fort size, on the one hand, and between field system size and labour expenditure on the other. Closer dating of hill-fort rampart constructions is required before further comment on hill-fort size and labour costs can be made.

The results of this analysis can be reformulated in terms of the nul hypothesis that the variations in labour expenditure are the result of increased site size, with the implication of concomitant increases in population. Thus, it can be proposed that the main reason for the far larger labour expenditure on Nadin was that it was a larger hill-fort than others in the sample. Nadin encloses more than double the area of Trojan, and three times the area of Kutlovica; by comparison, the median labour expenditure for Nadin is twice that of Trojan and four times that of Kutlovica. Hence, while there is partial support for the nul hypothesis, it does not explain all of the hill-fort data. It may be proposed that an additional element of prestige monumentality may be responsible for the added labour costs of the largest hill-fort in the central Ravni Kotari.

A second hypothesis to explain labour variability concerns the size of population from which the labour force is drawn. It could be argued that central places had the greater political control necessary to extract corvée labour from a wider area than smaller hill-forts within the tribal territory. Such a notion is reminiscent of the debate concerning the status of lowland Mayan societies – state-level if they could extract corvée labour and chiefdom-level if public works were based on the contribution of household labour in return for redistributional products, luxury items or services (Erasmus 1965). Unfortunately, there is no clear evidence on the existence or otherwise of territorial divisions in the Bronze Age. By the Iron Age, the consolidation of kinship relations into larger aggregates is hypothesized, with the result that territorial boundaries between the main hill-forts can be drawn using Thiessen polygons (see below, fig. 176). On this basis, central places such as Nadin would have had access to a far larger pool of labour than any other single hill-fort. The critical question is whether or not the work force was composed of household labour or a more highly organized corvée group including slaves from a wider area. One of the benefits of the work study is that it permits a tentative answer to just such a question.

An initial question concerns the form in which the labour estimate is expressed. A statement in people-days (PDs) allows ready conversion into household daily labour contributions, while expression in people-years (PYs) makes an assumption of a permanent, or full-time labour force. Čače (1985) makes a persuasive case for the existence of slavery in the Liburnian Late Iron Age, though hardly earlier than *c.* 400 BC. It is also reasonable to assume the existence of full-time stonemasons and quarrymen, as specialists who built at least the taller hill-fort walls, in addition to generalist builders who could construct field walls and small domestic buildings. It will be assumed that, for the sites of Nadin, Trojan, Kutlovica and Vijenac, specialist builders would have contributed labour for payment in kind and/or subsistence, in addition to the less skilled, household labour for haulage and lifting. For the other, smaller hill-forts and both the field systems, specialist builders are not taken into account; instead, members of local households are assumed to have been capable of building smaller structures. Female and child labour is by no means excluded from the majority of drystone wall building tasks (Hart 1980, 24).

Any labour expression in people-years or people-days poses a second dilemma; there is no *a priori* way of telling how long the work took to complete. Before turning to this question, it is worth recalling Simek's dictum (1948: repeated and elaborated by Neustupný 1977) that prehistoric hill-forts are not constructed in warlike times but rather in times of peace following hostilities, during a period of social consolidation. This insight implies that construction could proceed, if necessary, over a period of several years, since an immediate defensive function was unimportant. An important corollary to the time aspect is the size of the local or regional kinship network from which potential drystone wall builders can be drawn. Extrapolation of mating network theory (Wobst 1974, 1975, 1976) to tribal groups would imply breeding networks of several hundred people in any given region. This figure means a sizeable population of builders with kin relations to the leaders of the building project at any given time. A final general point is that much of the construction work, perhaps all carried out by local workers, would have been fitted into the lean parts of the agricultural calendar.

Let us begin the discussion by considering the smaller monuments. Sites such as Kruglas, with an estimated 1,000 PDs, could have been made by a local group of 50, supplying 30 workers for 33 days each, in a single season. If fifty workers from the local breeding network were available, the task could have been completed in three weeks. Similar small-scale building projects could have been completed within a year at the sites of Mutvica (1,800 PDs: 50 workers for 36 days) and the earliest enclosure at Čauševica (Čauševica II: 2,000 PDs: 50 workers for 40 days). Both Hogbin (1939) and Winans (cited in Erasmus 1965, 281) quote figures of 40–45 days per year as the time a household would devote to working on communal or chieftainly projects in return for redistributive services and/or products. It is also possible that monuments requiring labour of 2,700–3,000 PDs (e.g. Čauševica I and III) could have been completed within one year (45 days × 60 and 65 people respectively). However, without a major mobilization of labour, it seems unlikely that monuments requiring more than 5,000 PDs could have been completed in one year. Hence, the medium-sized monuments, such as Vinculja and the lower enclosure at Vijenac, may well have taken two building seasons to complete (Vinculja: 4,800 PDs: 60 people × 80 days; Vijenac: 5,700 PDs: 72 people × 80 days). Multi-period monuments such as Polača are likely to have been built over several years, if not added to over decades; hence, a small labour force of 20–30 people working for less than 40–45 days would have had no difficulty constructing this linear monument.

When we turn to the larger hill-forts of Trojan, the upper enclosure at Vijenac and Kutlovica, a range of between 10,000 and 20,000 PDs is required for each construction. Given a work contribution of 40–45 PDs per annum, a labour force of 250–500 people would have been required for completion within one season. Since this figure exceeds the estimated populations of each site and is probably in excess of the capacity of the local breeding networks, a building operation of 3 to 5 seasons seems more likely (if 3 seasons, 170 people for 40 days; if 5 seasons, 100 people for 40 days). Hence, the larger hill-forts could be built within a short span of time by members of the local breeding network without any need of corvée labour or outside assistance.

The largest settlement – Nadin-Gradina – has a labour requirement far higher than that of any other site. The labour input of 65,000 PDs may well have included a *c.* 50 per cent contribution by specialist builders, stonemasons and quarrymen. The assumption of full-time builders and masons has several interesting implications. First, the high status of the site's élite is underlined by their command of specialist craftsmen. Secondly, the success of the local redistributive economy underpins the hiring of such workers. Thirdly, the most efficient use of specialist builders involves a permanent building programme, the staffing of which requires a permanent non-specialized labour force. There are therefore two possible models for the construction of Nadin:

1. Part-time construction, without the aid of specialist builders. Given work contributions of 40–45 PDs, the work force required is 1,400–1,600 people. Even assuming central control from Nadin over the whole of the central plains of Zadar, it seems unlikely that a sufficiently large work force could have been assembled for completion within one building season. A construction time of three years allows for contributions by between 450 and 550 people, a figure more in line with the small political territory of even Late Liburnian hill-forts.
2. A full-time building programme, with 300 days' work in one year for 120 specialist craftsmen and 100 non-specialists (total labour force – 220 people). Given the low requirements for specialist builders outside of the Romanized areas of the central Mediterranean, it seems unlikely that such a large number of specialists would have been available in Liburnia. The alternative of full-time building over five years implies 24 specialists and 20 general workers – perhaps more in line with the surplus productivity possible from the Nadin territory and the availability of specialist labour in the region.

These calculations indicate that all of the drystone monuments in north Dalmatia could have been constructed within one and five building seasons and by a labour force drawn for the most part from the local breeding network of kin-related individuals. The only exception may have been Nadin, where the use of specialist builders would have shortened the construction time or diminished the size of the local labour force. The Nadin hill-fort is the only site where full-time construction, at the estimated rate of 300 days per annum, would have provided a significant advantage but required a large labour input.

In answer to the second hypothesis, there is no need to postulate a centralized political system based on an ability to extract corvée labour for the construction of large public monuments for either the Dalmatian Later Bronze or Iron Ages. The contribution of one day in 8 per annum to public works is as consistent with the scale of monument building in north Dalmatia as it is with a less stratified social structure, based more on redistribution and kin-based allegiances than on class relations. It is only with the construction of the Nadin rampart in the Late Iron Age that specialist craftspeople and/or slave labour are potentially significant. Even in this late period, the extraction of communal labour from kin and/or clients within

Table 18 Estimated construction rates for Wessex monuments

Monument	Estimated labour (people-days)		Estimated labour force
	Renfrew (1973)	Startin	(Startin)
Fussell's Lodge long barrow	less than 1,200	860	32–40
West Kennet barrow	–	1,960	100
Windmill Hill causewayed enclosure	12,000	7,845	80
Stonehenge I	–	1,375	45
Stonehenge II	–	45,000	over 100
Durrington Walls	120,000	62,500	250–500
Silbury Hill	1.2 million	500,000	250–500
Stonehenge III	3.7 million	218,750	600
Rams Hill enclosure	–	1,875	–
Ladle Hill hill-fort (if finished)	–	9,590	250–500
Danebury hill-fort	–	22,500	250–500

a larger political territory is a viable alternative to a more centralized building programme at Nadin.

Of the few work studies available for broadly comparable social structures, two projects deserve mention – the pioneering contribution of Renfrew (1973) for Wessex monuments and the later refinements of Startin (n.d.) for a similar range of sites. The estimated construction rates in PDs from both studies are presented above (table 18).

The Renfrew model for social differentiation in the Later Neolithic relies on hierarchy of labour inputs to a series of increasingly elaborate monuments. Startin suggests, however, that this hierarchy is blurred when a wider range of sites is taken into consideration. It is apparent that the Dalmatian data conform to the non-hierarchical, stepped pattern of a wide range of continuously graded labour requirements.

In terms of the range of labour mobilization necessary for the Wessex monuments, the smaller single-period Dalmatian sites are comparable to the mortuary barrows and small Bronze Age enclosures (1,000–5,000 PDs). The larger hill-forts are equivalent to causewayed enclosures and small hill-forts in Wessex (5,000–10,000 PDs), while Nadin hill-fort took as much labour as a Wessex henge-enclosure. There are no Dalmatian sites in the present sample which had a manpower requirement equivalent to the largest communal monuments of Wessex. These comparisons prompt the conclusion that the political control exercised by Dalmatian chiefs was by no means as great as that developed in a short period in the south British Bronze Age. This result supports the notion that the Dalmatian Bronze and Iron Age social structure was a relatively weakly developed hierarchical structure.

Conclusions

In conclusion, the work study of the Dalmatian drystone walled monuments provides one method by which hypotheses concerning the social structure of prehistoric populations can be assessed. Most of the Dalmatian forts could have been constructed by relatively small work forces drawn from the local kin group or breeding network, rather than through the use of slavery or corvée labour. The conditions of war and peace in the Ravni Kotari were not so fixed as to deter social groups from building operations for at least one major season per annum; most of the monuments in question could have been completed in one or two or, at the most, five seasons of work. The largest site – Nadin – required either a larger kin network for labour contributions or a smaller group of full-time labour, both specialists and general labourers. The relatively modest scale of most of the stone monuments supports the conclusion of a low-level hierarchy at the heart of later prehistoric social structure in north Dalmatia.

6 The excavations

A total of five excavations was mounted during the NDP, in order to provide a wide range of comparanda for long-term processes of subsistence and social change. This included larger excavations on four sites: Early Neolithic Tinj-Podlivade, Copper Age Bukovič-Lastvine, Bronze Age Mataci-Jazvinački Brijeg and the multi-period hill-fort of Nadin-Gradina. Smaller excavations, consisting of trial sections across ramparts and soil pits in adjoining areas, were conducted at two further sites: Čauševica and Polača-Dražice. The location of all excavated sites is presented above (fig. 79: see p. 111).

Tinj-Podlivade (figs. 125–36)

History of investigations

The site was discovered by K. Tomić in the late 1970s. Surface collections were made by NDP in 1983 and the Project excavated there in 1984.

Site environment

Tinj-Podlivade lies in a secondary basin formed on the slopes of the hill between the Vrana depression to the south west and the Tinj ridge to the north-east (fig. 125). Within the familiar catena of ridge-and-valley topography typical of the Ravni Kotari, this segment of terrain covers 3km from top of ridge to middle of valley. The Tinj site lies 1km from the top of the ridge, at an altitude of 45–50masl (fig. 126). There has been significant erosion from the limestone ridge which has deposited gravel at the break in slope. Within the site itself, there are minor but significant changes in topography, with gentle slopes from north-east to south-west and from south-east to north-west. The fact that the deep dark soil on the eastern side corresponds clearly to a well line suggests that it may have been wetter than the western side over a considerable period, and remains so today. In fact, this part of the area (shown on figure 125 as dark clay) may have been shallow Bottomland before soil loss from the ridge and drainage of Vrana depression altered the local hydrology. The vegetation in the vicinity of the Tinj site is almost entirely anthropogenic. A high proportion of the land within a 2km radius of the site is cultivated, either for cash-crops or for the more traditional cereals, vines and fruit trees. The distribution of land use classes around Tinj reveals a symmetrical pattern, with the Neolithic site located centrally on an oval area of arable land, with successively distant zones of Stony and Karst.

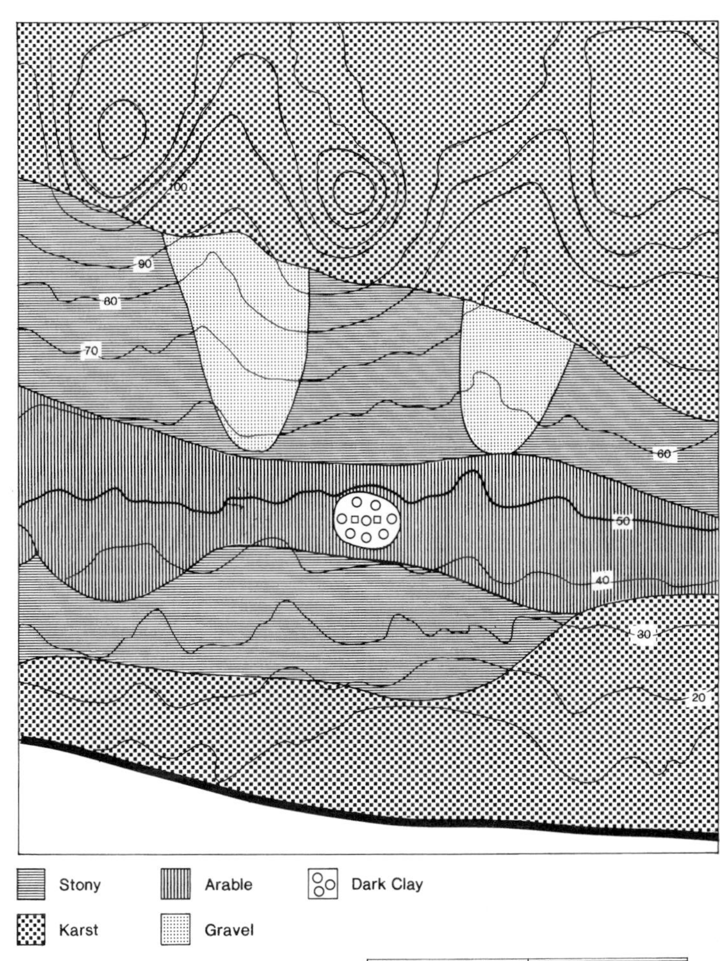

125. Topographical map of the Tinj area (site in centre)
126. General view of Tinj from north-east

Environmental changes

Environmental changes since the Neolithic relate to processes of hydrological change and soil erosion and deposition. The Bottomland on the western edge of the Neolithic site has now dried up completely though the water table remains high. Locally, surfaces have aggraded by over 50cm due to soil movement.

Surface survey and excavation strategy

Surface collection strategy at Tinj was guided by modern cultivation methods and local topographical conditions. The long, narrow north-east–south-west strip fields were used as the basic sampling unit. Systematic collection of all surviving surface finds was made from nine strip fields out of a total of twenty-five (fig. 127). The artefact scatter covered an area of 2.8ha (280 × 100m). Artefact densities per field were compared with the vegetation at time of survey and quartiles were calculated for each category of artefact. There is no pattern of density fall-off from the geometrical centre of the scatter, rather local concentrations of finds (e.g. Field 5: all finds; Field 22: pottery; Field 4: lithics).

The aims of the trial excavations at Tinj were threefold: the provision of a dated stratigraphic sequence from the Neolithic site; the recovery of a sufficiently large sample of biological data to define the subsistence base of the first farmers of the area; and the definition of environmental conditions in and around the site before, during and after the human occupation.

On the basis of the environmental information and the analysis of surface finds distributions, it was decided to excavate one trench in the south-western part of the site, closer to the margins of the lake/marsh (Trench B – British team), and another trench on the higher ground nearer the centre of the scatter (Trench A – Yugoslav team).

Stratigraphy and occupation sequence

The stratigraphic sequence in both trenches comprises a natural deposition of soil to a depth of 0.75m (fig. 128). The underlying geology was soft 'chalk'. The major features in each trench were cobbled surfaces which had been badly destroyed by recent cultivation (figs. 129–31). The limestone cobbles had been carried on to the site, presumably from the nearby Karst land. Four small refuse pits had been cut from the lower occupation levels – three in Trench A and one in Trench B (see Harris matrices: fig. 132). The far larger total of finds recovered from Trench A is probably explained by its lesser exposure to flooding from the seasonal lake on the south-west side of the site.

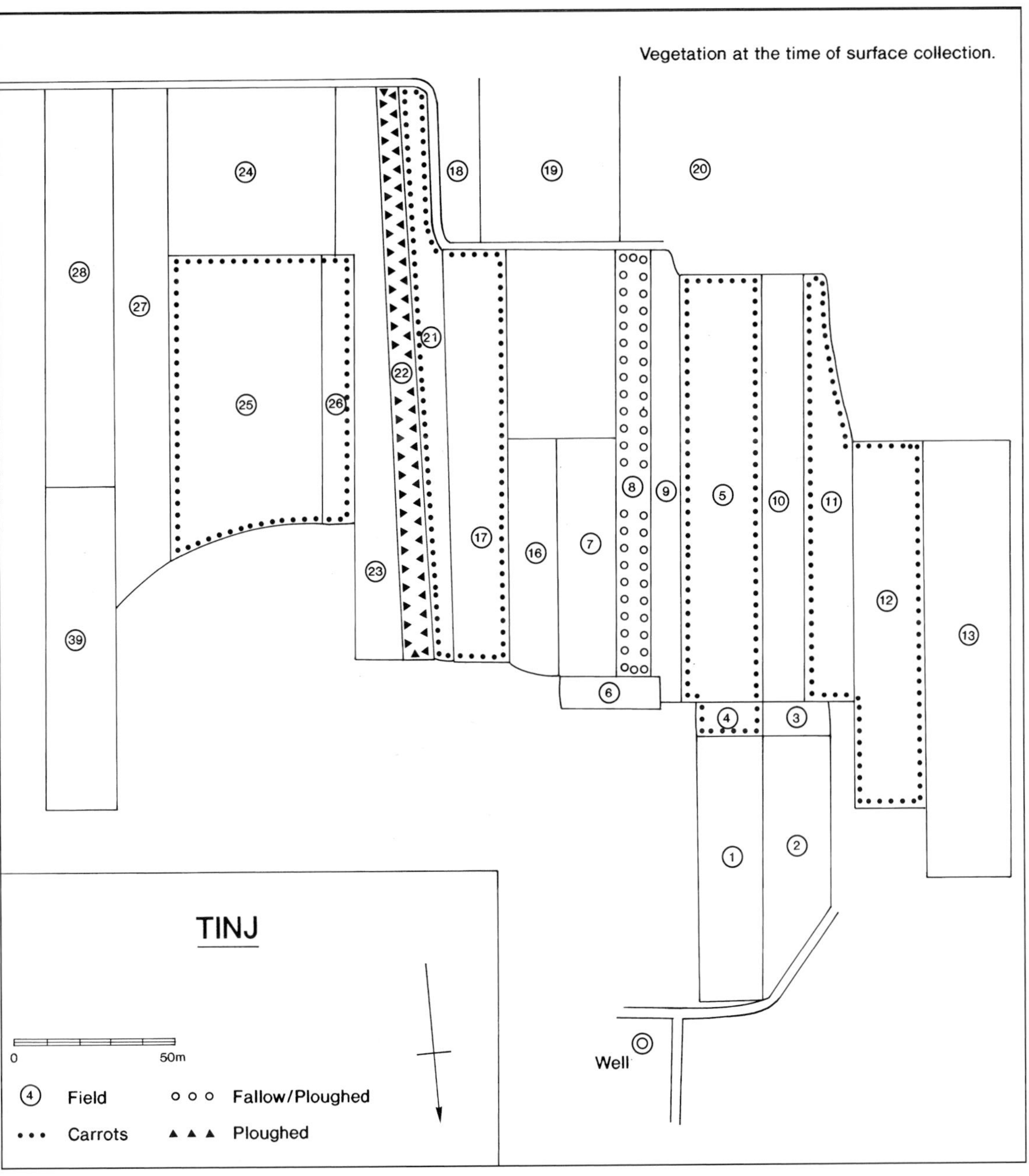

127A. Vegetation at Tinj-Podlivade

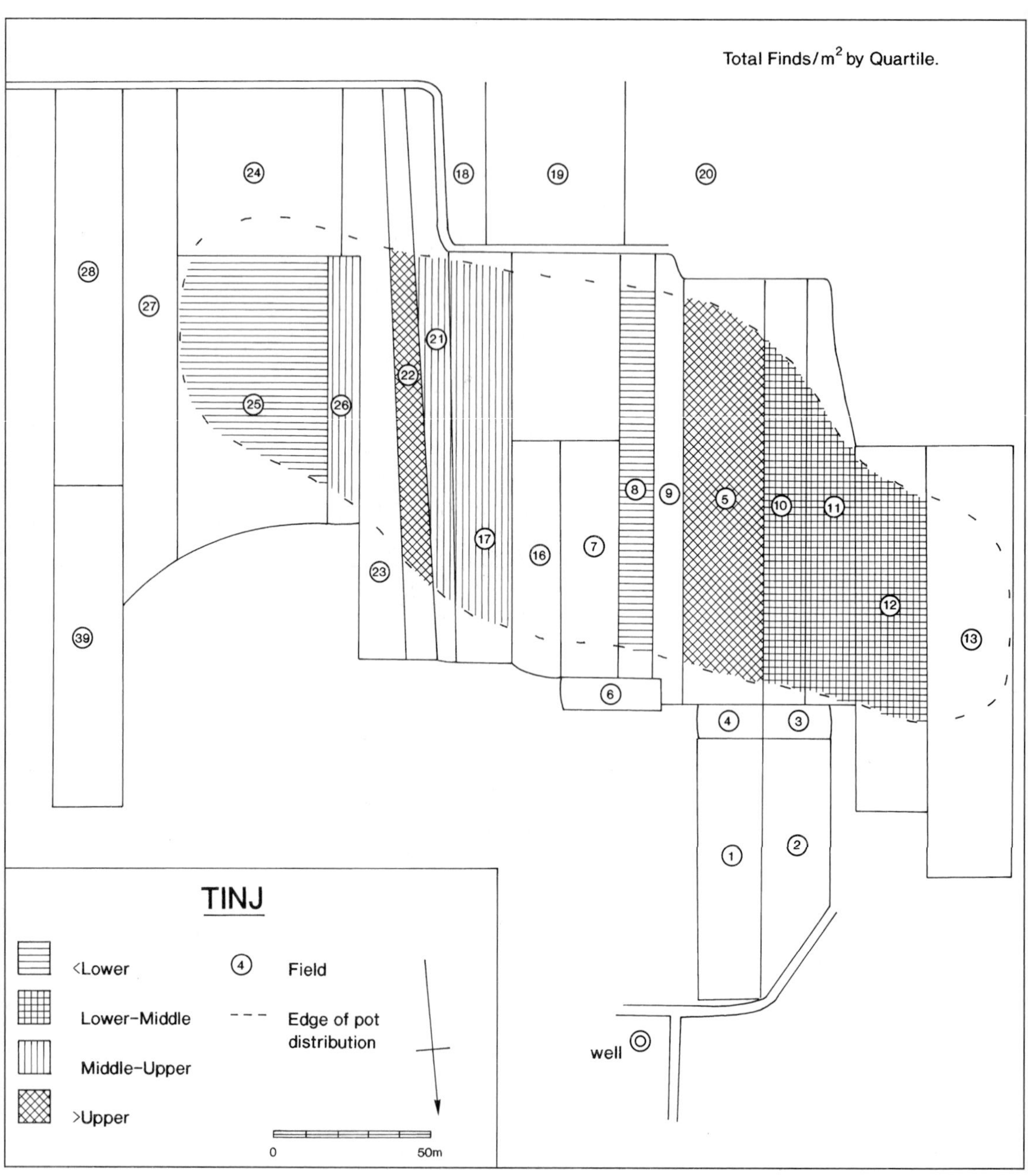

127B. Total surface finds, Tinj-Podlivade

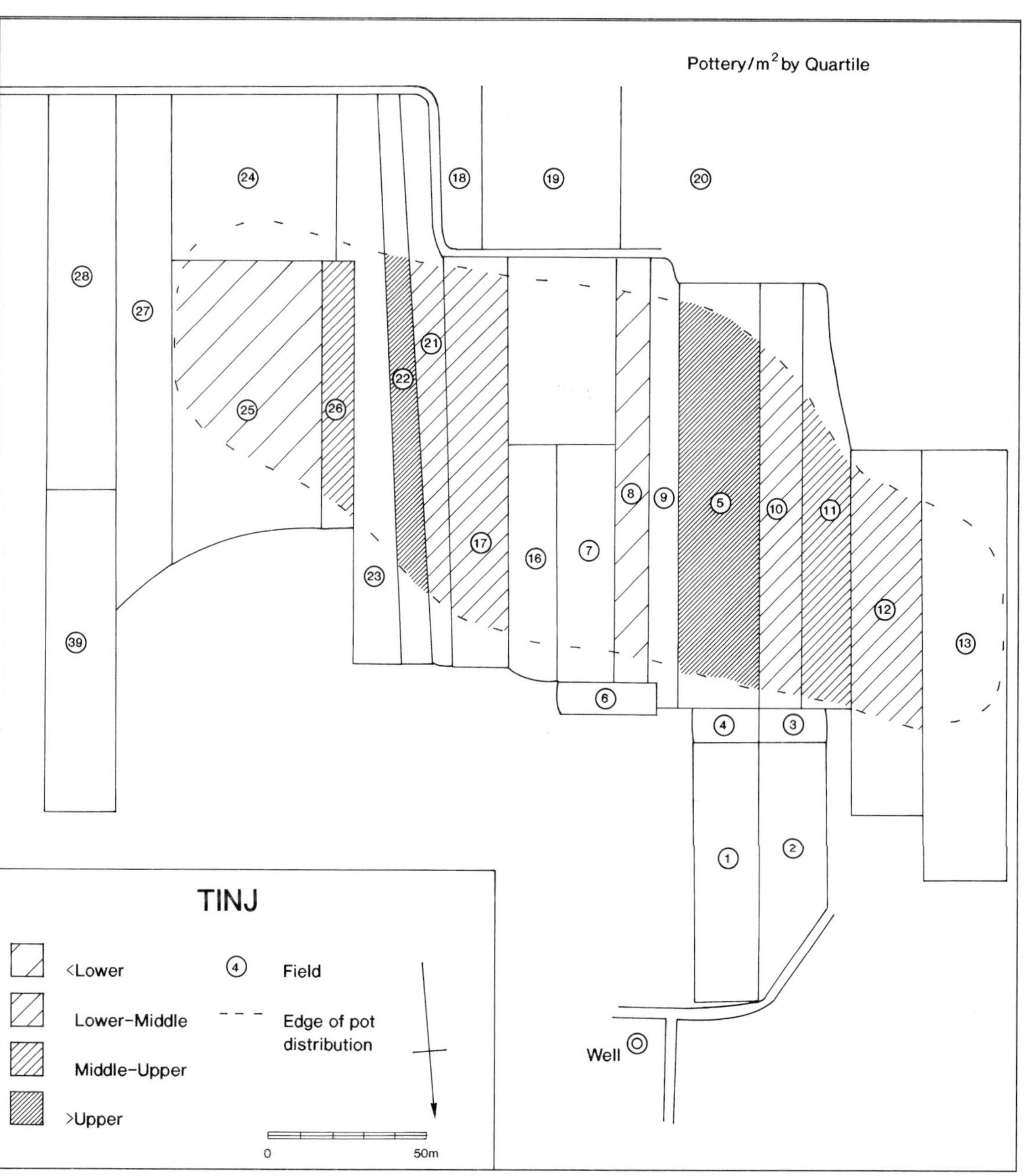

127C. Surface pottery, Tinj-Podlivade

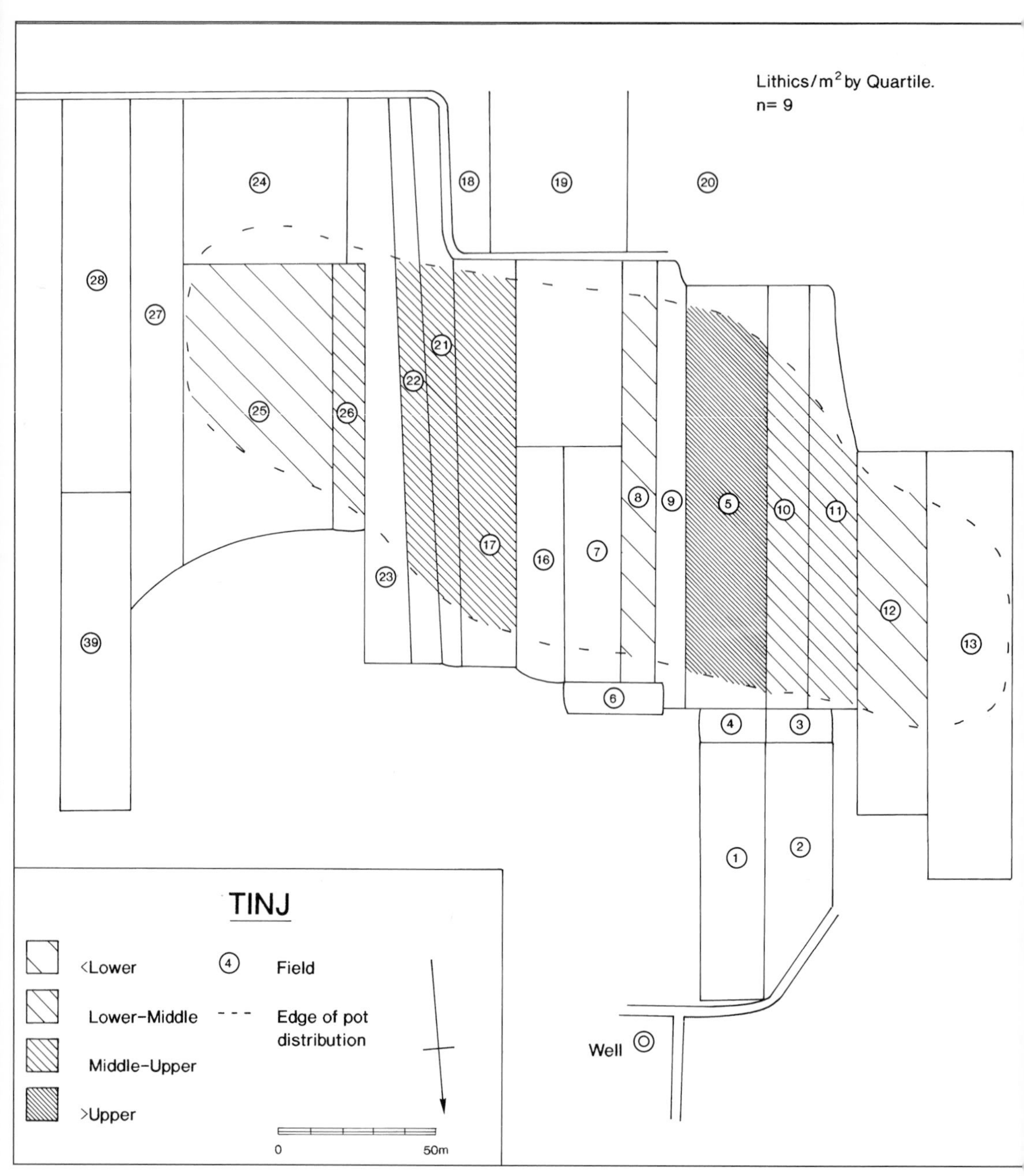

127D. Surface lithics, Tinj-Podlivade

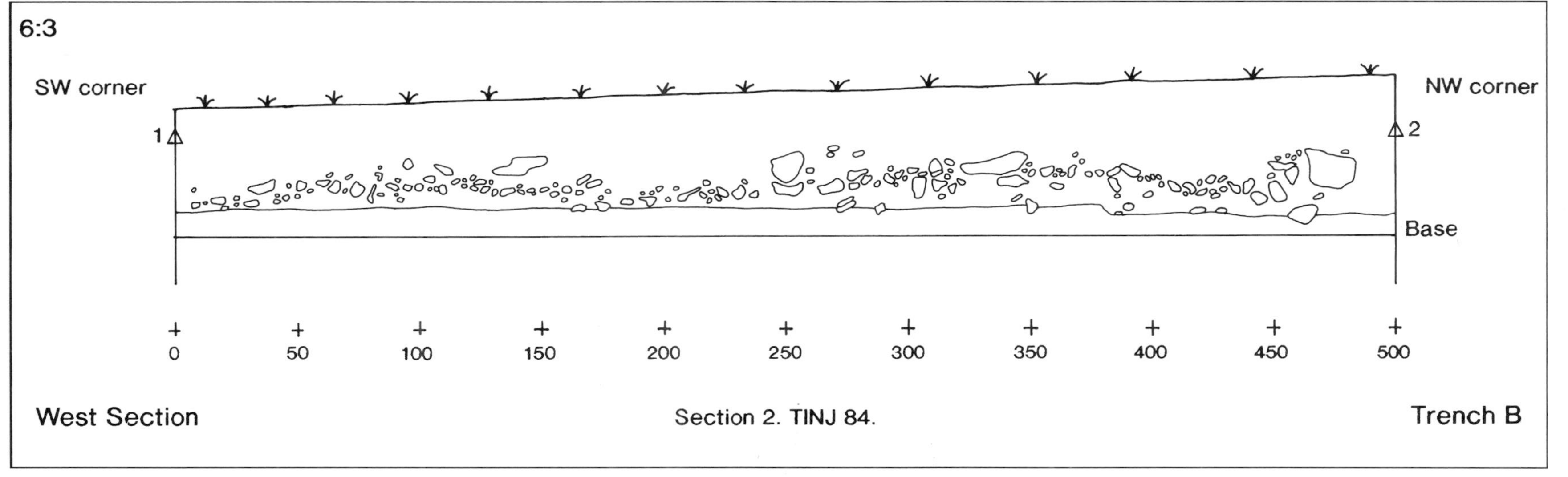

128. West Section, Trench B, Tinj (horizontal scale in cm)

6:4

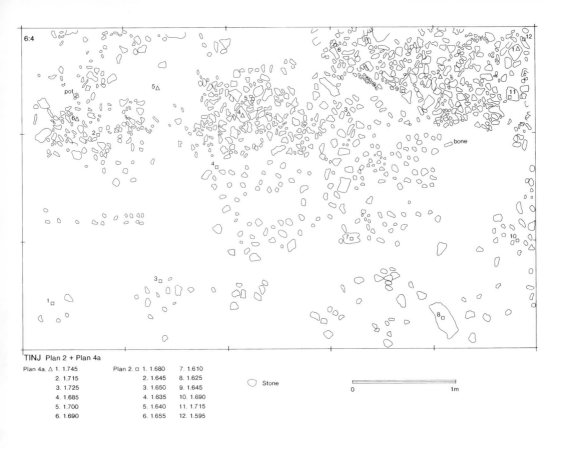

TINJ Plan 2 + Plan 4a

Plan 4a. △	Plan 2. □	
1. 1.745	1. 1.680	7. 1.610
2. 1.715	2. 1.645	8. 1.625
3. 1.725	3. 1.650	9. 1.645
4. 1.685	4. 1.635	10. 1.690
5. 1.700	5. 1.640	11. 1.715
6. 1.690	6. 1.655	12. 1.595

Stone

0 1m

129. Plan of cobbled surface, Trench B, Tinj

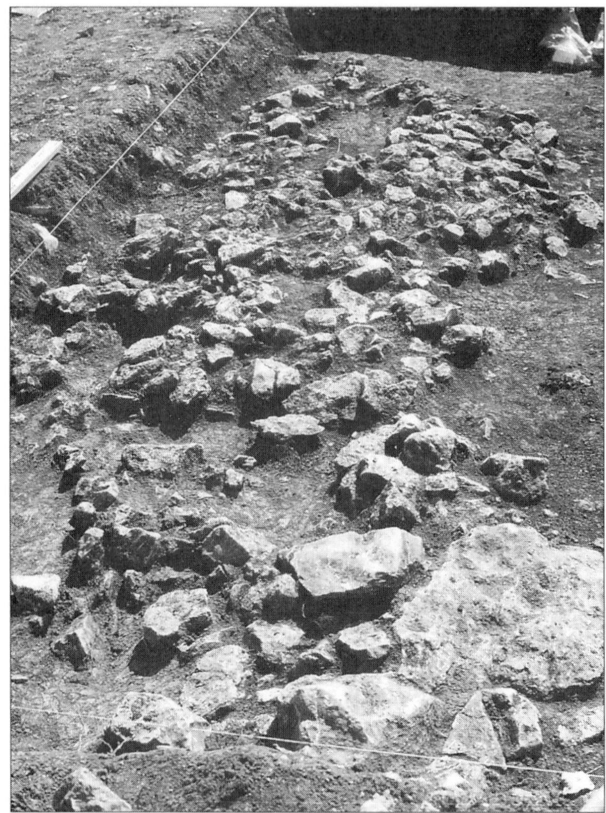

130. Cobbled surface, Trench A, Tinj

131. Cobbled surface, Trench B, Tinj

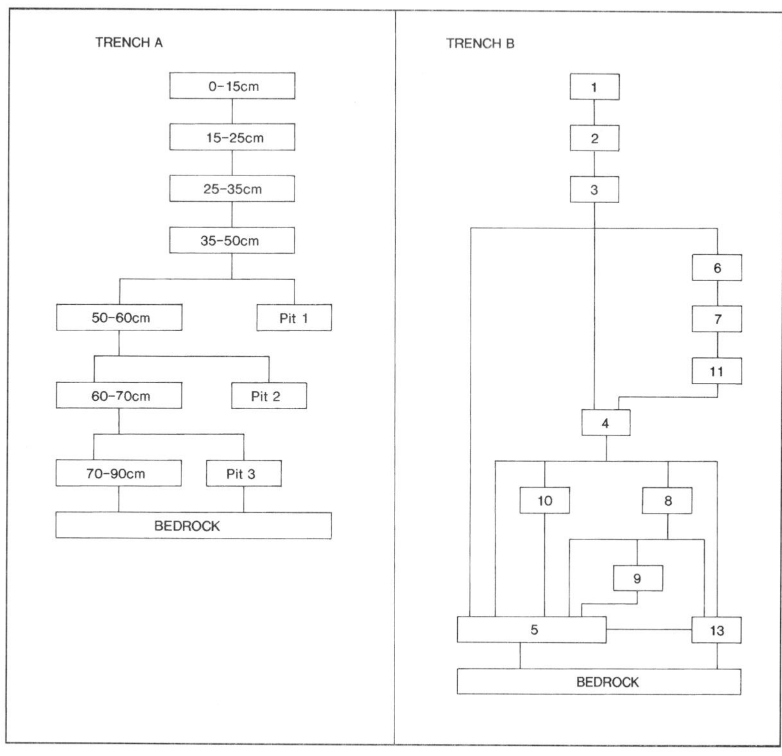

132. Harris matrices, Trenches A and B, Tinj

The radiocarbon dates

Three radiocarbon dates were obtained from water-sieved deposits from Tinj (table 19):

Table 19 Radiocarbon dates from Tinj-Podlivade

GrN no. Site	Context	Date	BP	Calibrated BC dates
15236 Tinj 1	Trench A/Pit 1	6980	± 160	5815, 5790, 5750 (*1)
15237 Tinj 2	Trench A/Pit 2	6670	± 260	5565 (*1)
15238 Tinj 3	Trench A/Pit 2	6280	± 210	5260, 5215, 5185 (*2)

These dates are some of the earliest dates for the establishment of a mixed farming economy in the east Adriatic zone (Chapman and Müller 1990; Chapman *et al.* 1992). The gap between the mean dates for Pits 1 and 2 is suggestive of either a repeated occupation or a lengthy occupation on the same site.

The finds

The faunal remains

By C. Schwartz

A total of 15,365 bone fragments was recovered from Tinj, with 3,212 identified to species (table 20). An additional 2,332 bones are identified only to element and the remainder, 9,821, are unidentifiable fragments. Most bones show signs of good preservation, being relatively free of leached chemical matter and there are few friable specimens. The vertebrate animal fauna is composed primarily of the caprines – sheep and goat (fig. 133). Included in the recovered domestic species are cattle, pig and dog, but they are relatively rare. Wild vertebrates such as red deer, roe deer and badger, as well as some birds, also appear in the later levels, significantly broadening the subsistence base of the village. Molluscs have the same

Table 20 Estimated minimum number of domestic stock, Tinj-Podlivade

	Immature	Juvenile	Sub-adult	Adult	Stratigraphy
Cattle	–	–	1	3	0–0.9m + Pits
Caprines	1	8	13	24	0–0.25m
	2	3	6	14	0.25–0.5m
	1	–	2	6	0.5–0.7m
	1	2	7	10	Pits
	5	13	28	54	Total
Pig	–	1	1	2	0–0.9m + Pits

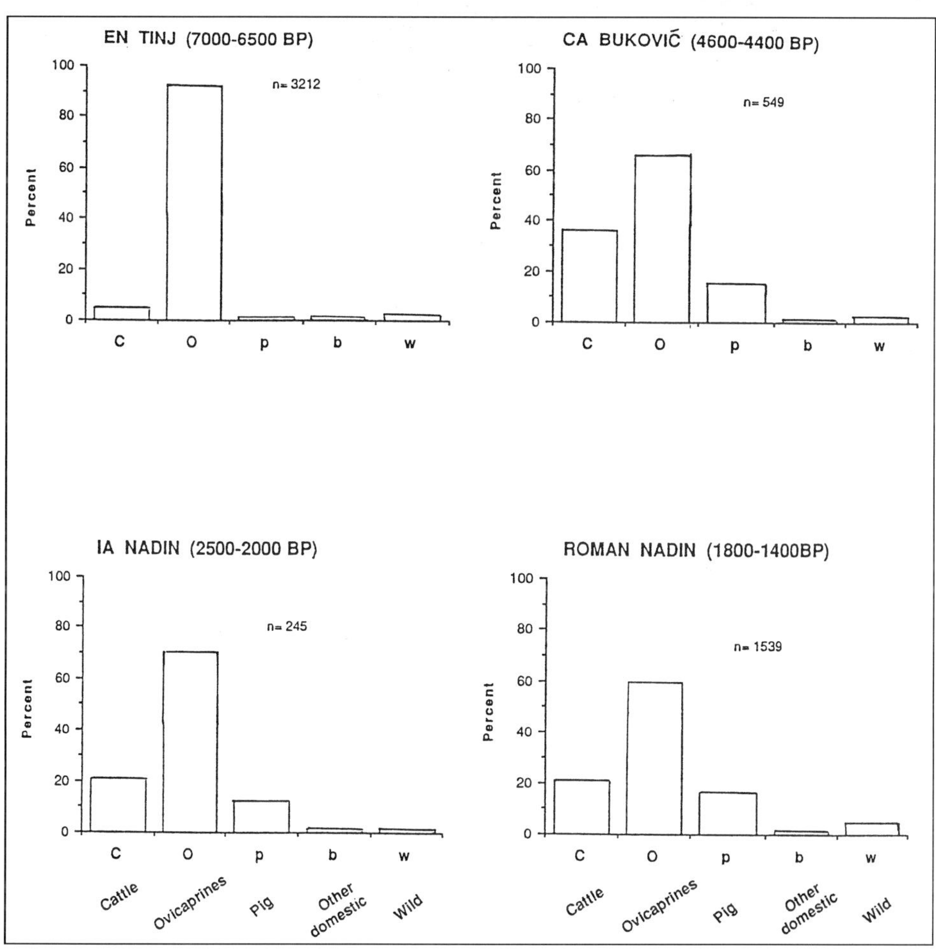

133. Distribution of animal species elements by periods, Tinj-Podlivade, Bukovič-Lastvine, Nadin-Gradina (Iron Age and Roman)

effect, adding minerals and vitamins not otherwise found in the diet (mainly mussels, oysters, topshells and murex). The kill-off patterns for ovicaprines and cattle indicate a preference for adult and sub-adult animals. No pathological characteristics were noted. The range of vertebrate species represented at Tinj compares closely with those at Smilčić and Obre II (Schwartz 1988; Bökönyi 1974).

The plant remains

By J. Huntley

Although few in number, the carbonized plant remains do indicate that at least three, possibly four, cereals were present in the area (table 21). These were barley, emmer and einkorn, and another wheat which is possibly the wild *Triticum*

Table 21 Botanical remains by context, Tinj-Podlivade

Plant species	Sample no.													
	1	2	3	4	5	6	7	8	9	10	12	15	16	17
Triticum grain	1	–	–	–	–	1	–	–	–	–	–	2	–	–
Hordeum indet. grain	1	–	–	–	–	–	–	–	–	–	–	–	–	–
Hordeum (naked) grain	–	–	–	–	–	–	–	–	–	–	–	–	–	–
Cerealia indet. grain	3	–	–	–	–	1	–	2	1	–	–	–	–	–
Triticum glume base	2	3	2	3	12	7	–	4	–	–	6	2	1	–
Triticum spikelet fork	–	–	–	–	–	–	–	–	–	–	–	1	–	–
Tr. aestivum grain	–	–	–	–	–	–	–	–	–	3	–	–	–	1
Tr. aestivum rachis	–	–	–	–	–	–	–	–	–	11	–	–	–	3
Tr. aestivum floret base	–	–	–	–	–	–	–	–	–	–	–	–	–	8
Triticum cf. spelta	–	–	–	–	–	–	–	–	–	–	1	–	–	–
Triticum spelta spikelet fork	1	–	–	–	–	1	1	–	–	–	–	–	–	–
Avena awn fragment	–	1	–	1	2	1	–	–	2	–	–	–	–	–
culm node indet.	–	–	–	–	–	–	–	–	–	–	–	–	–	1
Leguminosae	–	–	–	1	1	–	–	–	–	–	–	–	–	–
Veronica hederafolia	2	–	2	1	–	–	–	2	–	12	–	–	–	6
Portulaca oleracea	1	1	2	–	1	1	–	3	–	–	–	–	–	–
Chenopodium album	1	–	–	–	–	–	–	1	–	–	–	–	–	–
Chenopodium indet.	3	–	–	–	–	1	–	1	–	–	–	–	–	–
Gramineae indet.	1	–	1	–	–	–	–	–	–	–	–	–	–	–
Polygonum indet.	2	–	–	–	3	–	–	–	–	–	–	–	–	–
Polygonum aviculare	–	–	–	–	–	–	–	1	–	–	–	–	–	–

Key to contexts: 1–2 5/Pit 2; 3 – B/10; 4–6 - 5/Pit 2; 7 - 5/35–50; 8 - 5/25–35; 9 - B/6; 10 - 5/25–35; 11 - B/3; 12 - 5/Pit 2; 13 - 5/35–50; 14 - 5/Pit 1; 15 - 5/70–80; 16 - 5/Pit 3; 17 - B/4; 18 - B/9; 19 -B/13.

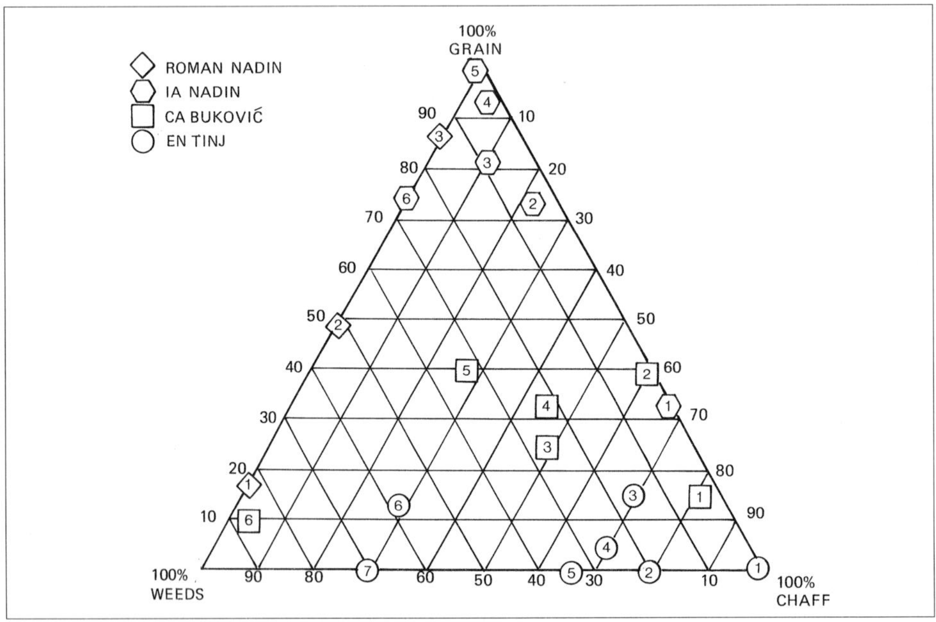

134. Tripole graph of botanical remains, Tinj, Buković and Nadin

boeoticum. The evidence for the various wheat species derives purely from chaff fragments. The weed seeds present were all from plants which are still present in the area today and are characteristic of disturbed and rather dry ground. The fact that most of the wheat remains and all of the oat remains are of chaff suggests that both a variety of wheats, and oats, were growing in the area, either as crops or adventitively, rather than that processed grain was being imported into the area. Division of the plant sample into cereal grains, chaff and weeds (Jones 1984, 1985; van der Veen 1985, 1992) produces a striking tripole graph, in which the greater part of the samples fall closest to the chaff corner (fig. 134).

The pottery

The ceramic assemblage at Tinj falls within the classic definition of Cardial Impressed Ware, with as many as 12 per cent of the sherds exhibiting cardial decoration in certain contexts. A primary defining characteristic of the Tinj pottery is the high frequencies of decorated sherds (fig. 135). In Trench A, 26.5 per cent of all sherds were decorated, a figure reduced to 19 per cent of the total pottery sample for both Trenches. Three fabric classes have been distinguished: fine/coarse – inclusions smaller than 3mm; coarse/fine – inclusions of between 3 and 6mm; very coarse – inclusions over 6mm.

Brakspear (1986) noted that surface colours varied continuously, as a reflection of fairly uncontrolled bonfire firing. Few burnished sherds were found and there were few thin-walled sherds. Three categories of surface treatment were used in the general pottery analysis: burnished ware, monochrome ware (often smoothed surface) and coarse ware (neither surface smoothing nor burnishing). The presence of carbonates in general as well as calcite in particular argues for firing temperatures lower than 750 °C. Oxidizing atmospheres were used for the firing of most of the Tinj sherds.

Five general shape categories can be recognized in the Tinj assemblage (fig. 136):

1. Dishes (4 shapes: straight-sided, convex, concave, carinated).
2. Bowls (2 shapes: convex, concave).
3. Necked forms (5 shapes: straight-sided neck, inverted neck, funnel neck, everted neck and necked, carinated).
4. Straight-sided forms (2 shapes: everted and inverted).
5. Miniature vessels (1 shape: rounded bowl).

Necked and straight-sided forms tend to be used more often for the small vessels, with dishes and bowls more frequent for medium-size pots. A small number of large examples of each general shape is also encountered. These conclusions

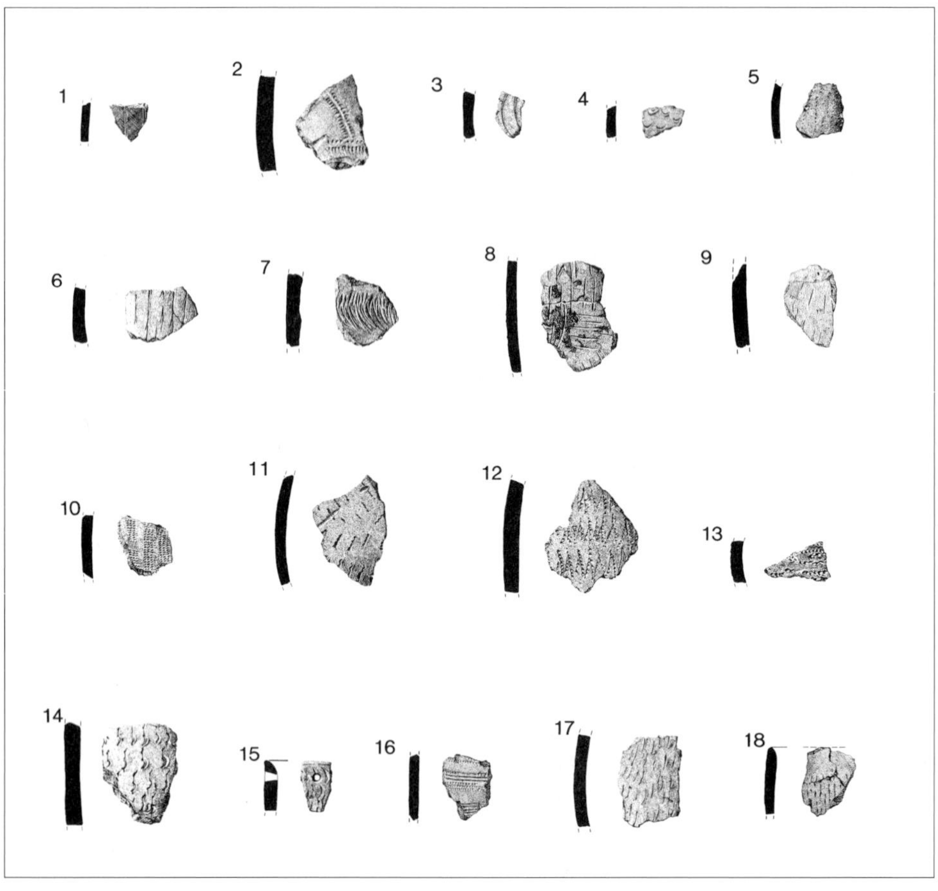

135. Decorated pottery, Impressed Ware, Tinj 1: Trench A/ 0–15cm depth; 2–3: A/15–25; 4: A/60–70; 5–9: A/15–25; 10–13: A/25–35; 14–17: A/35–50; 18: A/Pit I, 70–90

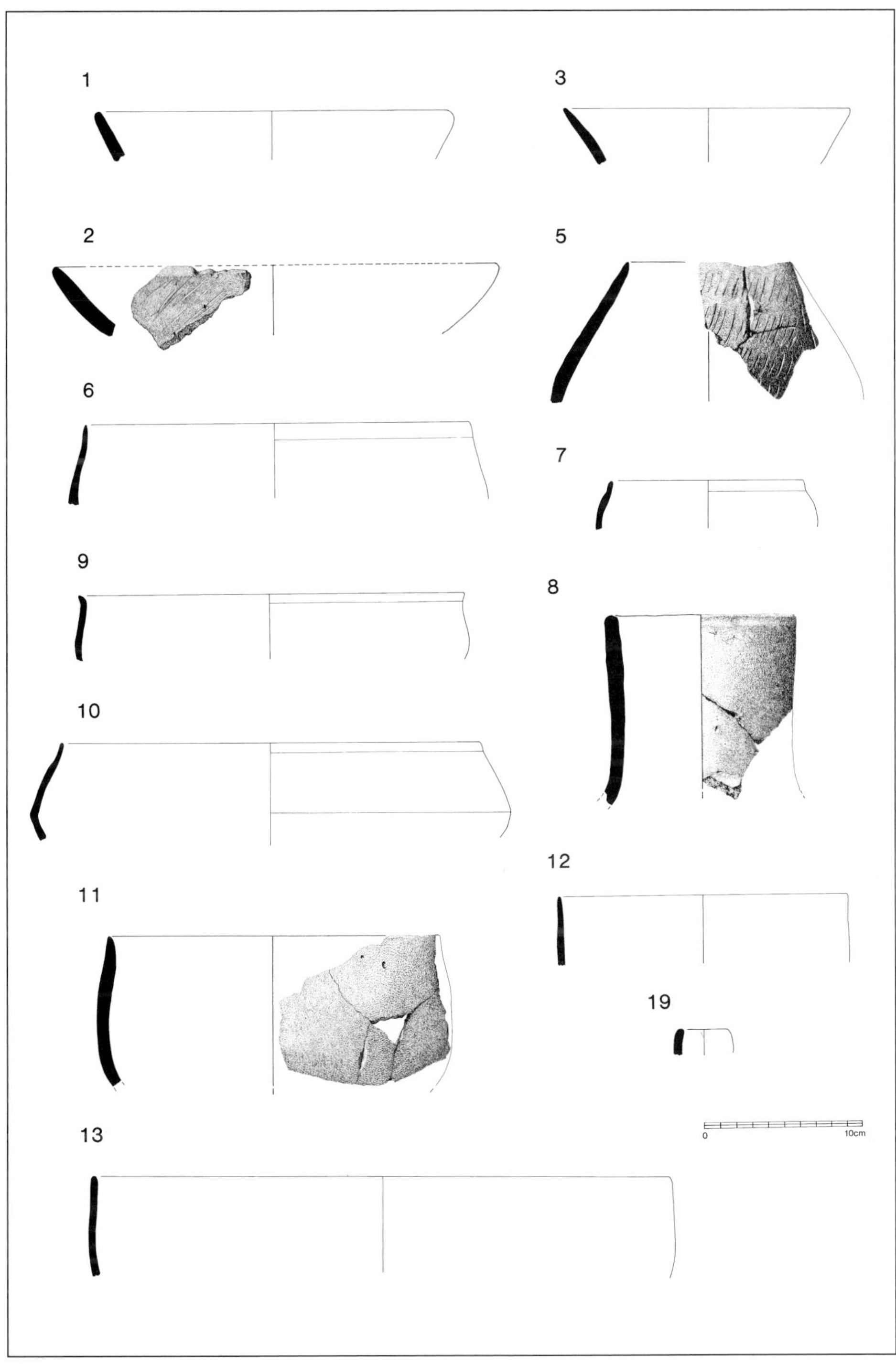

136. Vessel shapes, Tinj. Phase 1: 1–3, 5–7; Phase 2: 8–13, 19.

indicate minor functional differentiation amongst vessel sizes in the Tinj assemblage. It can be demonstrated that dishes and straight-sided forms are more frequently made in fine/coarse monochrome wares, and bowls and necked forms in coarse/fine monochrome ware. The classification of lugs and handles is simplified by the relatively undifferentiated forms used in the Early Neolithic. One handle type is known, along with four lug types (oval, upturned, extended and button). It is a sign of an early and undifferentiated potting tradition that there are only twelve recognizable lugs (or 0.2 per cent) in over 6,000 sherds.

Four main decoration styles can be defined at Tinj: non-cardial shell impressed, cardial impressed, stamped and other. Minor changes in time occur in the use of these styles: the main change is an increase in stamped and other decoration at the expense of shell-impressed ware, both cardial and non-cardial.

In summary, the biggest single variation in the assemblage is the far higher frequency of decorated pottery in Trench A compared to Trench B. The higher incidence of flooding in the area where Trench B was located suggests that a narrower range of activities was carried out there, with consequently lower discard rates. The fact that a high proportion of decorated sherds was found in fill deposits above the cobble level, particularly in Trench A, supports the idea of more intensive occupation in period 2, with a concomitant increase in pottery discard. There is no clear relationship between vessel shape and decorational style, probably because of sample size. Two main chronological differences can be pinpointed in the decorated sample. Increases in stamped and other decoration through time and decreases in sherds with complex decoration through time are probably significant at the 1 per cent level.

The decorational styles indicate that Tinj falls in Müller's Phase II of the Adriatic Impressed Ware group (Müller 1988a, 1988b, 1991). It is noticeable that almost every motif present at Tinj has a direct counterpart at the classic site of Smilčić, 12km distant (Batović 1966).

The lithics

A small sample of lithic artefacts was recovered at Tinj. A total of 255 pieces was found in the two excavated trenches. Twenty classes of raw materials have been identified in the Tinj assemblage: nineteen of these can be identified to geological type, whilst the twentieth (burnt flint) can be identified generically. In this assemblage, there are ten classes of flint, nine of chert and one quartzite. These classes are based on surface colour differences and may have sourcing potential. All these classes of raw material could derive from sources within the Ravni Kotari or the Bukovica. There is a strong preference for flint (93.7 per cent), with minor use of chert (5.9 per cent) and marginal use of quartzite (0.4 per cent). Even with a small sample, these figures show that most cherts and quartzite are represented by only one manufacturing stage, whereas most flint classes are found in two or more stages. This conclusion confirms the notion that flint was more intensively exploited as well as being merely selected for tool manufacture. While cherts and quartzite were collected systematically for initial experiments with production, they were fairly soon rejected in favour of the generally higher-quality flint sources available in the same overall region.

There is evidence for on-site manufacture, use and discard of flint tools and possible evidence for exchange relations involving cores or tool blanks. The Tinj lithics constitute a non-geometric, blade-based assemblage with a marked preference for truncations (66 per cent of all tools). Complete blades are rarer than flakes (8 per cent, cf. 26 per cent). All the blades and truncations were struck from prepared cores, mostly using a punch technique. Flakes were reduced in size from larger flakes through the use of secondary flaking. There are no true geometrics in the microlithic finished tools. Thus, the technology of the Tinj assemblage has few diagnostic characteristics. This relative unspecificity is perhaps related to the overall tool-using strategy of high discard and low tool curation. The basic character of the Tinj assemblage can be defined as a non-geometric, microlithic industry with a predominance of backed truncations. The number of retouched or notched pieces in the assemblage is fifty-nine (23.1 per cent). From these figures, it can be seen that fine retouch is very much the commonest style.

The presence of sickle gloss indicates a concern with cutting plant material, possibly the domesticated cereals discussed above. The absence of burins and awls may be significant; likewise, the rarity of 'scraper' retouch may indicate that scraping was not an important activity in the excavated areas. The frequency of backed truncations is a positive sign of interest in cutting materials. Otherwise, the most important functional aspect of the assemblage is that it is based on a multiplicity of small elements that could be flexibly arranged in composite tools or used individually when necessary. It is this flexibility of approach that may well account for the low curation rates of most of the pieces.

Other finds

Fragments of fired clay daub were recovered, mostly from Trench A. No daub fragment was larger than 10 × 8 × 7cm. Although the figure of 38kg found in Trench A seems a large quantity, Ammerman *et al.* (1990) have concluded that houses of the Early Neolithic Stentinello culture of southern Italy require as much as 1,000kg of clay in their constructions. Hence, the daub remains from Tinj would seem to represent the degraded remnants of structures outside the excavated areas, not *in situ* buildings. This interpretation is supported by the rarity of hearths or other fixed structures aside from the stone cobbling.

Summary

In summary, the exploratory excavations at Tinj reveal two phases of occupation, divided by the construction of cobbled surfaces in both trenches. Above and below the cobbling lie a series of largely undifferentiated midden deposits into which has been incorporated a large quantity of artefactual and biological material dated to the first half of the sixth millennium Cal. BC. The far larger quantities found in Trench A reflect its greater distance from the marsh with its likely seasonal flooding.

The occupation site was conveniently located for water, fertile Arable land and nearby grazing. The biological remains provide the first undisputed evidence that at least some Impressed Ware communities practised a mixed farming economy from the earliest period of Neolithic development. Compared to little reliance on hunting and gathering, local cultivation of four, perhaps five, types of cereals and the intensive rearing of ovicaprines define the economic strategy of the inhabitants. A small lithic assemblage indicates intra-regional procurement of raw materials, mostly for tools which were used and discarded fairly rapidly. The high incidence of decorated pottery indicates a wide range of social activities were carried out, presumably on the as yet unexcavated portions of the site. The ceramics fall within the known range of east Adriatic Impressed Wares, with close parallels both locally and across the Adriatic in southern Italy. The site indicates the development of a lowland mixed farming susbsistence economy at an early stage in the sixth millennium Cal. BC (Chapman 1994b).

Buković-Lastvine (figs. 137–45)

History of investigations

The Copper Age site of Buković-Lastvine was discovered in the mid-1970s by M. Savić, who excavated a single trench there in 1983. The stratigraphy of the trench included a metre of 'cultural layer' with pits which were cut as deep as 1.40m and well-preserved animal bone, pottery, house daub and some metal artefacts. The site has been assigned to the Copper Age Nakovani group (Čović 1983b, 135). Buković is one of the very few open-air, unenclosed Copper Age sites in Dalmatia.

The site environment

Buković lies at the junction of the plains of the Ravni Kotari and the limestone hill-country of the Bukovica, which rises to peaks of *c.* 600masl (fig. 137). The site lies on and near the edge of what is now drained Bottomland, on a low 'plateau' (fig. 138). Three landscape units make up the site topography:

1. *The Bottomland.* The lowest terrain in the neighbourhood, this former marsh, called 'Bare', lies at an altitude of 158–65masl and is floored with recent alluvium.
2. *The 'plateau'.* The 'plateau' lies between the Bare and the limestone hills, at an altitude of 165–200masl. The 'plateau' is an undulating area of Eocene shales and sandstones. The site lies at an altitude of 170–80 m and is set back some 50m from the very edge of the Bottomland, sheltered from the bura.
3. *The limestone hills.* The Tertiary limestone hills that extend north-east in a continuous chain to the summits of the Bukovica start at *c.* 200masl. The lower hills are rounded, with a thin if discontinuous soil cover and remnant maquis vegetation.

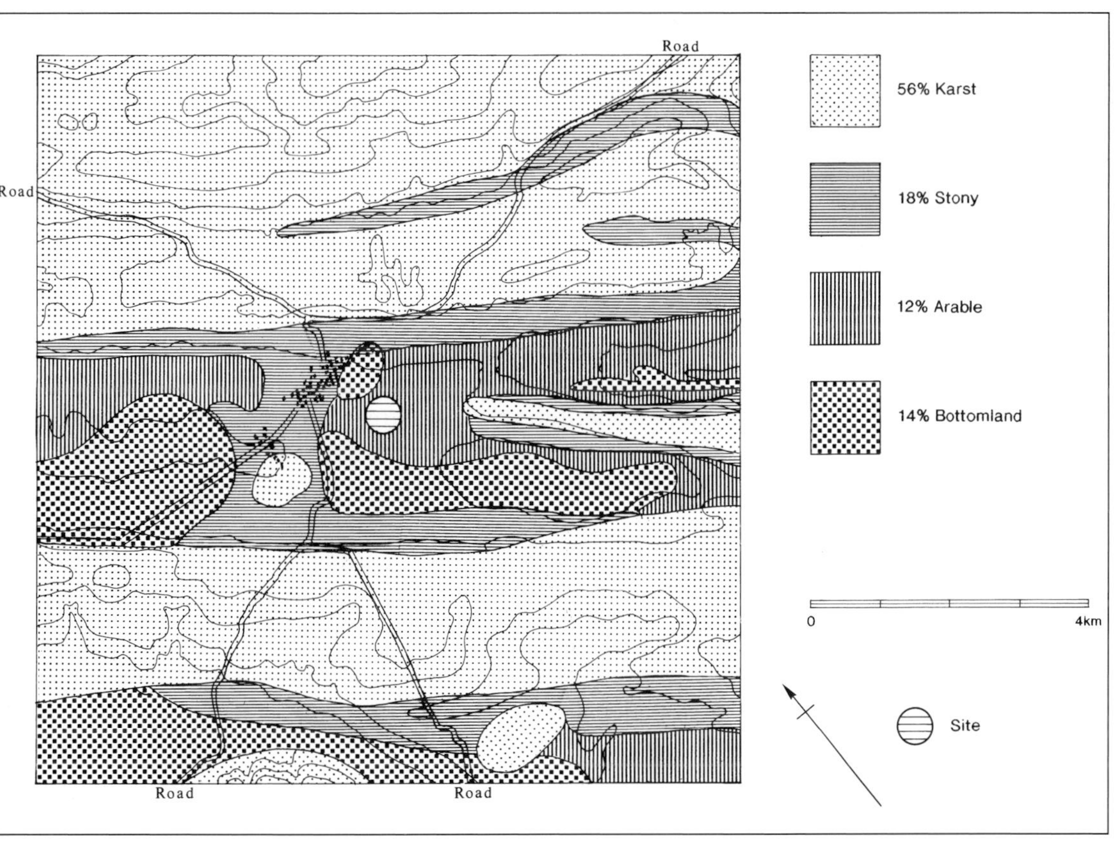

137. Location map, Buković

138. General view of Buković-Lastvine, from south-west

The hydrological advantages include a major area of at least seasonal water available on the Bottomland in front of the site, two streams within 1km of the site and two permanent springs within 1.5km. The overall land use potential of the site's 5km territory was closely related to the geological distinctions discussed above. Within 1.5km of the site Arable and Stony land, the two best classes, predominate, while Bottomland provides nearby summer grazing. The Karst grazings are more distant (fig. 137). Since the drainage of the bottomland of Bare, the entire area around Buković is covered in anthropogenic vegetation. Large parts of the former marsh are now utilized for cereal cultivation, while the limestone hills are a patchwork of maquis and small cultivated fields.

Environmental change

Changes in two important aspects of the site environment can be identified at Buković: hydrology and soils. The drainage of the Bottomland adjoining the site has removed important fish, shellfish and avian resources, as well as summer pasture especially valuable for bovids. The completion of the auguring of a 32m-long profile across the centre of the excavation site indicates that the area appears to have been covered by a fine sand/silt deposit in the post-Copper Age period. This deposit may relate to a period of deforestation in which soils on local limestone ridges were eroded and redeposited by wind on the 'plateau'.

Surface collection and excavation strategy

Savić defined the boundaries of surface pottery scatter at Buković as covering an area some 300 × 500m (fig. 139). Since the discovery of the site, however, the construction of a factory on the north side of the railway and extensions to the railway cutting itself have destroyed significant parts of the northern part of the site. In 1985, extremely low densities of surface material were found in the extant portion of the site. Given these unpromising surface conditions, it was decided that the best strategy was to define two foci for excavation: the area adjoining Savić' 1983 trench and the outer area of the site, characterized by lower surface pottery densities.

The aims of the Buković excavation were four-fold:

1. The definition of the character of the open Copper Age settlement form, which is so rare in Dalmatia.
2. The clarification of subsistence practices on site through the recovery of a representative sample of ecofacts. The importance of fourth millennium Cal. BC subsistence concerns the light shed on the 'Secondary Products Revolution' hypothesis (Sherratt 1979).
3. The definition and dating of the material culture of the site through the collection of radiocarbon samples from well-stratified contexts associated with diagnostic material.
4. The location of the site in its regional context of social networks of breeding, exchange and/or competition.

The results of the auger survey, by I. Maté and M. Lodder, indicated that there was a marked variation in geology and soil depth in the central area of the site. Prior to agriculture, the area seems to have been one of marked ridges, contrasting the harder and softer geological strata. The results of the auger survey enabled the location of the trenches to be closely related to predictable sub-soil conditions. The trenches in the main area were located to investigate the deepest stratigraphic sequences in the area, in a hollow some 1.8m deep by 18m across (fig. 140). The peripheral trenches were located to investigate the nature of occupation in other parts of the site.

139. Soil map, with location of trenches, Buković

Stratigraphy and occupation sequence

A total of eight trenches was excavated in a three-week season, an area of 68 sq. m. Six trenches were excavated within a 10m radius of the 1983 trench, while the remainder (Trenches 3 and 4) were located to explore other areas of the site (fig. 139).

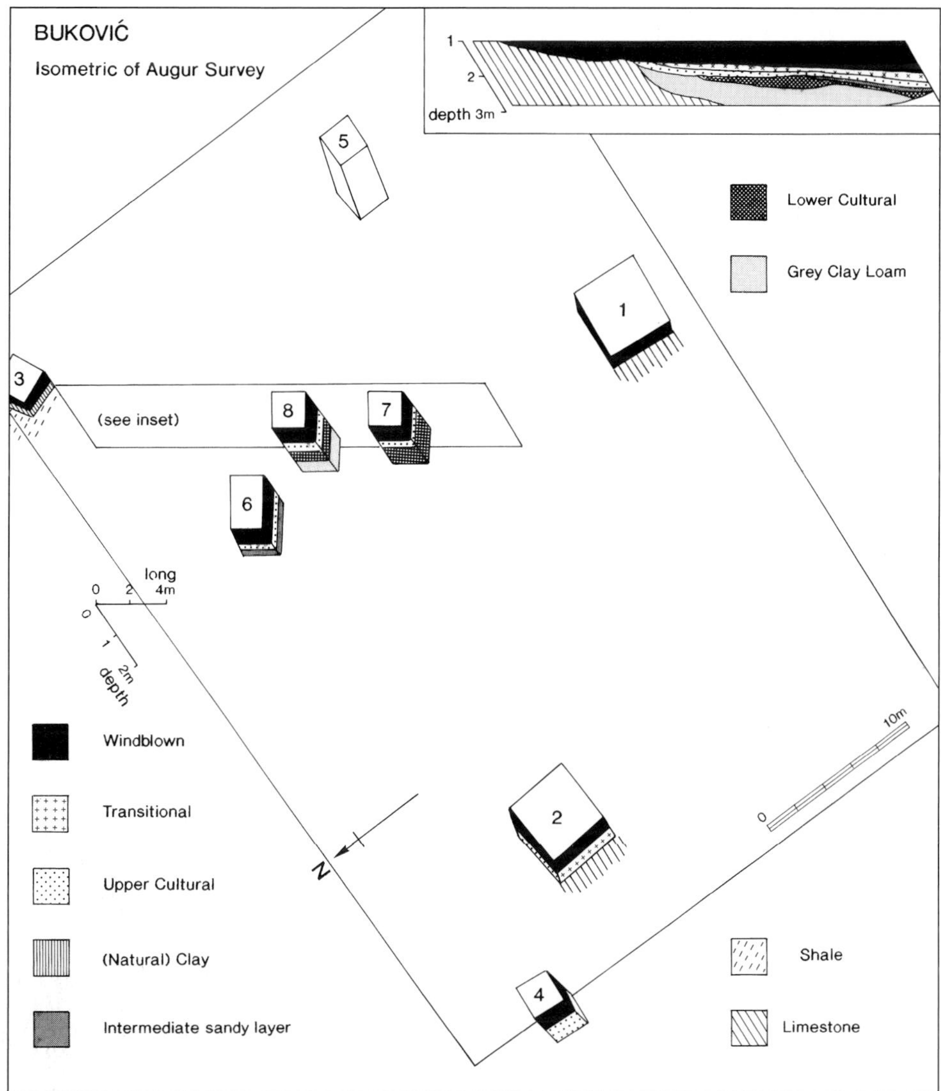

140. Auger isometric survey of central part of site, Buković

The following composite sequence was recorded from the auger profiles and the archaeological trenches (fig. 140):

1. A basal sterile grey layer (fine sandy silt loam: 10YR 6/6).
2. Lower 'cultural' layer (black clay with orange clay patches: 2.5Y 4/2).
3. Intermediate sandy layer (sandier than the lower levels: 10YR 3/2).
4. Upper 'cultural' layer (black, with more stones: 10YR 3/2).

5. Transition layer (black silty clay loam: 10YR 3/2).
6. Lower plough soil, relatively rich in pottery (Ap2/A1/plough pan).
7. Upper plough soil (Ap).

In this sequence, it is possible to identify three main periods of human occupation – the lower cultural layer, the upper cultural layer and the lower plough soil. The soils were also rich in charcoal, bone and artefacts, suggesting that the deepening and form of these soils was a product of organic-rich residues.

The most complete stratigraphic sequence is preserved in Trench 8, where both the lower and upper cultural layers are stratified between the basal grey layer and recent wind-blown deposits. A similar sequence is also found in Trench 5 (for basal outcrops, fig. 141). Both the lower and upper cultural layers are found in Trench 7, while the upper layer is present in Trench 6 and perhaps Trench 4. Minimal cultural material is sealed within wind-blown deposits in the upper parts of Trenches 1 to 3 (for Harris matrices, see fig. 142).

Almost all of the stratigraphic units at Buković are fills of one kind or another. This fact allows the derivation of a generalized sequence since each fill was laid down under similar conditions over much of the site.

141. General view of Trench 5, Buković

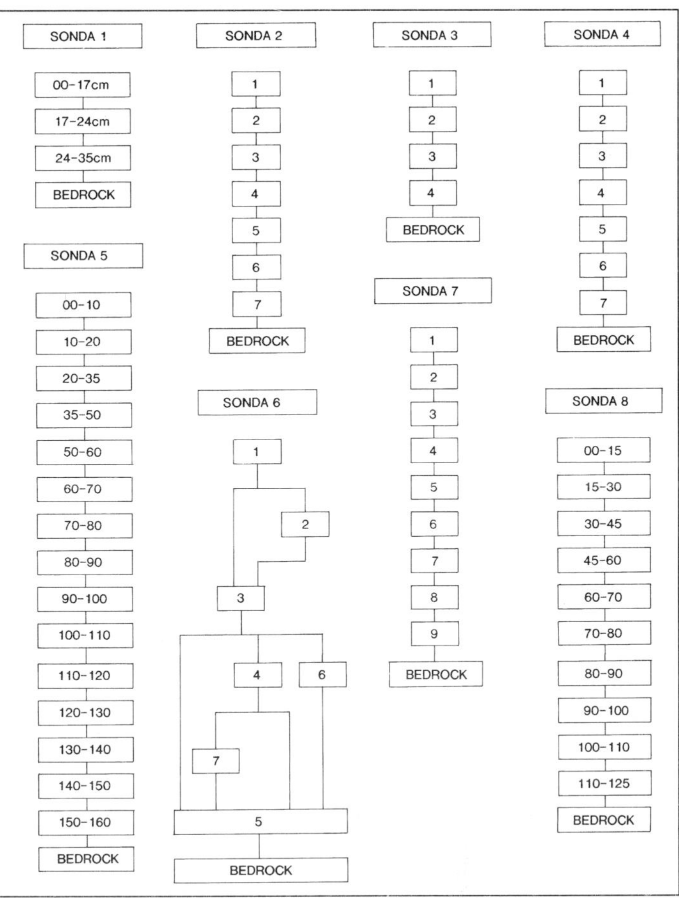

142. Harris matrices of archaeological trenches, Buković

On this basis, six depositional episodes can be defined, three of which incorporate archaeological material. The latter are designated Buković Periods 1–3: Buković 1 comprises the finds from the lower cultural layer, Buković 2 the finds from the upper cultural layer and Buković 3 the finds from the wind-blown deposits. The stratigraphic sequences in each trench can now be recategorized in terms of discard groups (henceforth 'Groups') (table 22).

The main difference between the deposits of these Groups is that the finds of Group 3 are less numerous, more heavily abraded and never horizontally bedded. In both Groups 1 and 2, horizontally-bedded bone and pottery is found in considerable quantity and in a far better state of preservation. There are two alternative interpretations of these differences, which depend on the interpretation of the anthropic soils in the central part of the settlement.

The first hypothesis is that the site was a settlement whose rather intensive occupation led to the development of *in situ* anthropic soils. It should be noted that structural remains of houses, whether postholes or bedding-slots, are seldom

Table 22 Occupation sequence, Buković-Lastvine (C.=context)

Trench	Group 1	Group 2	Group 3
1	–	–	0–0.65m
2	–	C. 5–7	C. 1–4
3	–	–	C. 1–4
4	–	C. 3–7	C. 1–2
5	1.00–1.6m	0.5–1.0m	0–0.5m
6	C. 7	C. 4	C. 1–3,6
7	C. 5–9	C. 3–4	C. 1–2
8	0.8–1.25m	0.5–0.8m	0–0.5m

found within these soils (for a full discussion, see MacPhail and Courty 1984; Courty *et al.*, 1989). An alternative model for the genesis of these anthropic soils is that the structures of the settlement were built on the harder rock ridges and that occupation debris was discarded down the slope into the natural hollows between the slopes, thus forming organic-rich sediments. According to the first hypothesis, the finds in Groups 1 and 2 are *in situ* refuse within an organically-rich area where settlement occupation took place, with the finds of Group 3 representing secondary deposition of refuse first discarded elsewhere (e.g. on the limestone ridges) but washed into secondary positions during the phase of erosion which preceded the deposition of the wind-blown deposits. The alternative is that the main settlement focus at Buković was on the dry, higher limestone ridges and that settlement refuse reached the trenches in two ways – direct discard of refuse by throwing into wet, perhaps marshy hollows during the period of residence (Groups 1 and 2) and discard on the limestone ridges of material which was later washed down into secondary positions and sealed by the wind-blown deposits (Group 3).

Two factors favour the second hypothesis of settlement on the ridges, with refuse deposition in the hollows: the damp conditions of the hollows for occupation and the high degree of abrasion in the faunal sample, interpreted as the movement of bones down the edges of gullies, together with ash and other organic residues. Such an incidence of abrasion is not found at Tinj, Smilčić or Obre.

The radiocarbon dates

Four C14 dates have been obtained from flotation residues from Buković (table 23): These dates indicate that deposition of the aeolian silt forming the matrix for Group 3 can be dated to the Later Bronze Age (GrN 15243), quite distinct from the dates for Group 1 (GrN 15241) and Group 2 (GrN 15242 and 15244). The latter are statistically barely distinguishable and derive from different trenches. The implication is that formation of the deposits of Groups 1 and 2 was broadly coeval, dating to the Copper Age.

Table 23 Radiocarbon dates from Buković-Lastvine

GrN	N Sample	Context	Date BP	Calibrated BC dates
15241	Buković 1	Trench 7/C9	4390 +/- 60	3015, 2970, 2940
15242	Buković 2	Trench 6/C4	4520 +/- 60	3335, 3230, 3190, 3160, 3145 3370, 3240
15243	Buković 3	Trench 4/C3	3090 +/- 50	1410, 1335, 1330 1400, 1330
15244	Buković 4	Trench 6/C4	4580 +/- 80	3350, 3385

The finds

The faunal remains

By C. Schwartz

The faunal sample from Buković-Lastvine represents one of the largest faunal collections from the third millennium BC in the Balkans. Of currently known samples, only that from Ezero, Bulgaria is larger. A total of 3,317 bone fragments was recovered from Buković, with 573 identified to species and an additional 510 only to element (table 24). Of the remaining 2,234 unidentifiable fragments, 17.4 per cent are burned. There are no whole bones and only fourteen measurable elements in the whole sample. Preservation is good, with the bones free of leached chemical matter. Many of the fragmented bones appear to have been altered in that their edges are not smooth but sharp. In all instances but two, the bones are fragmented prior to excavation. Examples of butchering and gnawing by carnivores is also attested.

Cattle remains from Buković are about half as frequent as those of caprovines, a total of 29 per cent (fig. 133). All the measurable bovid bones from Buković can be considered 'domestic' based on the criteria given in Bökönyi (1962) and Stampfli (1963). Most of the ageable bones recovered from Trenches 5–8 are adult specimens with the exception of three sub-adults, one juvenile and one immature specimen. The total number of individuals estimated (MNI) from all four trenches is eight. No pathological conditions are observed in the cattle sample.

Table 24 Distribution of identified species elements by group, Buković-Lastvine

Context	Cattle	Sheep/ Goat	Domestic pig	Dog	Red Deer	Hare	Hen	Total
Group 3	7	6	–	–	–	–	2	15
Group 2	34	49	9	–	1	–	–	93
Group 1	123	275	62	–	–	5	–	465
Total	164	330	71	–	1	5	2	573

The frequency of caprovine bones exceeds that of cattle. There is a predominance of long bone elements together with a paucity of axial bones. The absence of skull, pelvis and calcaneum elements distinguishes the caprovines from the bovines. Part of the discrepancy between the groups may consist of different butchering techniques. Most of the ageable bones are from adults.

Pig remains from Buković are low in frequency in comparison with those of cattle and caprovines, as at Tinj. Pig bones are dominated by mandible, metacarpal and calcaneum fragments. Most of the elements listed above are from adult individuals. Seven elements are from juveniles while two are from sub-adults.

Three bones of dog and red deer apiece have been identified, while five elements are recorded for the hare and two for the hen.

The Copper Age site of Buković-Lastvine is characterized by vertebrate remains composed primarily of caprovines (sheep and goat) and cattle. The representation of cattle at Buković is the highest found in any of the NDP faunal spectra; this is likely to be attributed to the incipient exploitation of secondary products in Dalmatia and the value of bovine traction (carts, ploughs). Included in the domestic sample are a small percentage of pigs and dog. Wild animals are represented by red deer and hare. The wild animals form an insignificant part of the overall total. One bird specimen has been identified – the hen. Burned bone occurred more frequently in the Buković sample (nearly 18 per cent) than in either Tinj (see p. 186), Smilčić (Schwartz 1988) or Obre (Bökönyi 1974).

An additional source of food is the sea, some 10km from the site, and brackish marshy areas close to the site today. The ecological niches represented by the molluscan species are the mesolittoral, infralittoral, stagnant water and land. Exploitation of the littoral is confined to a few species – mussels, oysters, cockles and turret shells. All marine species are low in frequency compared with the Neolithic site of Tinj (see p. 186–7). Moreover, the range of species is narrower and is collected from fewer ecological niches. Hence, it seems unlikely that marine molluscs played an important role in the diet of the Buković inhabitants. It seems unlikely that land snails contributed much to the Buković diet either; there are few *Helix* shells and *Valvata* appears to be inedible. However, the food source of the latter, the reeds of the semi-saline area, could easily have been transported to the site, where it could have had several uses (roofing, burning to ward off insects, etc.).

The plant remains

By J. Huntley

A total of twenty-four samples was collected from the eight trenches at Buković. These samples, which were of approximately equal volume, were floated on site over 0.5mm mesh sieves. The material was examined using a Wild stereoscopic microscope at a magnification of × 12 and all carbonized plant material was removed. Twelve of the twenty-four samples examined had identifiable material present. Samples 4, 9, 13 and 16–24 were barren.

Palaeobotanical studies confirm that the Buković population was engaged in mixed farming, with the local cultivation of emmer, einkorn and oats and possibly barley and a small-seeded legume (table 25). A low level of weed species had built up, perhaps indicating short-term cultivation in the area. Charcoal remains of oak, juniper and olive indicate some components of the local flora. Plotting of the Buković results on a tripole graph indicates the existence of uncleaned grain as well as the remains of crop-cleaning activities on site (fig. 134).

The pottery

The pottery assemblage from Buković-Lastvine is one of the largest groups to be excavated from an open, undefended Copper Age settlement in the West Balkans. The Buković sample consists of a total of 14,020 sherds, weighing 44.828kg. Most of the pottery surfaces are well preserved but the assemblage is heavily fragmented. The range of fabrics and decoration provides important comparanda both on the Dalmatian coast (e.g. the Nakovane group: Petrić 1975) and inland (e.g. the Cetina group: Marović and Čović 1983).

Table 25 Botanical remains by context, Buković-Lastvine

	1	2	3	5	6	7	8	10	11	12	14	15
Triticum glume base	–	1	–	3	4	–	14	2	4	3	–	–
Cerealia indet. grain	1	2	3	1	3	–	3	2	5	1	–	–
Portulaca oleraceae	1	–	–	–	–	–	–	–	–	–	–	–
Chenopodium album	–	–	1	–	–	–	–	–	1	–	–	–
cf. Triticum grain	–	–	–	1	–	1	–	–	–	–	1	–
Triticum spikelet fork	–	–	–	1	–	–	3	–	–	–	–	–
Labiatae undiff.	–	–	–	1	–	–	–	–	–	–	–	–
Chenopodiaceae undiff.	–	–	–	1	1	1	–	–	–	–	–	–
Galium cf. verum	–	–	–	–	1	–	–	–	–	–	–	–
Gramineae undiff.	–	–	–	–	–	–	1	–	1	–	26	–
Avena awn	–	–	–	–	–	–	1	1	–	–	–	–
Avena sativa floret base	–	–	–	–	–	–	–	–	–	–	2	–
legume less than 4 mm diameter	–	–	–	–	–	–	–	1	–	–	–	–
cf. Hordeum grain	–	–	–	–	–	–	–	–	1	–	–	–
Echinochloa sp	–	–	–	–	–	–	–	–	1	–	–	–
Atriplex patula/hastata	–	–	–	–	–	–	–	–	1	–	–	–
Rumex acetosella	–	–	–	–	–	–	–	–	1	–	–	–
cf. Setaria	–	–	–	–	–	–	–	–	–	–	2	–
CHARCOAL												
Quercus sp.	–	–	–	–	–	–	–	–	–	–	2	2
Juniperus/Taxus	–	–	–	–	–	–	–	–	–	–	1	–
cf. Olea	–	–	–	–	–	–	–	–	–	–	2	–

KEY TO CONTEXTS: 1 8/90–100; 2 8/60–70; 3 6/4; 5 5/130–140 6 8/90–100 7 7/9; 8 8/80–90; 9 8/45–60; 10 7/5 11 8/70–80; 12 8/100–110 13 6/3 14 2/3; 3 3/1

The main difference between the Tinj and Buković assemblages is the far lower proportion of decorated ware in the latter. The wares could be divided into two basic classes, on the basis of surface treatment and inclusions (Brakspear 1986):

1. *Fine ware*: black burnished wares, with abundant fine quartz grains and fine regular fabric.
2. *Coarse ware*: unburnished wares in a variety of colours (orange, buff, brown, black and grey), with predominantly limestone temper but also the use of ironstone and quartz.

Further sub-division of the assemblage into seven fabrics indicates variable production, probably household-based and using bonfire firing: (1) fine black burnished ware, (2) fine brown burnished ware, (3) coarse black burnished ware,(4) coarse brown burnished ware, (5) red coarse ware, (6) dark coarse ware and (7) other coarse ware.

The distribution of sherds by trench indicates considerable variation in the quantity of material deposited over the site. While Trench 3 contained no pottery at all, a total of 7,211 Copper Age sherds (22.249kg by weight) was recovered from Trench 5. There is considerable variation in the frequency of fabrics by trench, such that fine wares (fabrics 1–4) are very rare in Trenches 1–4. There is little evidence to contradict the supposition that the Buković pottery represents generalized refuse dominated by a high proportion of non-feature sherds.

The study of vessel form at Buković is based on a sample of 415 measurable rim sherds (*c.* 3 per cent of the total sample). The vessel shape typology developed for the Tinj assemblage was extended to incorporate a wider range of morphological variation; the same five general shape categories were present but more sub-types had been made (n = 22). The Buković assemblage is dominated by rounded rims with both edges curved (fig. 143). The size range of the Buković assemblage resembles that of the Tinj ceramics: vessel size ranges from 50mm to 600mm in diameter. A vessel diameter histogram of all measurable rims indicates that three size ranges are present: 50–200mm; 210–400mm and over 410mm (namely, small, medium and large). The size ranges of dishes, bowls and necked forms overlap to the extent of a reduction in functional differentiation. Even with the straight-sided forms, small vessels hardly outnumber medium sizes and there is a marked lack of large vessel sizes in the whole assemblage.

In contrast to the relatively undifferentiated range of lugs and handles at Tinj, the Buković assemblage boasts eight lug/handle types – 5 lug types, 2 handle types and a broken type. A total of forty-two sherds with lugs or handles is known from Buković (or 0.3 per cent of the assemblage). The potters at Buković made sizeable handles with complete horizontal perforations, as well as a range of five lug types. Strap handles are the most important type. A total of 123 bases was found at Buković (or 0.9 per cent of the assemblage).

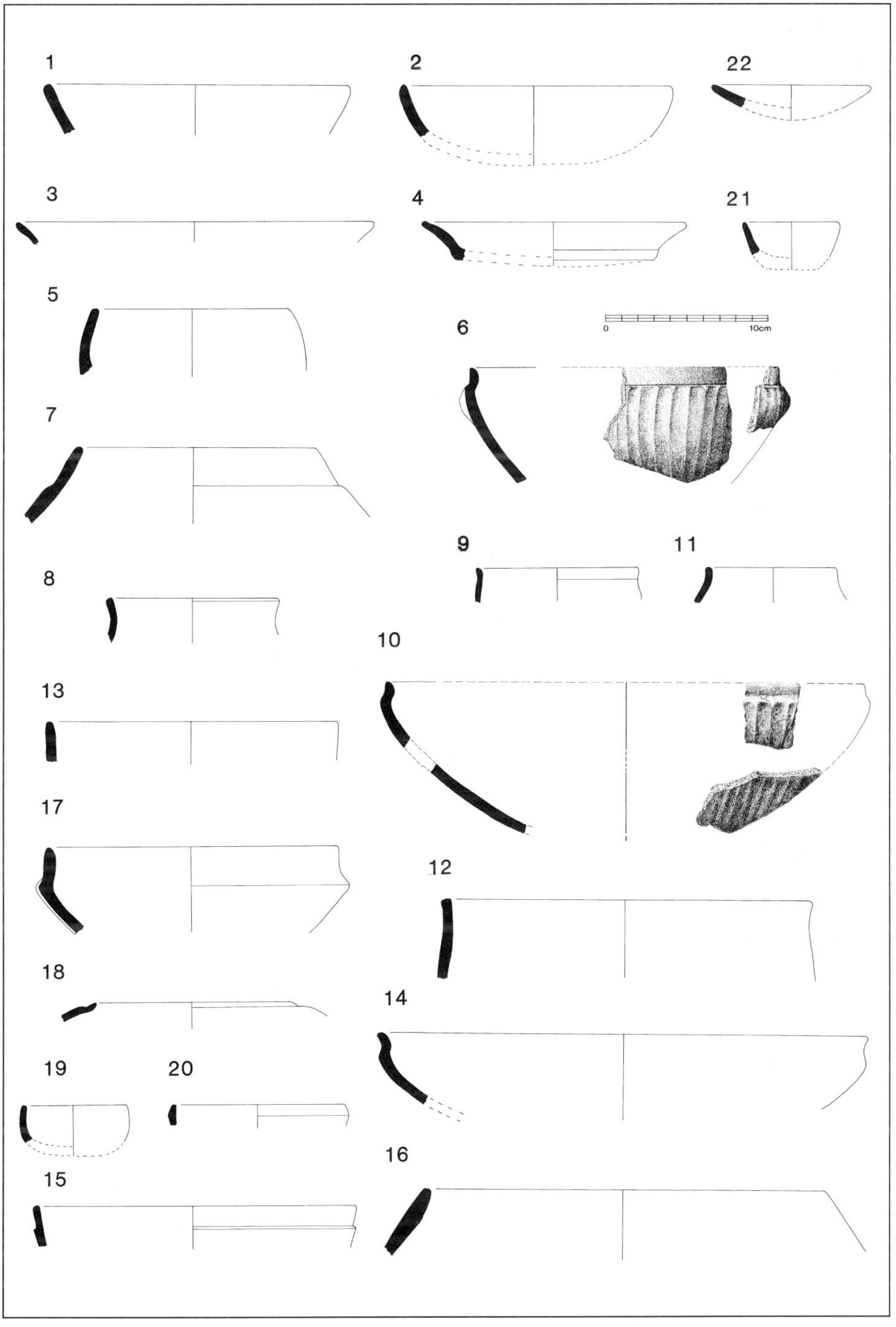

143. Shape classes, Copper Age pottery, Buković. Group 1: 1–6, 10–12, 15–20; Group 2: 7–9, 13–14, 21–22.

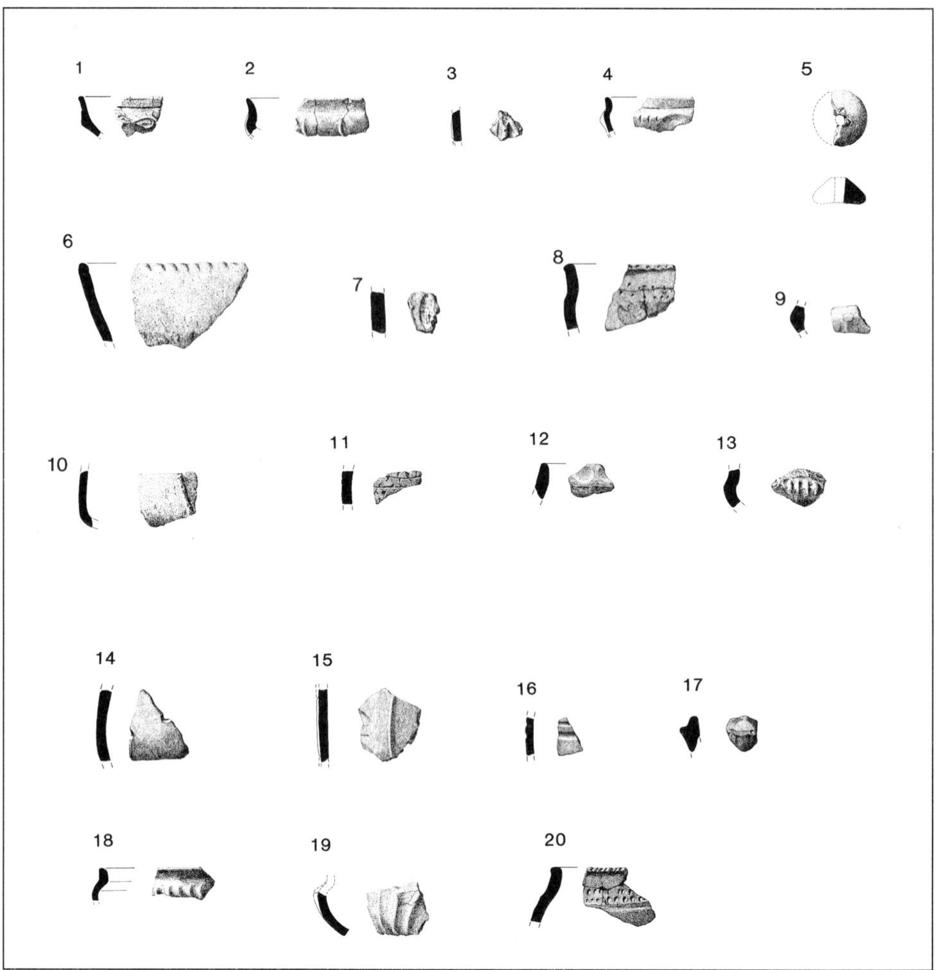

144. Decorated wares, Buković. 1: Trench 8/80–90cm depth; 2: 8/80–90; 3–5/ 80–90; 4: 7/Context 9; 5–6: 7/C. 9; 6: 7: 5/60–70; 8: 8/60–70; 9: 9/C. 4; 10: 8/45–60; 11: 8/0–15; 12: 8/90–100; 13: 8/45–60; 14: 5/90–100; 15: 6/C. 6; 16: 8/100–110; 17: 5/90–100; 18: 5/130–140; 19: 4/C. 4; 20: 8/60–70

In addition, twelve classes of base have been distinguished – 3 types of flat base, 3 types of pinched base, 3 of omphalos, a ring base, rounded base and a broken base. The flat base is by far the commonest form of base.

Although a low percentage of the assemblage bears decoration, there is a wider range of decorative styles at Buković than at Tinj. Seven styles are used at Buković: channelled, incised, impressed, plastic, grooved, excised and scribble burnish. Yet an eighth style represents a combination of channelled and plastic styles. Both Groups 1 and 2 contain sizeable quantities of dark burnished ware, some with channelling (fig. 144). The channelling is found on all four fine ware fabrics – fine black, coarse black, fine brown and coarse brown. Grooved decoration was limited to Group 1 coarse wares. In all of the levels with material of Groups 1 and 2, channelled ware is associated with red and brown coarse ware, rarely decorated with incised, excised, impressed and plastic decoration. The incised and excised decoration is not dissimilar to the decorated wares of the early Cetina group from Ravlica pećina Level IIIa (Marijanović 1980–1). Thus the Buković dates are the first such for the Nakovane facies anywhere in western Yugoslavia; the site confirms that channelled fine wares are consistently associated with those same incised coarse wares hitherto believed to be the sign of a different 'cultural group'. An alternative explanation is that the two different styles represent a domestic and a prestige ceramic set, with little other differentiating characteristic save for surface finish and decoration. The pottery found in the burnt level of Trench 4 is undifferentiated, with no decorated sherds in the assemblage at all. The associated date indicates a Later Bronze Age attribution.

The lithics

The lithic assemblage at Buković consists of a small sample of exactly one hundred pieces, weighing a total of 0.165kg; the fourteen different classes of raw material indicate a generalized collection strategy for most raw materials (except Class 01, comprising over 50 per cent of the assemblage). The distribution of lithics by manufacturing stage indicates a dominance of tools/tool blanks in the assemblage. It seems likely that finished tools were imported into Buković in combination with a strategy of local opportunistic tool preparation and use.

Four classes of retouched 'tool' are represented at Buković. Two examples of true geometric microliths are found – both retouched trapezes. This ranks as one of the latest occurrences of geometrics in the Adriatic zone. In addition, backed blades and a single example of an awl indicate possible functions, although, in the absence of microwear studies, these conclusions can be but tentative. Only 40 per cent of the tools/tool blanks have been modified by retouch.

Lithics play a far smaller role at Buković than at Tinj, with a smaller and less varied assemblage based on a narrower range of raw materials. The similarities lie in the opportunistic manner of raw material exploitation and the relatively low curation and high discard strategies found at both sites. Both assemblages are characterized by a preference for microlithic backed blades and bladelets, with a minor geometric component at Buković and more varied styles of backing at Tinj.

Other finds

The single small find consisted of an undecorated copper pin with circular cross-section (fig. 145), found in Group 2 level in Trench 6/Context 4 and dated by two C14 determinations to *c.* 3300 Cal. BC. According to EPMA analysis by the late R. F. Tylecote, the pin was a work-hardened arsenical copper reduced from an oxide ore with residual sulphur.

Summary

The middle reaches of the Benkovac trough were occupied in the Neolithic period at Benkovac but the settlement of Buković, some 3km away, was first occupied in the Copper Age. The settlement was established on the margins of a marsh or seasonal lake, with fertile Arable land backing the site. Although no structural remains were excavated, it seems most probable that the buildings were constructed on the limestone ridges within the site and that domestic refuse was discarded, or fell, into the intervening hollows which formed anthropic soils. Although the site territory bears a close resemblance to that of Early Neolithic Tinj, their mixed farming practices appear to be somewhat different. The increase in domestic cattle relative to ovicaprines at the latter may be a reflection of different herd strategies, in which cattle traction was more important than previously. The cultivation of a similar range of crops and legumes is striking, although the wider range of weed seeds may indicate a longer occupation at Buković than at Tinj.

The Copper Age dates from Buković provide the first absolute dates for the Nakovane facies and for pottery of Early Cetina style, indicating its contemporaneity with a period of ceramic diversification dated 3400–3100 Cal. BC,

145. Copper pin, Buković

the Late Neolithic–Early Copper Age transition in the central Mediterranean. Like Tinj, the site was used continuously or discontinuously, for a period of several centuries. Subsequently, Buković was abandoned for a period of more than a millennium. Short-term reuse in the Later Bronze Age corresponds to a period of local erosion and soil instability.

Mataci-Jazvinački Brijeg Bronze Age enclosure (figs. 146–55)

For history of investigations, site environment and site survey, see pp. 111–13 and figs. 80–1, 146–7).

Excavation strategy

The strategy for the 1983 excavation was based on four aims:

1. The identification of traces of occupation in the interior of the enclosure.
2. The definition of the form and construction technique of the primary rampart.
3. The identification of past land surfaces preserved beneath the rampart or cairn.

146. Mataci-Jazvinački Brijeg from south-west; site on hill in front of forest

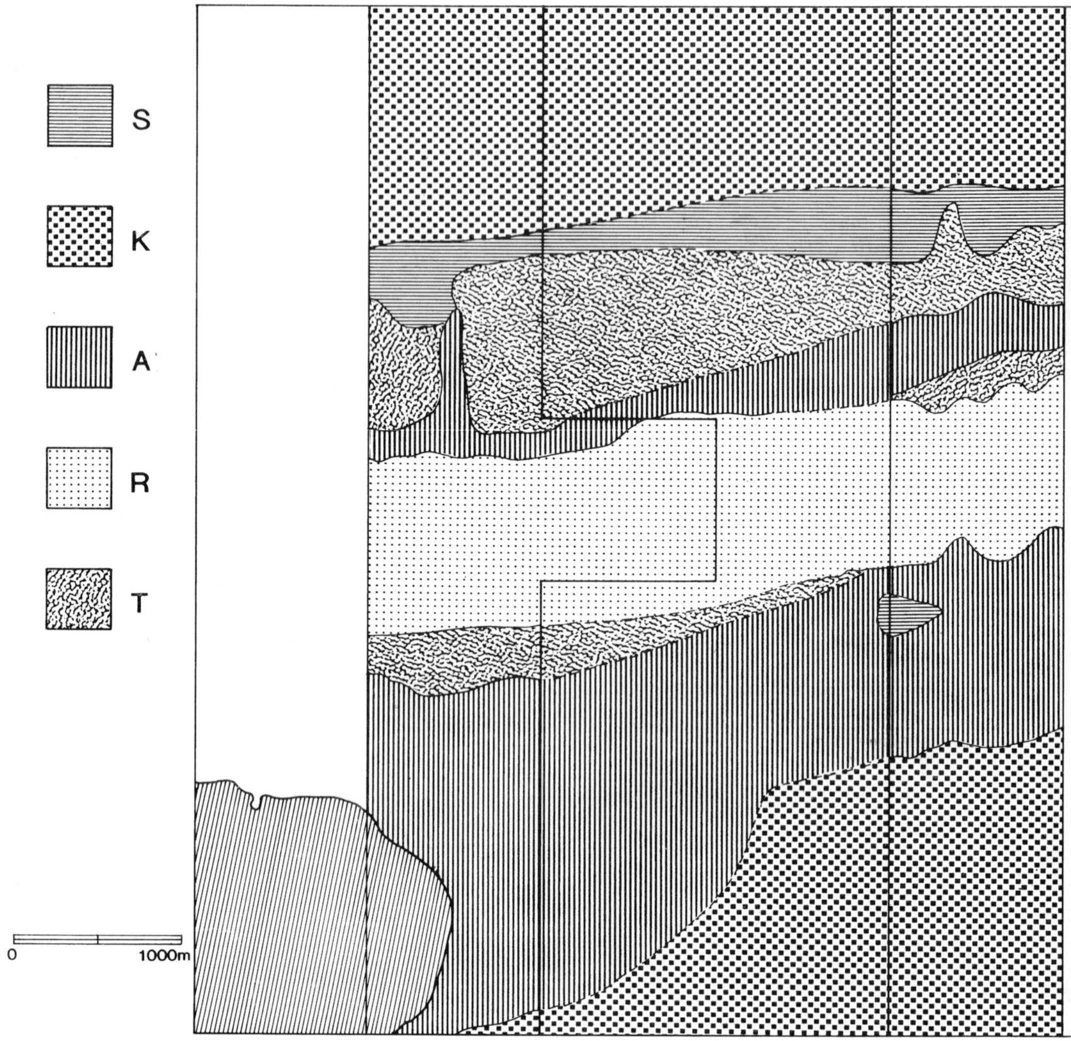

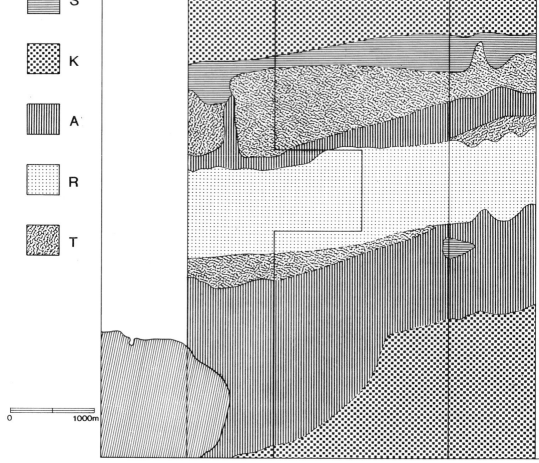

147. Land Use Capability map of Mataci territory (S = Stony, K = Karst, A = Arable, R = Ridge, T = Terrace land class)

4. Recovery of economic and other data pertaining to the function of the enclosure.

Three excavation trenches were laid out, two inside the enclosure walls on the plateau along the apex of the ridge (less than 3 per cent slope) and a third across a well-preserved section of the enclosure rampart.

Stratigraphy and occupation sequence

The stratigraphies of the three trenches at Mataci present a consistent picture of the sequence of processes and activities at the site (for Harris matrices, see fig. 148). On the basis of these stratigraphies, a sequence of eight phases can be identified at the Mataci site, starting with the pre-occupation environment and ending with recent erosive damage to the site (fig. 149).

1. The pre-occupation landscape consisted of an intact soil horizon of brownish-yellow silt under what, by analogy with the nearby dated Bokanjačko Blato pollen diagram (see p. 39) was probably mixed oak forest. Silt is not typical of a 'sandstone' matrix from which the site is presumed to have developed. The soil was probably already more acid than is typical of the Ravni Kotari and grykes would have already begun to form in the underlying limestone. There is no indisputable evidence of a pre-enclosure occupation from the excavated areas. Similarly, there is no clear dating evidence for the construction of the tumulus now lying inside the enclosure.
2. The first use of the site is defined by the construction of a stone and earth rampart round an area of 0.2ha. The primary rampart on the north side of the enclosure was *c.* 2.5m wide and composed of large limestone blocks (figs. 150–1), as opposed to the rubble placed on top of it. An inner revetment bank, *c.* 1.4m wide, and made of earth (colour 10YR), smaller stones and sherds, was constructed against the inner face of the north rampart.
3. Forest clearance inside and in the vicinity of the enclosure prompted erosion of the A-horizon of the silty loam soil. The exposure of limestone in localized areas of thinner soil increased the rate of karstification of some areas of the enclosure interior. Small quantities of pottery were found in the resultant grykes, suggesting discard of some pottery during use of the site.
4. After an undefined period of time, the site went out of use and the rampart began to collapse both inwards and outwards (figs. 152–3). The preservation of areas of pre-enclosure soil beneath rampart tumble confirms the relatively localized erosion patterns during site use. The pottery incorporated into the rampart tumble derived from the rampart construction of phase 2 and cannot necessarily be associated with the period of site use.
5. The process of rampart collapse continues, with rampart tumble now sealing the grykes which deepened in phase 3.
6. The process of karstification continued in areas of the site not covered by rampart tumble, leading to extension of the clints and grykes. Pottery incorporated into these grykes derives from the main phase of site use.

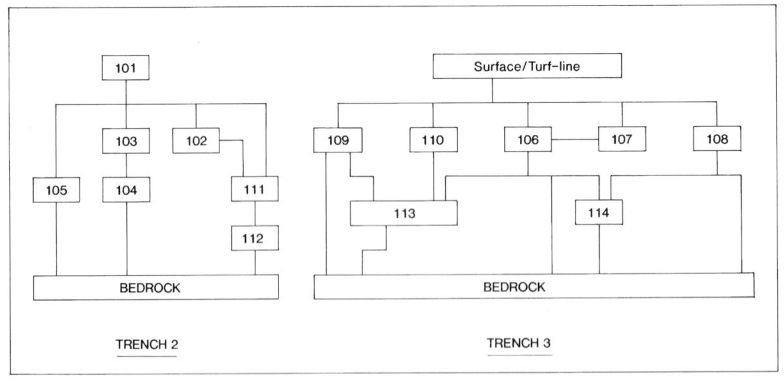

148. Harris matrices of archaeological trenches, Mataci

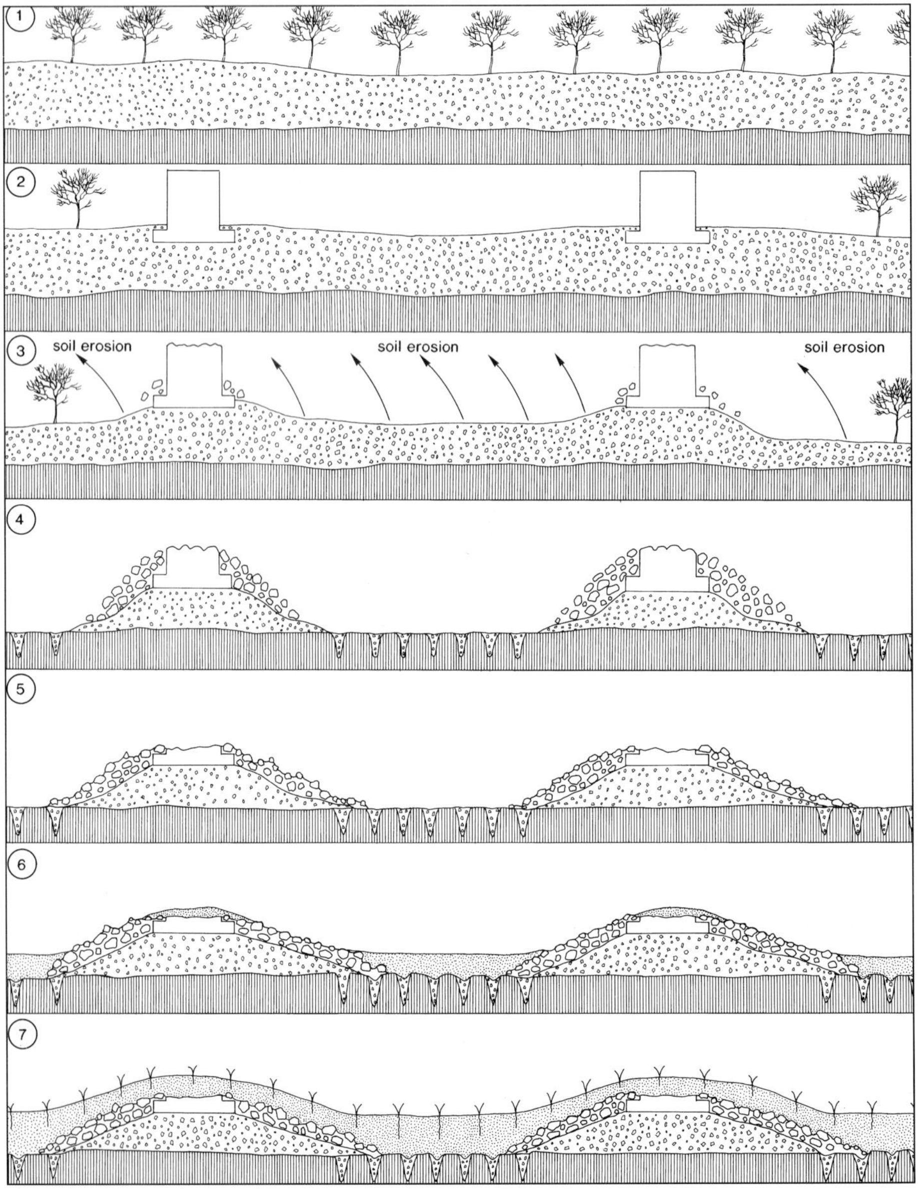

1
2
3 soil erosion
soil erosion
soil erosion
4
5
6
7

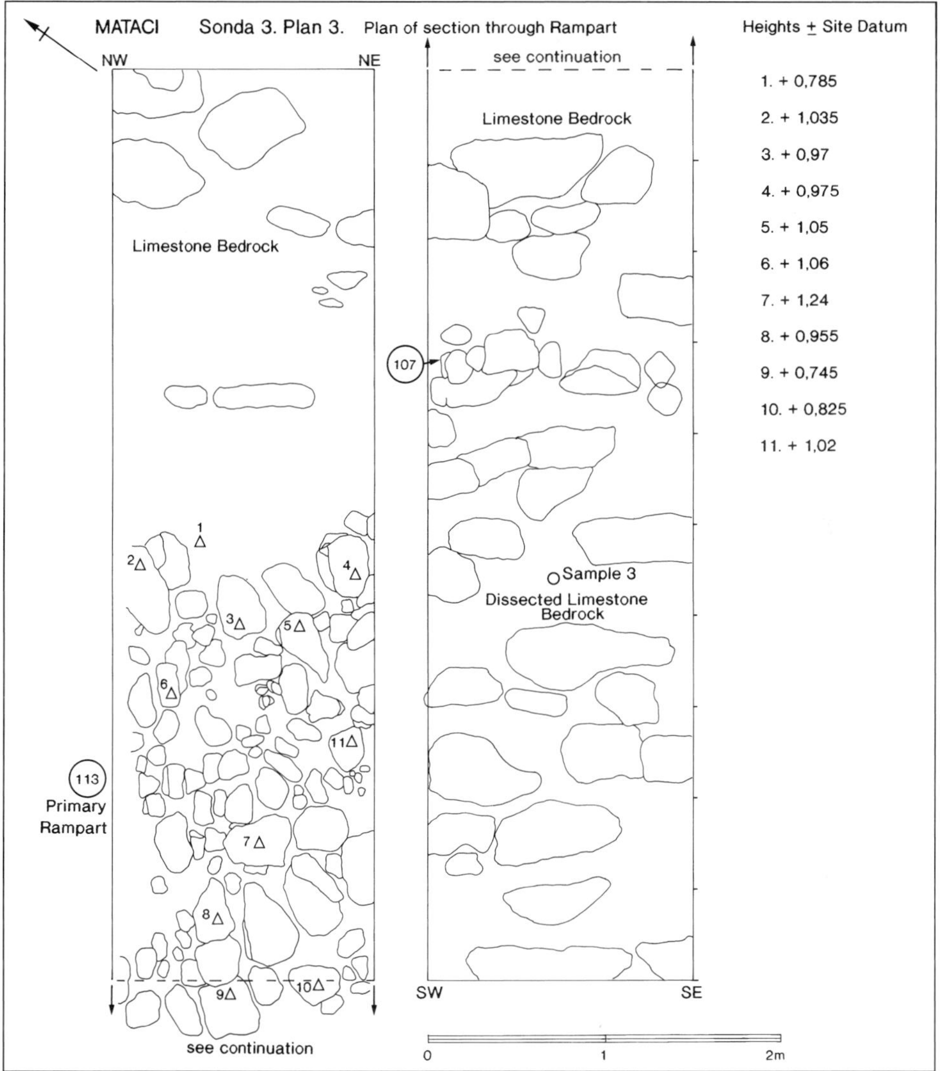

150. Plan of Trench 3, Mataci

7. After a phase of soil erosion following initial deforestation of the area, a post-occupational (?post-Bronze Age) phase of deposition is attested by the sediments sealing the rampart tumble and the clints-and-grykes system. These deposits may derive from local materials following deforestation, as at Buković (see p. 197) or alternatively represent aeolian silt blown in from the Velebit Mountains. The pottery and flint sealed within this deposit represents primary debris from the main period of site use.

151. Primary rampart from south-west, Trench 3, Mataci

8. A period of more severe erosion, of as yet unknown date, removed not only part of the Phase 7 sediments but also part of the south-east and north-west rampart. This erosion exposed the clint-and-gryke structure and led to more rapid run-off, increased erosion and increased karstification.

Although the site occupation appears to be complex (fig. 149), the human occupation at Mataci appears to have been of relatively short duration, although its impact on the environmental balance was considerable. The artefacts associated with the monument can be divided clearly into two overall periods: finds primarily produced in the pre-enclosure period (Phases 2, 4 and 5), and finds relating to the actual use of the enclosure (Phases 3, 6–9).

The radiocarbon dates

Two samples from Trench 1 were submitted to the Zagreb laboratory:
Z-1265 *Jazvinački brijeg No. 1.* Modern. Charcoal from top level, 0– 0.1m.
Z-1264 *Jazvinački brijeg No. 1.* 560 ± 100 BP. Charcoal from second layer, 0.1–0.3m depth.
Both dates are much younger than the occupation, presumably owing to modern contamination (Srdoč *et al.* 1987, 138).

MATACI Sonda 2. Plan 2.

Plan of Rampart tumble and Bedrock areas.

Rampart rubble

Fragmentary Yellow rock

Dissected bedrock

0 1m

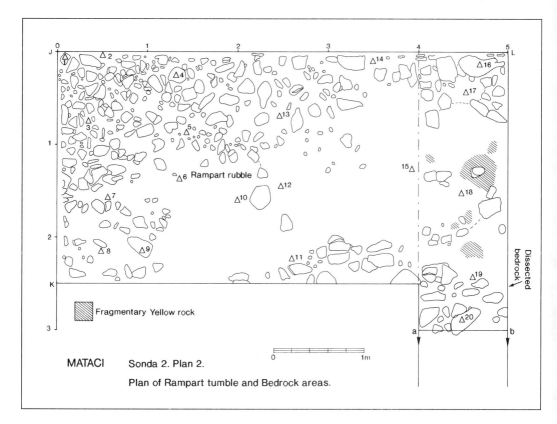

152. Plan of Trench 2, Mataci

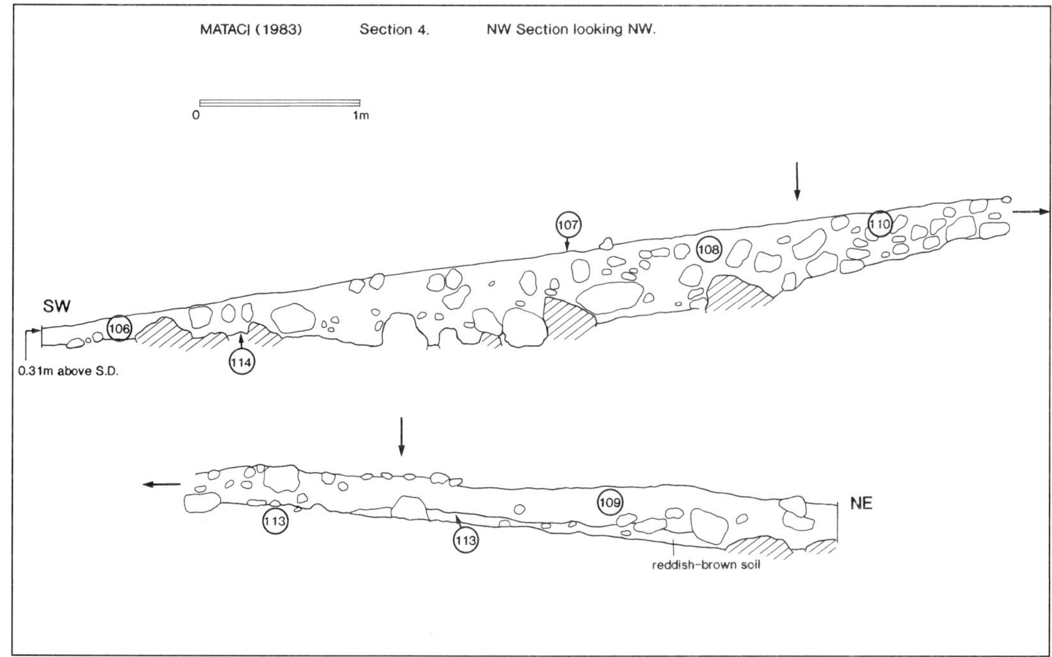

153. North-west section, Trench 2, Mataci

The finds

The biological remains

Despite flotation and wet-sieving operations, the only ecofact found at Mataci was a single animal bone, unidentified to species, preserved in the fill of the primary rampart. Two factors may have affected preservation of plant and animal remains: soil acidity and the absence of excavated contexts for good preservation (no pits, hearths or living structures). It is also pssible that neither plant and animal processing nor discard of food waste after consumption took place within the enclosure.

The pottery

A total of 1,085 sherds, weighing 5.5kg, was excavated from Trenches 1–3. A feature of the assembly is the poor condition of the pottery. Many sherds have lost their original surface, leaving a red-brown sub-surface devoid of decoration or surface treatment. It is suggested that the high levels of acidity in the ridge soils at the site were the primary cause of surface deterioration.

Five fabrics were recognized in all: (1) red-brown, (2) grey-black and (3) yellow-grey coarse wares and (4) brown and (5) black medium fine wares. On the basis of the sixty measurable rim sherds, three classes of vessel shapes were defined: dishes, bowls and necked forms. These classes were sub-divided into a total of eight shape types (fig. 154: 1–8). The assemblage is characterized by a predominance of rounded shapes, with few carinations and sharp divisions. Dishes and necked forms, on the one hand, and bowls, on the other, show a complementary size range, with only a few larger vessels present. The considerable variety of rim forms is suggestive of pottery production by a number of potters, probably at household level. Eight handle and lug types are found in only twenty-four examples; there is no evidence for handled cups, dippers or jugs – the characteristic Bronze Age range of vessels related to serving and consumption of liquids. Five classes of bases are found. Five styles of decoration are found: grooving, excision, incision, impression and plastic (fig. 155:1–3, 5). However, none of the incised patterns resemble the Cetina wares found at Buković and in the Sinj region (Marović and Ŏvić 1983). Despite this variety, prestige fine wares are absent. Many of the Mataci pots are consistent with a cooking function, especially the dishes.

The Mataci assemblage is dominated by preparation and serving vessels. The apparent rarity of storage jars is matched by a total absence of lids. Cooking and food serving vessels are more common than storage jars. The use of funnel-necked forms for water carrying and storage is paralleled by local ethnographic instances.

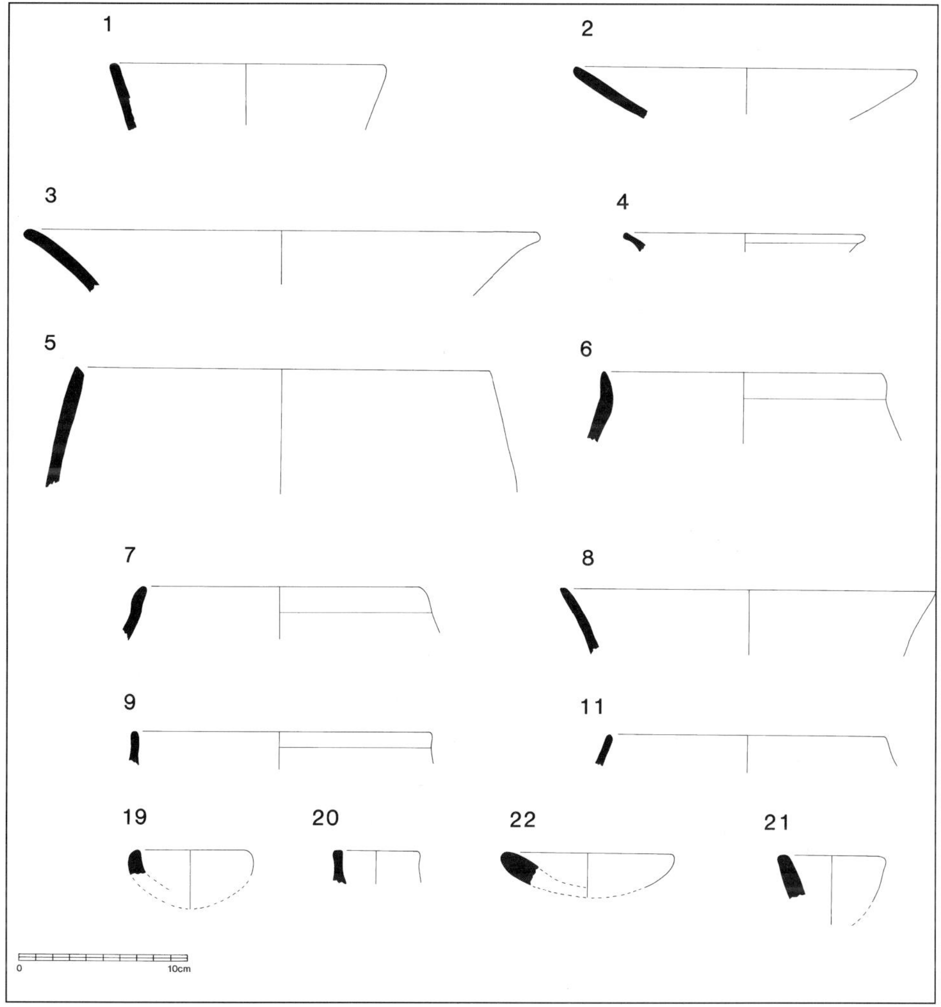

154. Vessel shapes of Bronze Age pottery 1–8: Mataci; 9, 11, 19–21: Čauševica

The lithics

Seven examples of humanly modified lithics were found in the excavations at Mataci. They comprise five pre-cores and two waste flakes – an indication of limited core production on a ridge where Bronze Age chipping floors abound. The scanty finds reflect the small amount of knapping activity carried out at the enclosed site. Given that tool preparation may be expected on a site with sporadic occupation, perhaps as a stock enclosure, it is curious that such small quantities of lithic debris were found.

Summary

Prior to the construction of the drystone-walled enclosure at Mataci, a linear group of cairns dominated the Mataci-Stojići ridge, an area already favoured for its plentiful, if low quality, pebble flint. Despite the acidity of the soil and incipient karstification, Later Bronze Age groups built several small enclosures north-east of the cairns. While it is possible that pre-existing cairns were incorporated into each enclosure, broken, worn sherds from nearby were clearly incorporated into the rampart. The enclosure pottery consisted of more cooking and serving vessels than storage jars or prestige forms. The composition of the pottery assemblage and the paucity of plant and animal remains is suggestive of a short-lived occupation or a series of brief occupations. The low rampart is consistent with stock control rather than defence. The survival of a fragment of a field boundary near the enclosure and the existence of many clearance cairns (some used also for burial) indicates that agriculture was also practised on the ridge. After the abandonment of the enclosure, the processes of soil erosion and karstification intensified and heathland formed on some parts of the ridge. In the Iron Age, the main focus of settlement shifted northwards to the Venac hill-fort and its related mortuary enclosure.

Čauševica Bronze Age farmstead (figs. 154–9)

For history of investigations, site environment and site survey, see pp. 131–3 and figs. 102–3).

Excavation strategy

There were four aims of the trial excavation at Čauševica:

1. The dating of the rampart in Enclosure 1.
2. A comparison between the soil profiles of Enclosures 1 and 2 and the soil sequence beneath the rampart.
3. The recovery of environmental samples from sealed contexts beneath the rampart.
4. The testing of conditions of preservation of artefacts and ecofacts under the rampart and within the enclosures.

One archaeological trench at Čauševica was excavated in conjunction with two soil trenches laid out to define the pedological sequence in two different areas of the site – Enclosures 1 and 2.

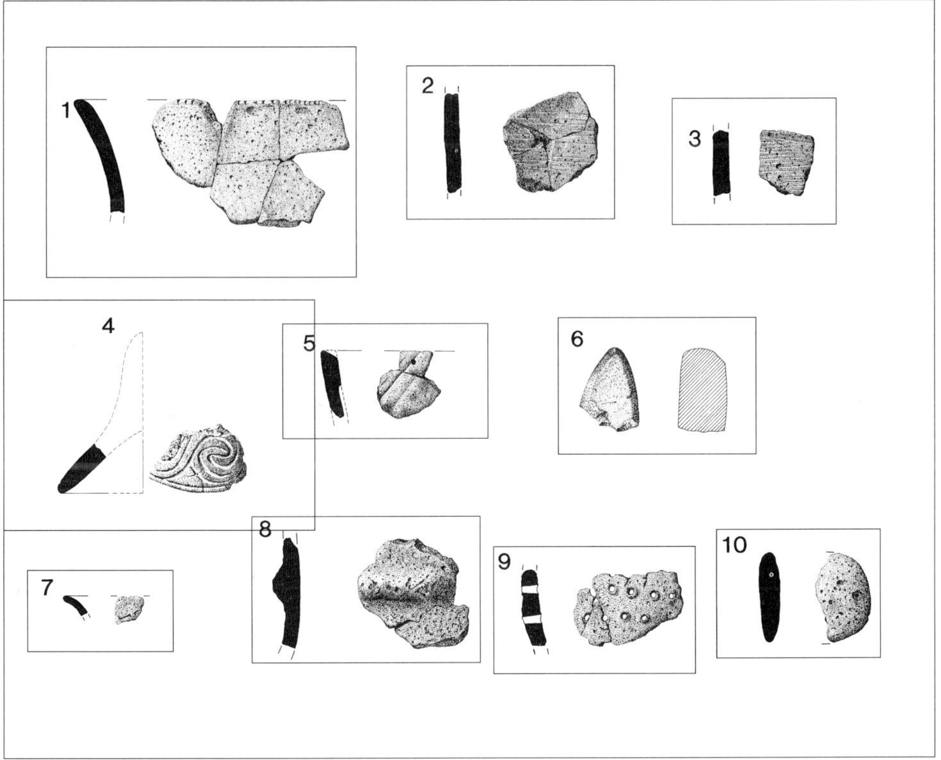

155. Decorated wares: 1–3, 5: Mataci; 4: Kula Atlagić surface find; 6: Polača-Dražice surface find; 7–10: Čauševica

Stratigraphy and occupation sequence

The soil in Trench 3 appears to be plaggen, as indicated by the large quantities of Bronze Age artefacts and its dark humose colouring (fig. 156). The latter indicates that there must have been a large input of organic matter to the soil in earlier times in order to mask the red colours which typify the natural limestone-derived Terra rossa soils.

In Enclosure 1, Trench 2 shows no accumulation of dark organic matter. However, soil similar to that found in Trench 3 has been preserved under the drystone wall 10m away from Trench 2. This suggests that any man-made soil in Enclosure 1 has subsequently been eroded away, being preserved only under the drystone walling and the tumble therefrom. The large quantities of artefacts and animal remains, as well as the apparently high organic matter content indicated by the dark brown soil colour, would imply that Enclosure 2 was not just a temporary shepherds' area but was occupied on a more permanent basis.

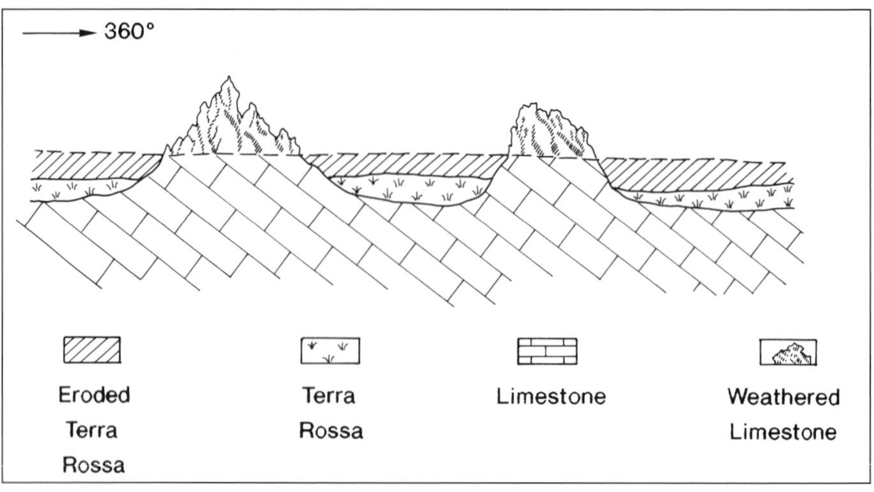

156. Geological section through site, Čauševica

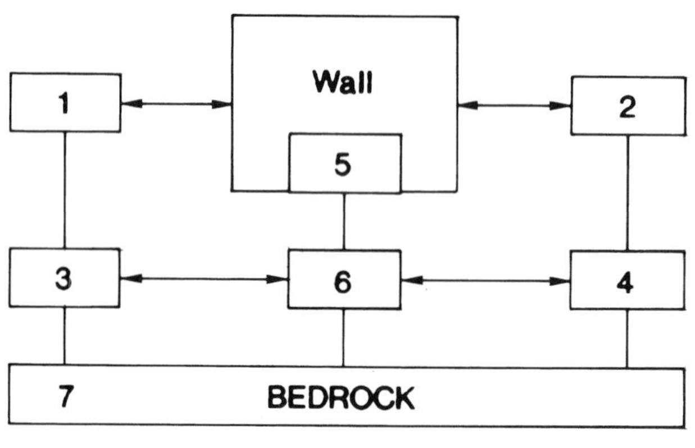

157. Harris matrix, Trench 1, Čauševica

Analytical survey indicates that the Čauševica enclosures are a multi-period structure, with a minimum of three periods of construction, with Enclosure 1 assigned to Period 2 (see above, pp. 132–3). Based on the excavation of the three trenches (for Harris matrix, see fig. 157), four occupation phases can be defined for Enclosure 1:

1. *Pre-enclosure phase.* This phase is represented by the main culture level in Trench 3 and by the sealed occupation deposits (contexts 3, 4 and 6) in Trench 1. The deflated remains of this phase may be represented in modified and eroded form in Trench 2.

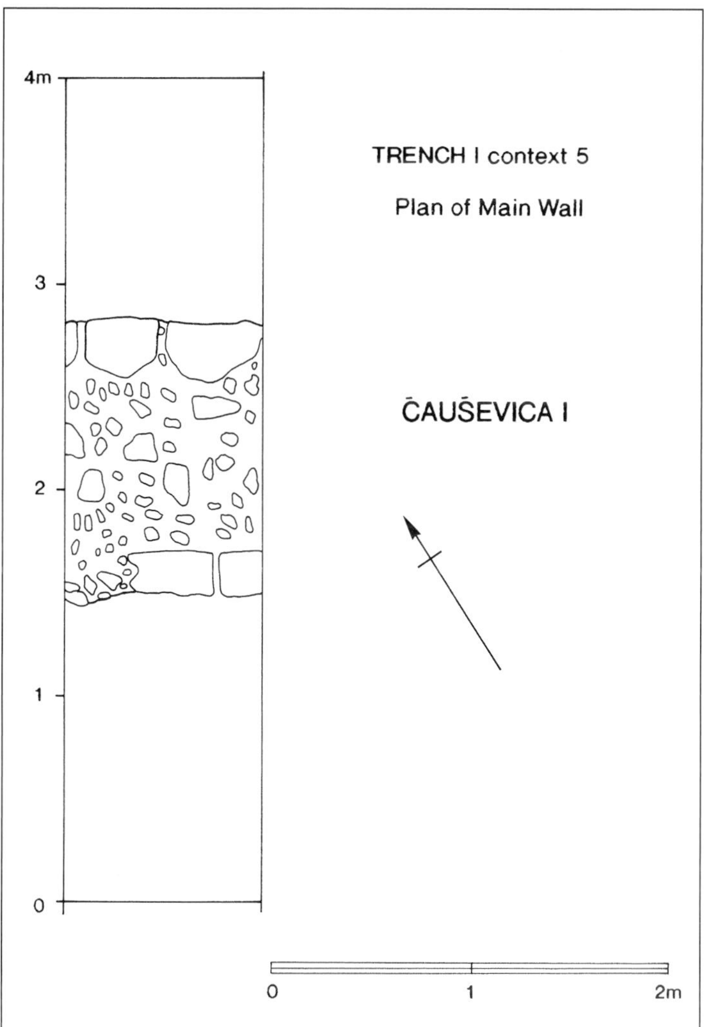

158. Plan of primary rampart, Trench 1, Čauševica

2. *Construction of rampart.* The main construction of the drystone wall of Enclosure 1 (context 5). The wall is 1.20m in thickness and comprises limestone blocks with earth and pottery fill (figs. 158–9), possibly deriving from Phase 1. The dating of this phase of site use to the Later Bronze Age is inferred from the absence of pottery of any other date from Trench 1.

3. *Abandonment of rampart.* The wall of Enclosure 1 falls into disuse and stones from the primary rampart fall off to north and south. This stone tumble (Trench 1/contexts 1 and 2) covers intact, uneroded occupation horizons dating to Phase 1.

4. *Erosion phase.* A phase of soil erosion removed 0.20–0.30m of soil cover from Enclosure 1, as indicated by *Karstrillen* analysis and the truncation of the soil profile in Trench 2 as compared with Trench 1. This phase postdates the collapse of the rampart tumble, which seals uneroded deposits.

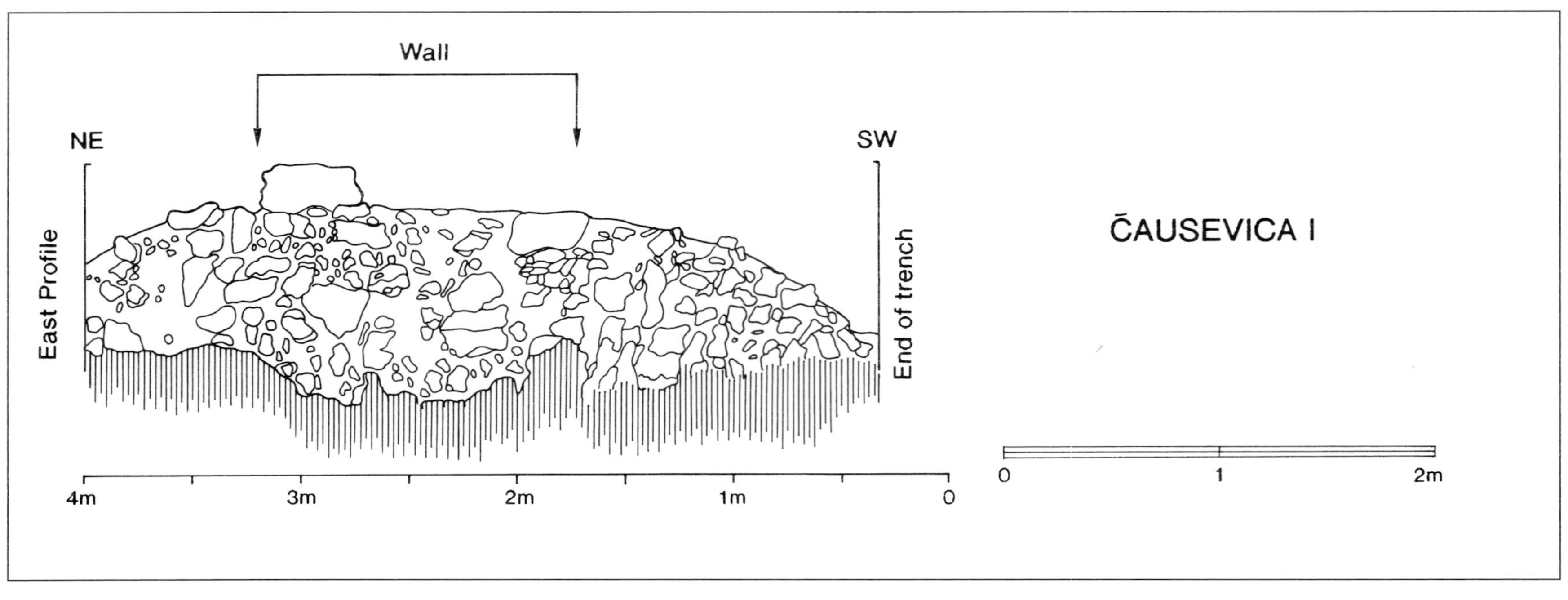

159. Section of primary rampart, Trench 1, Čauševica

While the four phases of site use and abandonment form a chronological sequence, the same cannot be said for the artefactual material incorporated into the excavated deposits. There are no stratified artefacts which unambiguously relate to Phases 2, 3 or 4 of the sequence. The only finds which are securely associated with deposits in which the original discard took place are the sherds from Phase 1 in Trench 3 and Trench 1/contexts 3, 4 and 6. The finds discovered in the primary wall of Enclosure 1 are most likely to have originated from the pre-enclosure occupation rather than from discard into an enclosure wall contemporary with its use.

The finds

The faunal remains

By C. Schwartz

A total of eighty-two bones was found, with fifty identifiable to species. Of the unidentifiable fragments, ten specimens were burnt and nine more were identifiable to element. All the bones were discovered in Trench 1, in the main fill of the wall. Species present at the site include a predominance of domestic species – cattle, pig, sheep/goat (caprovines) and only one wild species – roe deer. Most of the sample comprises adult individuals, except in the case of pig (four juveniles) and cattle (one sub-adult). No pathological conditions were observed on any bone. The presence of so many bones in the primary fill of the rampart suggests that the earth was collected from a pre-existing cultural level for inclusion into the dry-stone wall.

The plant remains

By J. Huntley

Only two samples from the Čauševica excavations contained macro-botanical remains. Both samples derived from Trench 1/context 6, a sealed occupation deposit assigned to the pre-enclosure Phase 1. Sample 1 contained twenty juniper pips and twelve *Olea* stone fragments; Sample 2 had one grain of *Gramineae* and four grains of small-seeded *Gramineae* (cf. Setaria). These results indicate the use of local wild resources (olives, juniper, grasses) as well as the possible use of a domesticated cereal, Italian millet. The discovery of wild olive stones in Bronze Age contexts is the earliest occurrence of this plant remains in Dalmatia (cf. the Early Bronze Age finds in the Aegean and Italy: Barker 1981, 1985; Runnels and Hansen 1986).

The pottery

The trial excavations at Čauševica yielded a total of 835 sherds, weighing 4.35kg. Of this total, most of the material came from contexts in Trench 1 (65.7 per cent by number), while the remainder comprises the undifferentiated residue found in the soil pit, Trench 3. Two main fabric classes are found – fine wares and coarse wares, differentiated by the presence and absence of burnishing on the outer surface of the vessel. The colour and inclusions varied considerably. Four materials are present as pottery inclusions – fine sand, limestone, grog and shell; surface voids are also common. Voids and fine sand are restricted to fine wares.

Coarse wares outnumber fine wares by *c.* 9:1 and undiagnostic sherds outnumber feature sherds by almost 12:1. The pottery fragmentation rate (or PFR) for the pre-enclosure occupation level is far higher than that for the pottery in the fill of the wall, which comprises the lowest PFR on site. Four out of the five general shape categories are represented: dishes, bowls, necked forms and miniature vessels (rim total = 30) (fig. 154:9, 11, 19–21). The proportion of large vessels to small and medium (1:6) is higher than at Buković, Mataci and Tinj. There seems to be a tendency for dishes to be selected for larger vessels, necked forms for medium-size use and bowls for smaller vessels. There is a total of nineteen lugs and handles in the assemblage, with strap handles predominating. A total of twelve bases is known from Čauševica (three types). A low percentage (0.6 per cent) of the Čauševica ceramics is decorated, in only one style. The incised motifs are similar to those at Mataci (fig. 155: 7–10).

The relative frequency of large vessels in the measurable rim sample, as well as hints at a relationship between vessel size and form combines to suggest that the Čauševica ceramics may be rather more differentiated than those from Tinj, Buković and Mataci. There is a predominance of food preparation and serving vessels, with rather few storage jars. The decoration of pottery at Čauševica provides least evidence for differentiation.

The lithics

No lithics were found in any of the trenches at Čauševica, nor on the surface during survey collection.

Summary

The Čauševica hill was settled for the first time in the Later Bronze Age. An unenclosed settlement of unknown size and duration was replaced in the same phase by an enclosure, on to which were built at least two other enclosures. The soil evidence from Enclosure 2, morphologically the nucleus of occupation, indicates a relatively long occupation; this is supported by the multi-period development of the drystone remains. The field divisions and the faunal remains indicate a mixed farming subsistence base, supplemented by the gathering of wild olives and juniper berries. In the latest occupation phase, land management became a problem, with the clearance of large quantities of limestone rocks from the enclosures. Perhaps this increase in effort prompted abandonment of the farmstead. Following site abandonment, further soil erosion is indicated in Enclosure 1, leading to the impoverishment of the area for future cultivation. The site is now Karst but was formerly Stony land until the Later Bronze Age.

Polača-Dražice Bronze Age field system (figs. 160–1)

For history of investigations, site environment and site survey, see p. 139 and figs. 111–12).

Excavation strategy

The goals of the trial excavation were threefold:

1. Definition of the date of the construction of the Polača wall.
2. Determination of the history of soil development, erosion and deposition.
3. An assessment of the conditions of artefact and ecofact preservation both in the vicinity of the wall and in open parts of the site.

Stratigraphy and occupation sequence

The results of the excavation of four trenches at Polača-Dražice permit the combination of archaeological and pedological information. Six separate 'events' can be distinguished in the history of the site (for stratigraphy, see fig. 160; for Harris matrix, see fig. 161), not all of which can be securely located in a putative occupation sequence:

1. Early phase of pre-enclosure occupation: defined as the activities which caused the deposition of pottery in the gryke fill of context 5/1.
2. Late phase of pre-enclosure occupation: represented by sediments sealed by rampart tumble (fig. 160) in Trench 1 (especially the horizontally-bedded sherds in Trench 1/5, but also context 1/5 upper, 1/2 and the materials found in the B horizons of Trenches 2 and 4).

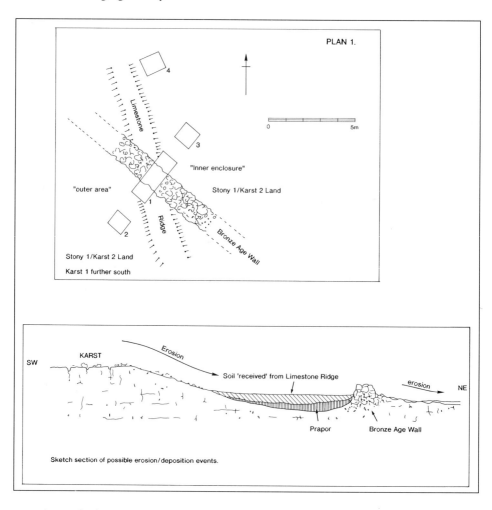

160. Plan and schematic section, Polača-Dražice (Grabar)

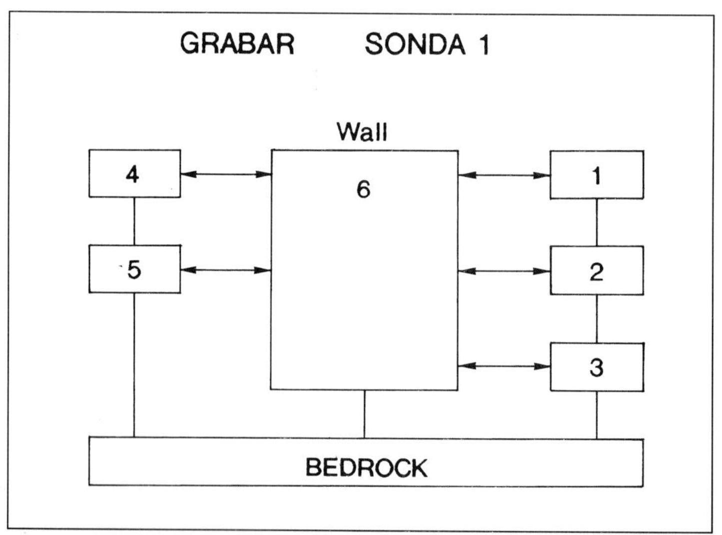

161. Harris matrix, Trench 1, Polača-Dražice (Grabar)

3. The construction and use of the wall: the finds in contexts 1/6 and 1/7 define the building phase of the wall. The use phase of the wall may be correlated with the artefacts in the A horizon of Trench 4 but this cannot currently be demonstrated.
4. The abandonment and subsequent collapse of the wall: comprising the deposits and finds of contexts 1/1, 1/2 and 1/4.
5. Soil erosion from upslope of the wall, with deposition into the 'terrace' adjoining the wall: the A horizon in Trench 2 defines the *terminus ante quem* for this 'event'; the Bronze Age pottery sealed by context 2/A in context 2/B defines the *terminus post quem*.
6. Soil erosion from downslope of the wall: soil studies indicate the likelihood of soil erosion from the area of Trench 3.

The excavated section of the main wall at Polača was partly constructed on the top of a low limestone clint which runs at a 40-degree angle to the alignment of the Bronze Age wall (fig. 160). Small limestone stones, on average 100 × 100mm in size, were placed to bed the larger stones of the lowest course onto the ridge. Of the two courses which survive in the wall, both are built using large limestone blocks up to a maximum size of 300 × 300mm. The drystone technique resembles that of Čauševica and Nadin. The average width of the wall in Trench 1 was 1.50m; the two courses reached a height of 300mm. As at Čauševica and Mataci, it seems very likely that the pottery, animal bone and shell in these contexts derives not from *in situ* deposition of finds during construction but rather the incorporation of finds from elsewhere on site. These finds raise the possibility of a pre-enclosure phase of occupation at Polača.

The soil descriptions of Trenches 2 and 3 demonstrate the difference in soil conditions immediately 'inside' and 'outside' the Bronze Age wall. Rather than having shallower, more stony soil on the 'outside' of the wall, with deeper and less stony soils 'inside' the enclosure, the deeper soil was in fact in the outer area. Furthermore, the depth of the 'inner' soil is extremely irregular due to the clints and grykes. This has important consequences for ease of cropping, as irregular depth produces a heterogeneous spread of crop size and maturity, making harvesting extremely difficult.

The greater depth of soil 'outside' the wall suggests that eroded upslope material from the limestone ridge was prevented from travelling further downslope and banked up against the Bronze Age wall, possibly being preferentially used for cultivation in the later Bronze Age. The inner enclosure was perhaps used for less intensive agriculture or stock control, the arrangement of small walls at right angles to longer walls is reminiscent of sheep-shearing divisions, often made using hurdles.

The finds

The faunal remains

No animal bones were recovered from either the excavation or the flotation.

The plant remains

Four 10kg earth samples from Polača-Dražice were processed by flotation. No botanical remains were recovered from this operation.

The pottery

A small quantity of largely undiagnostic pottery was found, mostly in the fill of the rampart in Trench 1. The majority of the finds were red coarse ware dishes and bowls, with a few storage jar shapes and some necked vessels. No decoration was observed in this group. The style of the pottery closely resembled that of Čauševica and Mataci.

The lithics

No lithic artefacts were discovered at Polača-Dražice, either during the course of the field survey or in the excavations. The situation is similar to that at Čauševica, where an absence of lithics is equally surprising.

Summary

Two settlements were newly founded during the Later Bronze Age on the north slopes of the Tinj Ridge – the Muvača enclosure and the Polača field system. The similar form of small fields in each site suggests a close relationship between the two groups of residents. The linear boundary at Polača can be dated to the Later Bronze Age, along with the fields and clearance cairns. Although neither plant nor animal remains were found, there is a strong likelihood of mixed farming at Polača: the field wall is best interpreted as a stock control feature rather than as a defensive barrier, while the fields and cairns imply cultivation of Stony land. The scale of the wall and the number of cairns and cross-walls convey the impression of a lengthy occupation. Soil erosion both below and above the wall is attested after the abandonment of the site. In the Iron Age, the focus of settlement shifts to the higher summits of the Tinj Ridge. As at Čauševica, the land was at best Stony in the later prehistoric period.

Nadin-Gradina multi-period hill-fort (figs. 162–73)

For history of investigations, site environment and site survey, see p. 116 and figs. 47–8, 86–95).

Excavation strategy

A number of questions could be clarified by small-scale excavations, without prejudice to any future long-term explorations of this central place. Perhaps the most basic question concerned the date of site occupation in various parts of the site, both inside and outside the hill-fort wall. Two kinds of excavation were required: the excavation of trenches in interior areas with major depths of stratigraphy and the excavation of specific extra-mural structures. The excavation of a section across the main rampart was beyond the scope of NDP (but NB fig. 87, recorded after an illicit 1987 excavation!).

The choice of excavation structures revolved around the range of structural classes represented at Nadin. It was decided that the study of funerary structures, roads and quarries was of lower priority than the excavation of settlement remains. Hence, attention was focused on the interior of the hill-fort, enclosures, 'houses' and terraces. Two trenches (Trenches 1 and 3) were excavated in different parts of the hill-fort interior. Trench 1 was located near a known focus of Roman occupation close to the well-preserved Roman cistern, while Trench 3 was located at the opposite end of the hill-fort, near the north rampart. Two enclosures stood out in terms of size and location in the site plan – the upper enclosure abutting the south-west section of the rampart (Enclosure 908), and a large enclosure in the southern district (Enclosure 907), associated with potential stock control walls to the south. Hence, Trench 5 was excavated across the wall of the hilltop enclosure 908 and Trenches 6 and 7 were laid out to investigate the construction of Enclosure 907 and the associated soil sequence.

The final decision concerned selection of a structure 'associated' with an adjoining terrace. Since no terraces in Dalmatia had hitherto been excavated and hence dated, the Nadin terraces with their related buildings seemed an obvious opportunity. A recurrent pattern in the settlement plan was the co-occurrence of a structure and a terrace, termed by NDP the 'house-and-garden' complex. This co-occurrence raised several questions of sequence, association and function: were the terraces built to facilitate the construction of houses or were they built separately, with their own specific function (e.g. agricultural)? Were house and garden contemporary and, if so, what were the functional relations between the two? What were the construction techniques of the terraces and how did these relate to construction techniques of the structures?

In order to answer such questions, even in a preliminary way, it was important to select a 'house-and-garden' complex of moderate size, so as to permit excavation of a section through the entire terrace and house. Given slope conditions and the density of surface stone on much of the hillslope, choice was restricted to one of three possible combinations. The decision to excavate Building 037 and Terraces 219 and 220 was based on the good preservation of the building and the terrace walls and the small size of the structures.

As with the excavation strategies for other sites, it was the aim of the project to define a representative sequence of material culture for the site occupation. In this respect, Nadin was particularly important for the Roman period since, hitherto, there has been no published sequence for Roman fine wares and coarse pottery from north Dalmatia. In addition, it was a project aim to recover subsistence data by way of faunal and botanical material for an investigation of local husbandry and crop practices. A subsidiary aim was to investigate possible differences in resource utilization between the interior and the exterior of the hill-fort, whether for plants, meat or traded goods. Given the size of the Nadin site and the short time available for trial excavations, it was clear that definitive answers to the largest questions were unlikely but that a focus on manageable problems had the potential to lead to significant advances.

Stratigraphy and occupation sequence

Since the trenches or pairs of trenches were separated by considerable distances (fig. 84), it proved impossible to form any convincing stratigraphic links between them; hence the occupational relations between each trench/pair of trenches will be determined by the datable finds in their stratigraphic context. The archaeological stratigraphies in each respective trench are summarized below.

Trench 1

Trench 1 (4 × 2m) was located near the Roman cistern on the hill-top. The trench was excavated to establish the building sequence in the southern part of the hill-fort. The stratigraphy of Trench 1 represents a sequence of refuse deposits from Roman and Late Antique structures, one of which is located in the trench itself (fig. 162). Late first-century AD finds occur in the silty clays below the floor level. The compact floor level is the floor of an early Roman house. Its walls and building refuse form a deposit from *c.* 1.13 to 1.85m, radiocarbon-dated to 1840 ± 60 BP, into which later material dating to the second and third centuries AD has been deposited. Above these building levels was a deposit of building refuse, whose latest find is a Byzantine belt-buckle dating to the seventh century AD (fig. 173:8). This find appears to postdate the latest datable ceramics by one century.

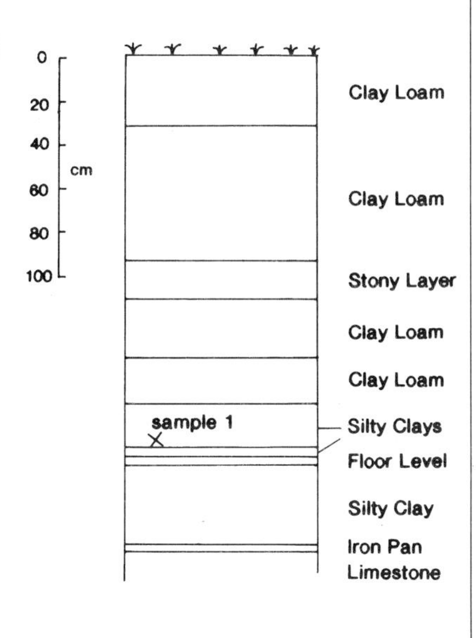

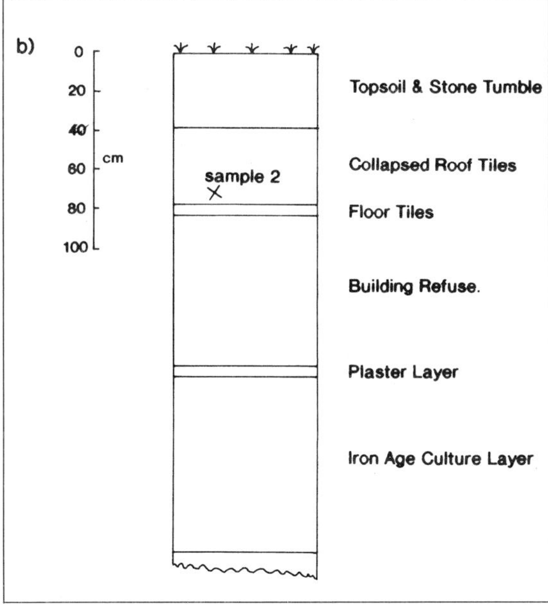

162. Schematic sections, Nadin: (a) Trench 1; (b) Trench 3

Trenches 2 and 4

Trench 2 (6 × 2m) and Trench 4 (3 × 1.5m) were located together to investigate the date, nature of construction and stratigraphic relationships between structure 037 (figs. 163–6) and terraces 219 and 220.

There are four phases of activity in the history of Structure 037: the development of a terrace filled with garden soil prior to the construction of Building 037; the construction of 037, dated 50 BC–AD 50; the deposition of organic-rich sediments on the terrace outside 037 (first–third centuries AD); and the abandonment of 037 (undated) (fig. 164).

The principal event recorded in the stratigraphy is the construction of Building 037. From the dated pottery in Phase 1, it is clear that construction cannot have predated 50 BC–AD 50. The foundations of Building 037 were laid down on top of contexts 17–18–20. The sequence of garden soils comprising contexts 3–10, 12, 14 and 16 indicates build-up of deposits while the building was in use. During the use of the building, organic sediments or manure built up outside the south wall and inside the main room. These deposits may be partly interpreted as the accumulation of refuse deposits occurring over a long period. The final phase of Building 037 is its abandonment. No clear dating evidence for this phase was

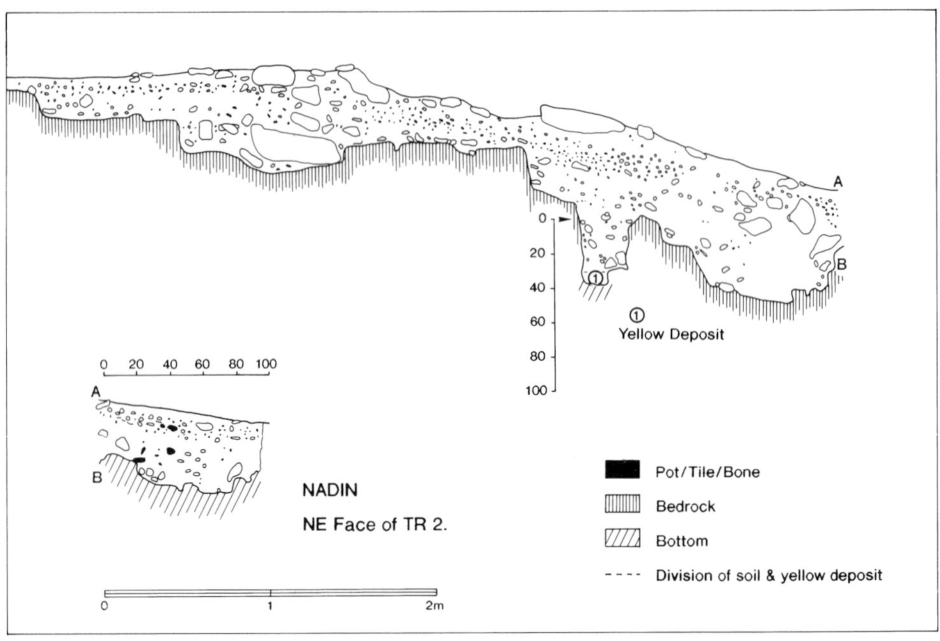

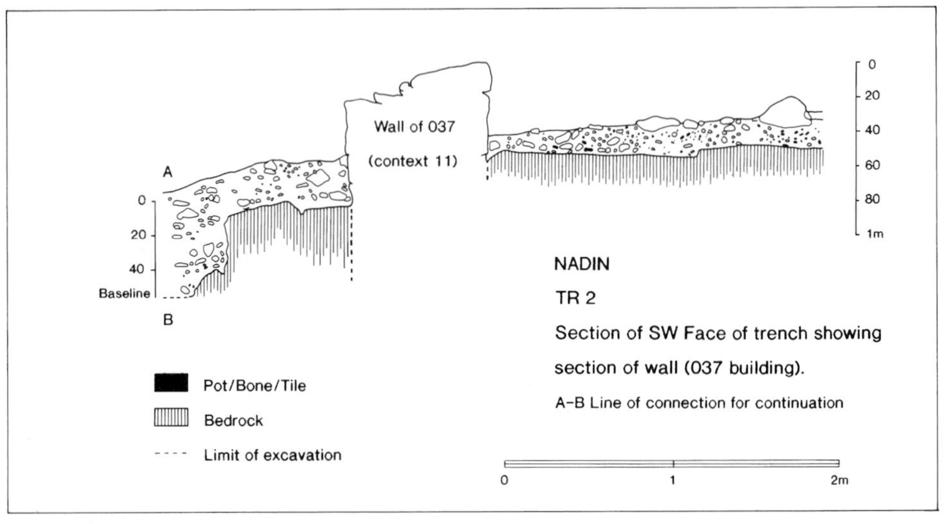

(b)

163. North-east and south-west sections, Trench 2, Nadin

recovered, for no datable pottery occurs from contexts 1 and 2, the rubble collapse both inside and outside the building, nor on the latest mud floor of the building (context 3). Judging by the quantity of rubble in and near the structure and the paucity of roof tiles, it seems likely that both wall stone and roof tiles were removed and recycled in another building.

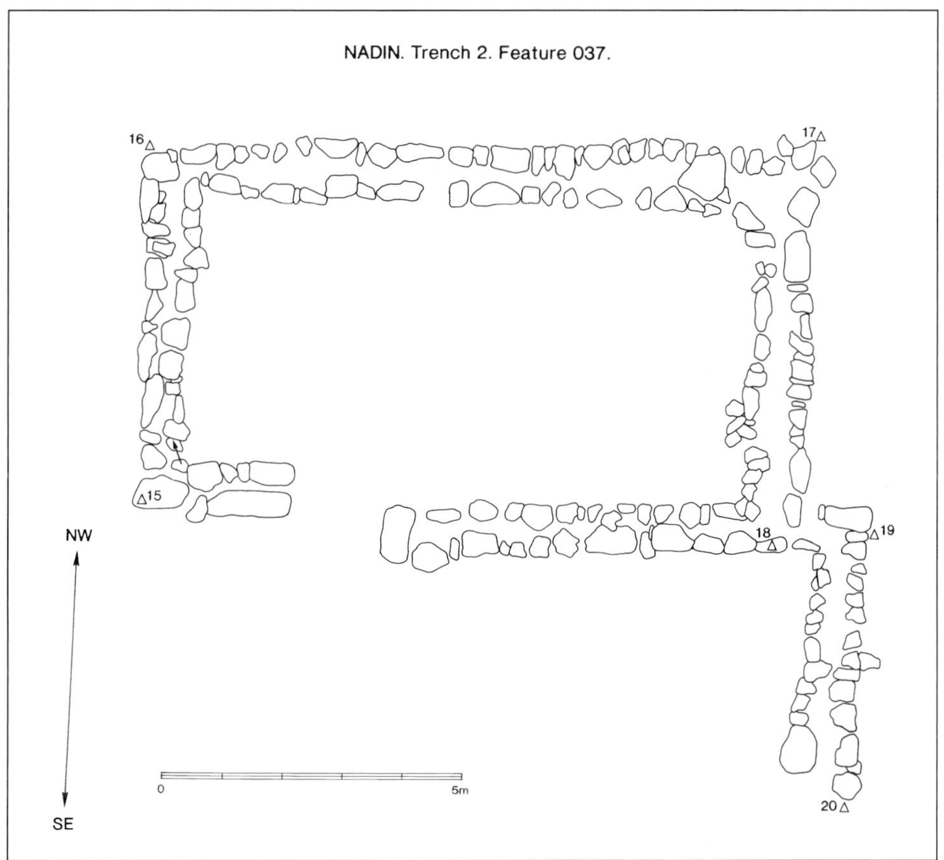

164. Plan of Building 037, Trench 2, Nadin

Building 037 has external measurements of 11.8m (length) and 6.8m (width) and also incorporates an offset wall, 4.2m in length, which abuts the south-east corner. The internal measurements of the single room are 9–9.3m × 4.3–4.9m (fig. 164). The structure is by no means rectangular. The foundation is laid out partly on an exposed limestone vein which runs transversely across the house plan. Large limestone blocks are laid directly onto this outcrop. The structure is built in a simple dry-stone wall technique (fig. 164). The largest stones are reserved for the doorposts and the threshold; the latter is composed of a large, thin limestone slab. The standard width of the double dry-stone walls varies from 0.9m to 1.2m.

In Trench 4, the sequence of terrace wall construction and use can be divided into three phases: pre-construction; construction; and use. Before the construction of the wall, a garden soil of dark greyish-brown silty clay loam developed on the gently sloping hillside. A group of three sherds of the second–first centuries BC provide a date for the early phase of this garden soil. Above the garden soil (context

165. Building 037, from its terrace, from south, Nadin

166. Building 037, from east, Nadin

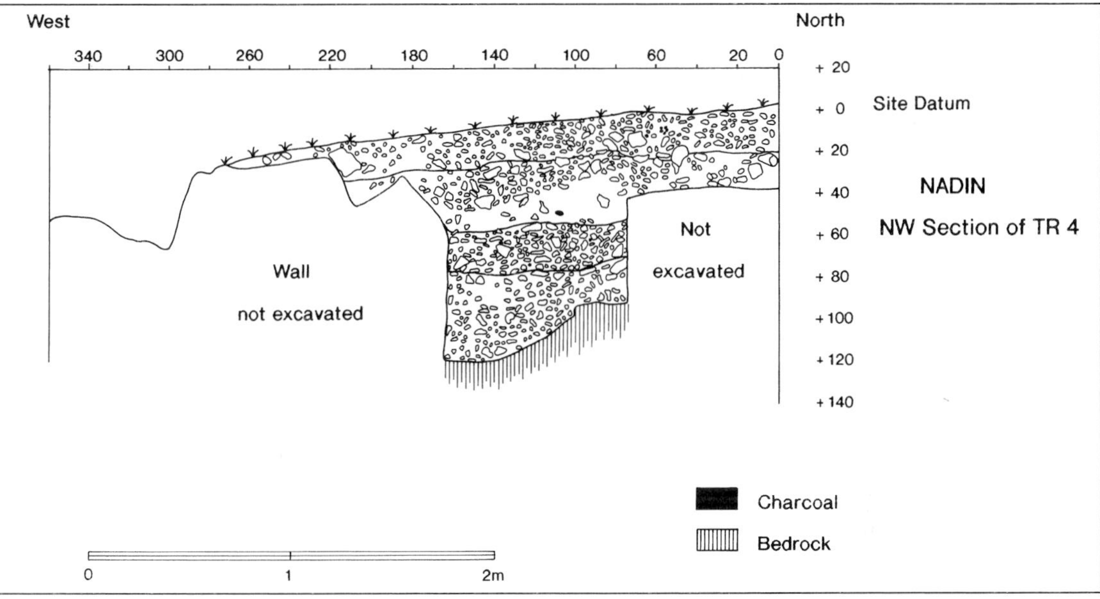

167. North-west section, Trench 4, Nadin

8), a simple, triangular wall was constructed of unfaced stones with no proper foundations or stone packing. This 'structure' was the result of a series of graded and small-scale reactions to continuing problems of soil loss; stones were piled up as and when necessary to form a gradually accreting revetment wall (fig. 167). The gradual filling up of the terrace above the wall indicates that this structure was successful in preventing soil loss. It is interesting to note that the latest sherd material from these contexts (dating to the third century AD) postdates the latest finds from Structure 037, perhaps by as much as a century.

There was little domestic activity close to Terraces 219 and 220 in late Roman times. The terrace wall, however, remained stable until present times; such stability of abandoned terraces would appear to be typical of the Nadin hillslopes in the post-Roman to modern period (by contrast, cf. van Andel and Sutton 1987).

Trench 3

Located just inside the north rampart of the hill-fort, this trench (3 × 2m) was excavated to investigate the sequence of occupation in the northern part of the enclosed area.

Since the stratigraphy consisted largely of building material, soil description proved impossible. Six phases can be distinguished in the sequence of building remains (fig. 158):

1. Occupation level, with hearths, associated with Iron Age pottery (third–first centuries BC).
2. Compact layer of plaster from an Early Roman house (*c.* AD 60–80).
3. Building refuse from Early Roman house, with later refuse (second–fourth centuries AD).
4. Floor tiles of Late Roman house (pottery dating to fifth century AD; C14 date of 1500 ± 30 BP).
5. Collapsed roof tiles from the Late Roman house (fifth century AD).
6. Topsoil mixed with building tumble (fifth century AD).

Trench 5

Trench 5 was located across the wall of the supposedly pre-Late Iron Age enclosure 908 south of the main hill-fort. The trench was excavated to provide a date for the enclosure and an understanding of its building techniques.

A complete, if disturbed, soil profile was discovered above limestone bedrock. The B horizon, a reddish-brown clay loam, contained Iron Age sherds dating from the fifth–first centuries BC. The A horizon, a very dark greyish-brown clay loam, contained the foundation of the wall and its lower courses, together with Late Iron Age, Attic Red-Figure and Roman pottery. Hence, the date of the wall is unclear but cannot predate the Late Iron Age. The enclosure is probably early Roman in date, with wall construction incorporating material deposited in a pre-Roman period.

Trenches 6 and 7

Two trenches were laid out in Enclosure 907 to date the enclosure wall and investigate any existing buried soils in relation to other surviving soil profiles. Trench 6 (4 × 1m) was laid out across the wall of Enclosure 907, while Trench 7 (1 × 1m) was a soil pit excavated on the inner side of the enclosure wall.

Two courses of the wall were found *in situ* within the top 220mm of the profile (fig. 168). Early Roman pottery was found within and beneath the wall courses. Late Iron Age pottery was found only within the limestone grykes, below 0.58m, sealed beneath wall tumble on the inner side of the wall (context 8). The associated finds suggest pre-wall activity in the Iron Age and construction of the enclosure wall in the early Roman period (first century AD).

Within Trench 7, the dark colour of the two upper soil horizons suggests that they were cultural in origin. The greater depth of the two upper horizons preserved beneath the enclosure wall as compared with that found in Trench 7 suggests some soil loss in the enclosure or post-enclosure period.

168. Enclosure 907, Trench 6, from east-south-east, Nadin

The finds

The faunal remains

By C. Schwartz

A total of 7,977 bone fragments was recovered from Nadin, with 1,785 identified to species (table 26). An additional 942 bones are identified to element. Of the remaining 5,617 unidentifiable fragments, 2.8 per cent are burnt; these consist mostly of blackened fragments of long bone and indicate on-site roasting as one form of cooking. There are thirty-eight complete measurable specimens in the sample. The sample is dominated by domestic ovicaprines, with a small number of domestic cattle, pig, horse and dog, as well as wild deer and hare, birds, turtle, frog, fish and shellfish (fig. 133). Significant differences were observed between the fauna of the three main periods, mainly reflecting changes in the importance of pig from Iron Age to Early Roman and from Early to Late Roman. This increase is perhaps a

Table 26 Species element distribution by period, Nadin-Gradina

Species	Period							
	Iron Age		Early Roman		Late Roman		Total	
Mammalia								
Domestic								
cattle	51	(20.8)	165	(20.1)	169	(23.5)	385	(21.7)
sheep/goat	160	(65.3)	526	(64.0)	366	(51.0)	1052	(58.9)
pig	29	(11.8)	86	(10.5)	143	(19.9)	258	(14.5)
horse	5		4		1		10	
dog	–		10	(1.2)	1		11	
Wild								
red deer	–		1		1		2	
brown hare	3		22	(2.7)	14	(1.9)	39	(2.2)
Aves								
birds (unident)	–		3		9		12	
hen	–		1		7		8	
Amphibia								
turtle								
frog	–		2		–		2	
Fish	–		–		4		4	
Total	248		820		715		1783	

Figures in parentheses refer to column percentages
Early Roman: first–second century AD; Late Roman: third–fifth century AD

reflection of the increased importance of markets in the Roman period. A related decrease in the frequency of ovicaprines from Early to Late Roman period is a subsidiary cause. Age distributions for cattle, caprovines and pigs indicate a predominance of adults. In the Iron Age caprovine and pig samples, the total number of adults is less than the combined total of other ages; the reverse is the case in the Roman levels.

The plant remains

By S. Nye

Identification of charred plant remains (table 27) indicate that many of the remains are of food plants, such as olive, juniper, cereals and grape. The olive has long been cultivated in areas of Mediterranean climate for its fruit, which contains a high proportion of oil, useful for cooking and as fuel in lamps. The cereals identified were emmer, spelt wheat, barley, broomcorn millet and probably Italian millet. The barley was a hulled, six-row variety of *Hordeum vulgare.* Millets can be used for making bread and porridge, alcoholic drinks and as animal feed; the straw can also be used for thatch and animal bedding. Some fragments of chaff were noted, indicating that at least the wheat was threshed and cleaned on site. The

Table 27 Remains of food and weed species, Nadin-Gradina

	Sample numbers																								
	01	03	05	07	08	09	11	12	13	15	16	17	18	19	20	21	22	24	26	27	28	29	30	31	32
SUB	x	x	x	x	x	x	x	x	x	x	x	x	x		x			x	x	x			x		x
SPP																									
1	–	–	–	–	–	–	–	–	–	–	–	1	–	–	–	–	–	–	–	–	–	–	–	–	–
2	–	–	–	–	–	–	–	–	–	–	1	–	–	–	–	–	–	–	–	–	–	–	–	–	–
3	–	–	–	–	–	–	–	–	1	–	–	–	–	–	–	–	–	–	–	–	–	–	–	–	–
4	–	–	–	–	–	–	–	–	–	–	1	–	–	–	–	–	–	1	–	–	–	–	–	–	–
5	–	–	–	–	–	–	–	–	–	–	–	–	–	–	–	–	–	–	–	–	1	–	–	1	–
6	–	–	2	–	–	–	1	–	–	–	1	–	6	–	–	–	–	–	–	–	9	–	–	1	–
7	–	–	–	–	–	–	–	–	–	–	–	–	85	–	–	–	–	–	–	–	12	–	–	–	–
8	3	–	–	–	–	–	–	–	–	–	–	–	–	–	–	–	–	–	–	–	–	–	–	–	–
9	–	–	2	–	–	–	–	–	–	–	–	–	–	–	–	–	–	–	–	–	–	–	–	–	–
10	1	–	–	–	–	–	–	–	–	–	–	–	–	–	–	–	–	–	–	–	–	–	–	–	–
11	–	–	–	–	1	–	–	–	–	–	–	–	–	–	–	–	–	–	–	–	1	–	–	–	–
12	1	–	–	–	–	–	1	–	–	–	–	–	–	–	–	–	–	–	–	–	–	–	–	–	–
13	2	–	–	1	–	–	100	–	–	–	–	–	–	–	–	–	–	–	–	–	–	–	–	–	1
14	1	–	–	–	–	–	–	–	–	–	–	–	–	–	–	–	–	–	–	–	–	–	–	–	–
15	–	–	1	–	–	–	–	–	–	–	–	–	–	–	–	–	–	–	–	–	–	–	–	–	–
16	9	–	–	–	–	–	–	–	–	–	1	–	2	–	–	–	–	–	–	–	2	–	–	–	–
17	1	–	–	–	–	–	–	–	–	–	–	–	–	–	–	–	–	–	–	1	–	–	–	1	–
18	–	–	–	–	1	–	–	–	–	–	4	–	10	–	1	–	–	–	–	–	3	1	–	–	–
19	–	–	–	–	–	–	–	–	–	–	–	–	–	–	–	–	–	–	–	–	1	–	–	–	–
20	–	–	–	–	–	–	–	–	–	–	4	–	3	1	–	–	–	–	–	–	11	–	3	–	–
21	–	–	–	–	–	–	–	–	–	–	–	–	7	–	–	–	–	–	–	–	7	–	–	–	–
22	–	–	–	–	–	–	–	–	–	–	–	–	–	–	–	–	–	–	–	–	9	–	–	–	–
23	–	–	–	–	–	–	–	–	–	–	1	–	4	–	–	–	1	–	–	–	7	–	1	–	–
24	–	2	–	1	–	–	–	–	–	2	2	–	45	–	–	–	–	–	1	–	5	1	–	–	–
25	–	–	–	–	–	–	–	–	–	–	–	–	–	1	–	–	–	–	–	–	–	–	–	–	–
26	1	2	3	1	2	6	3	2	–	2	31	1	85	–	–	1	3	9	–	1	50	3	2	–	–
27	1	–	–	–	–	–	–	–	–	–	–	–	12	–	–	–	–	–	–	–	10	–	–	–	–
28	–	–	–	–	–	–	–	–	–	–	–	–	8	–	–	–	–	–	–	–	8	–	–	–	–
29	–	–	–	–	–	–	–	–	–	–	2	–	2	–	–	–	–	1	1	–	–	–	–	–	–
Tot	20	4	8	3	4	6	105	2	1	4	48	2	269	2	1	1	4	11	2	2	136	5	6	3	1

KEY: 01, *Juniperus* sp.; 02, *Cruciferae*; 03, cf. *Cruciferae*; 04, *Caryophyllaceae*; 05, *Chenopodium* sp.; 06, *Vitis* sp. (whole pip); 07, *Vitis* sp. (pip fragments); 08, *Leguminosae* (cf. *Ulex* type); 09, *Vicia/Lathyrus*; 10, *Umbelliferae*; 11, *Rumex* sp.; 12, *Olea europaea*; 13, *Olea* stone fragments; 14, *Galium* sp.; 15, cf. *Galium* sp.; 16, *Gramineae*; 17, *Triticum* sp.; 18, *Triticum* cf. spelta; 19, *Triticum* cf. dicoccon; 20, *Triticum* glume base; 21, *Triticum* cf. spelta glume base; 22, *Triticum* cf. diccocon glume base; 23, *Triticum* spikelet glume base; 24, *Hordeum vulgare*; 25, *Hordeum* internode; 26, *Cerealia* indet; 27, *Panicum miliaceum*; 28, small *Gramineae* (cf. Setaria); 29, indet.
Sub = sub–sample taken from botanical sample for the context

grape pips from Nadin are closer in size to the wild than the domestic form. The charcoal fragments recovered were probably remnants from fires. The genera tentatively identified all include species which grow in the Mediterranean today. The most abundant charcoal was oak; also frequent were olive, ash and juniper or yew. Almost all the cultivated species were present in both Iron Age and Roman levels (table 28). Exceptions are emmer and the olive. The absence of emmer may reflect a preference for the higher-yielding hexaploid wheats. The distribution of food plants provides strong evidence for continuity in resource usage across the Iron Age–Roman transition.

Table 28 Botanical remains by period, Nadin-Gradina

Seeds	PRIA	Roman	Charcoals	PRIA	Roman
Spelt wheat	X	X	Oak	X	X
Six-row barley	X	X	Olive	X	X
Emmer	–	X	Elm	–	X
Millet	X	X	Pine/spruce	X	X
Grape	X	X	Apple type	X	X
Olive	–	X	Buckthorn	–	X
Legumes	–	X	cf. willow	X	X
Dock	X	X	Juniper/yew	X	X
Fat hen	X	X	Hazel	X	X
Cabbage family	X	X	Ash	X	X
Carrot family	–	X	Rose	–	X
Pink family	X	–	Plum sp.	X	X
Bedstraw	–	X	Ilex	X	–
			Grape	X	–

Presentation of these results on a tripole graph indicates that most of the Iron Age samples consisted of cleaned grain, while the Roman samples represented cleaned or uncleaned cereals with an admixture of weeds (fig. 134). It is unlikely that grain was grown within 1km of Nadin and it seems reasonable that at least some cleaning of grain occurred before the crop was taken some distance.

In summary, the dated subsistence information from Nadin provides our first glimpse of the way in which traditional plants and animals were incorporated into a Roman market economy in the early Roman period. The continuity recorded in the subsistence data matches that displayed in the settlement pattern record; both aspects of the archaeological data base indicate that, with the exception of pigs, the changes consequent upon Romanization of the coastal strip of Dalmatia concerned the organization and scale of crop production rather than the productive resources of the region themselves.

The pottery

By K. Griffiths and J. Hayes

Study of the Nadin assemblage began with the establishment of the chronology from the well-known imported wares and proceeded by relating that chronology to the associated coarse wares. The pottery came from seven different trenches (fig. 84). The heavily abraded condition of the pottery from Trenches 2 and 4–7 prevented quantitative analysis of the coarse pottery; identification of only some fine wares was possible. The pottery from Trenches 1 and 3 was in much better condition.

A numbered type series of the non-fine wares was established using the fabric analysis recommended in the Museum of London Department of Urban

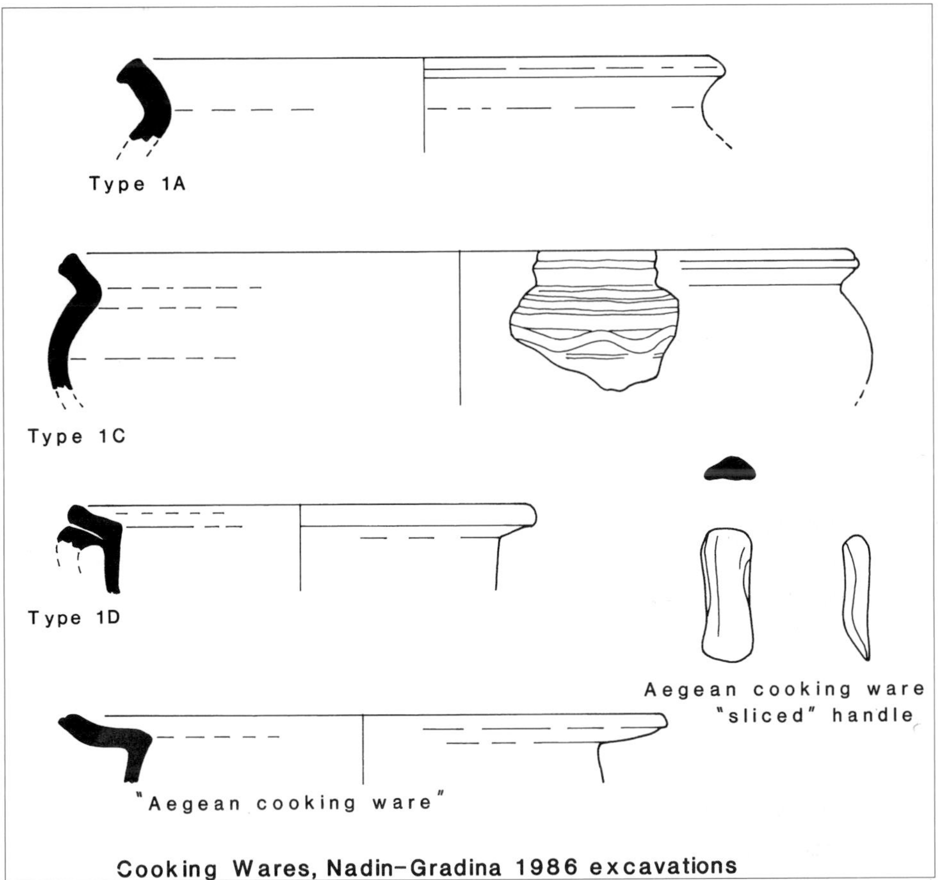

169. Fabric 1 vessels, Nadin

Archaeology Finds Processing Manual (Department of Urban Archaeology 1984). Some twenty major fabric divisions were created in this manner. An unexpected feature of the assemblage was the huge percentage of imported wares – not only African red slip wares and Italian *terra sigillata* but also the large numbers of amphorae and even cooking wares which were not locally made. In fact, no contemporary pottery workshops have hitherto been found in the region.

A notable feature of the upper levels from Trenches 1 and 3 were the so-called Fabric 1 wares of the Nadin Type series. These were reminiscent of Black Burnished wares, (bonfire-fired, hand- or wheel-made, common in jars with an everted rim, wavy line combed decorations: fig. 169). Such wares have previously been dated to the early medieval period in Yugoslavia, as in the upper layers at Nadin. However, they were also being manufactured in the fifth century AD and earlier. In Trench 3 at least, their numbers peak at the same time as those of the African red slip wares

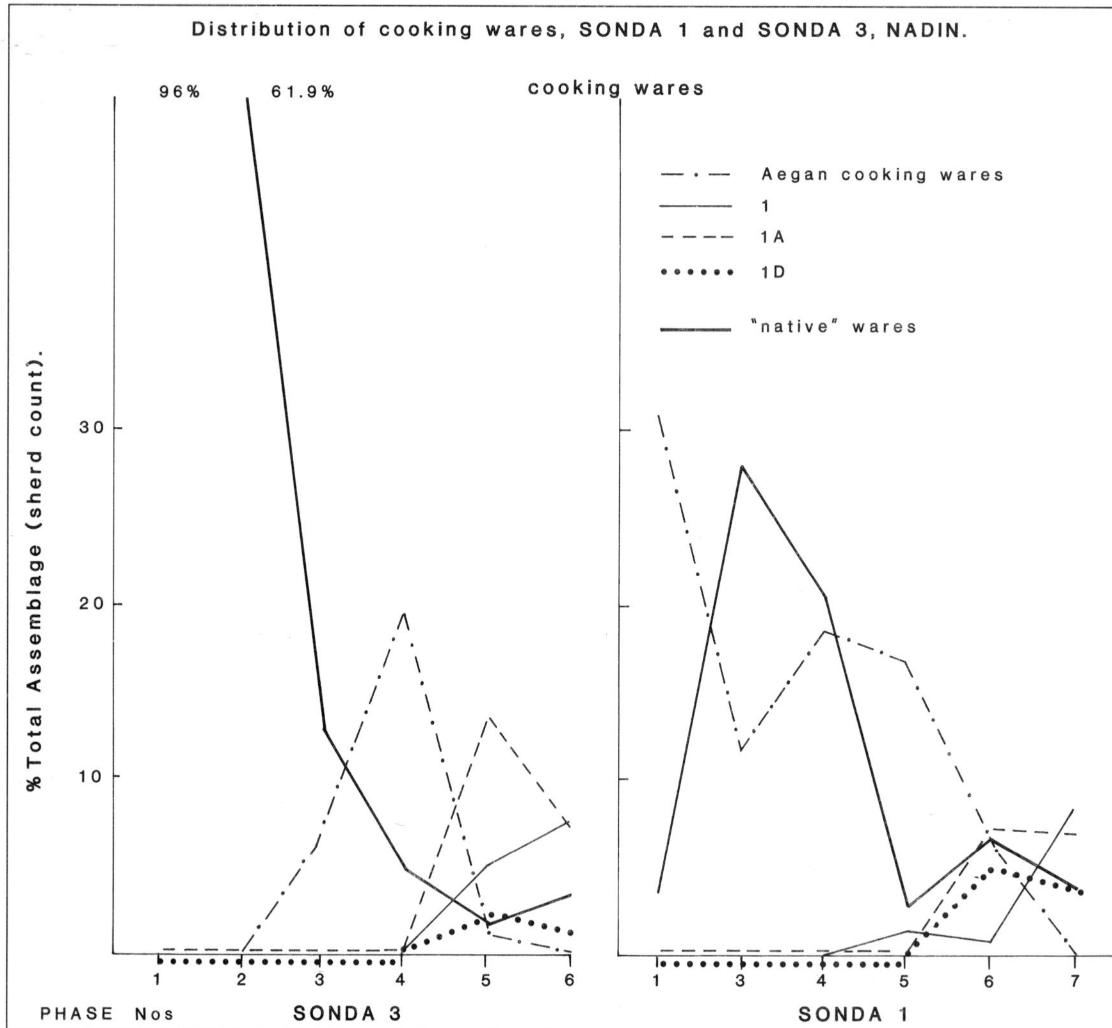

170. Frequency of coarse ware fabrics, Nadin

on the site (figs. 170–1). Some of the Fabric 1 wares, namely Fabric 1D, are quite finely made and must have been wheel-thrown (fig. 169*c*). Their fabric is much less heavily gritted than others of Fabric 1 and in fact on examination bears some resemblance to that of the second and third century AD so-called 'Aegean' cooking wares (fig. 169, 1). The 1D forms are also in some respects similar to the Aegean flat-rimmed, handled casseroles. The graph (fig. 170) demonstrates the apparent replacement by the Fabric 1 vessels of the Aegean cooking wares, which had themselves previously replaced the ubiquitous heavily calcite-gritted cooking wares of the Iron Age. No doubt many of the latter continued to be manufactured well into the Roman period. It should be stressed that these three wares were really the only obvious cooking wares found in Trenches 1 and 3 other than the occasional African casserole and baking lid.

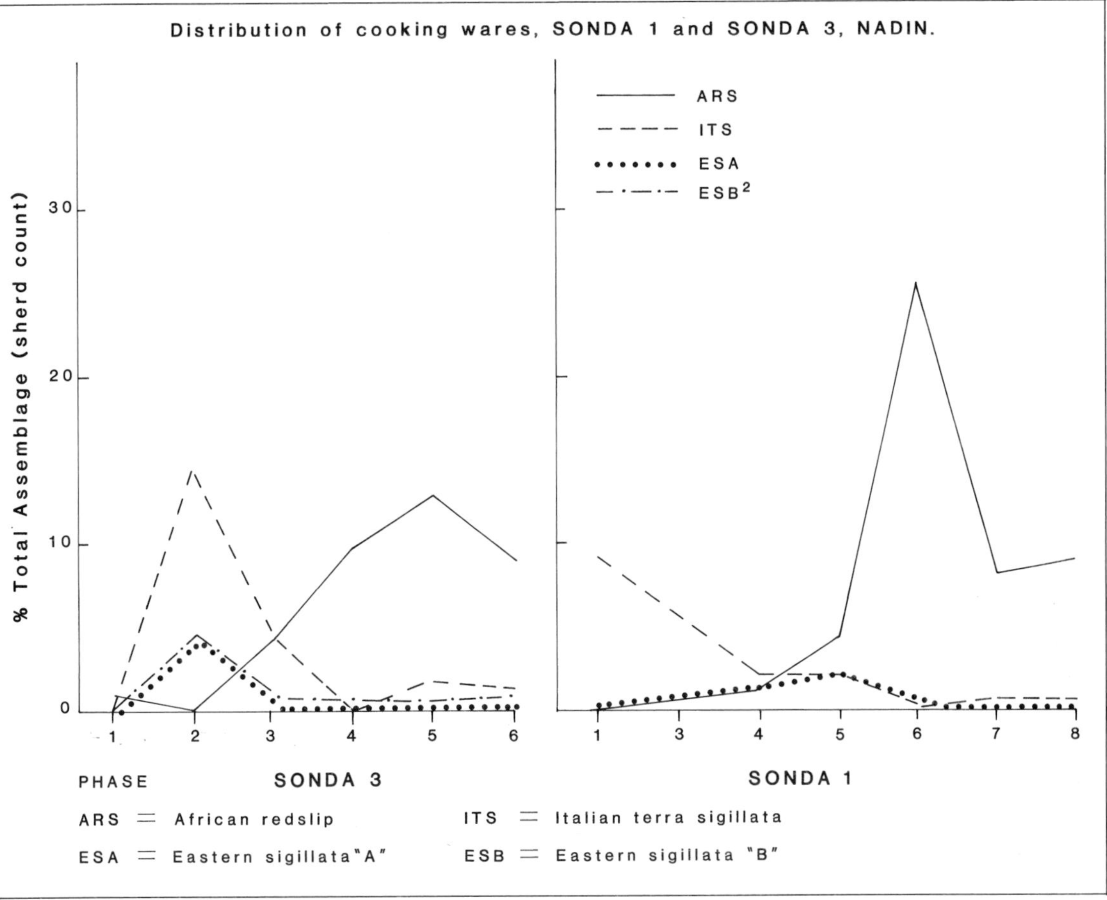

171. Frequencies of Eastern *terra sigillatas*, Nadin

There seems no doubt that fine Aegean cooking wares were imported into Dalmatia. Many thousands of these vessels were discovered lying on the sea bed at the ancient port of Zaton (pers. comm., Z. Brusić, 1988). Thus we cannot look to them for a local pottery production. Though the heavy cooking wares from the Iron Age levels never really die out, their numbers do clearly decline throughout the Roman period. It may be postulated that they are superseded to some extent from the second and third centuries AD, by the imported Aegean cooking wares and, in the fourth–fifth centuries by a new source of cooking wares, the Fabric 1s. The heavy often burnished cooking wares of the Iron Age/Roman period seem strong candidates for a local production site or sites.

The economic growth of Nadin-Gradina during the Roman period is indicated by the appearance of fine *terra sigillata* from Italy and the Eastern *sigillatas* A and B from Syria and Asia Minor (fig. 171). By the second and third centuries AD, imports of African red slip wares begin to rise. However, by the time imports of the latter peak in the fifth century, the importation of Aegean cooking wares has declined, very possibly to be replaced by the Fabric 1 wares. Though probably locally made, their uniformity and similarity of fabric to some of the Aegean wares might point to a source further afield.

The analysis of the other imported wares by John Hayes held no surprises. The range of sources again indicates the status of Nadin during the whole of the Roman period (first century BC–sixth century AD) (fig. 172). There were large amphora imports at all periods from the late first century AD onwards. The dominance of African sources in the fifth century AD is clear. Many of the amphora fabrics however remain to be identified and sourced.

As for the fine wares, there was the expected range of sources, including exotics like the Knidian pine cone *Thymiaterion* fragments, Corinthian lamps and

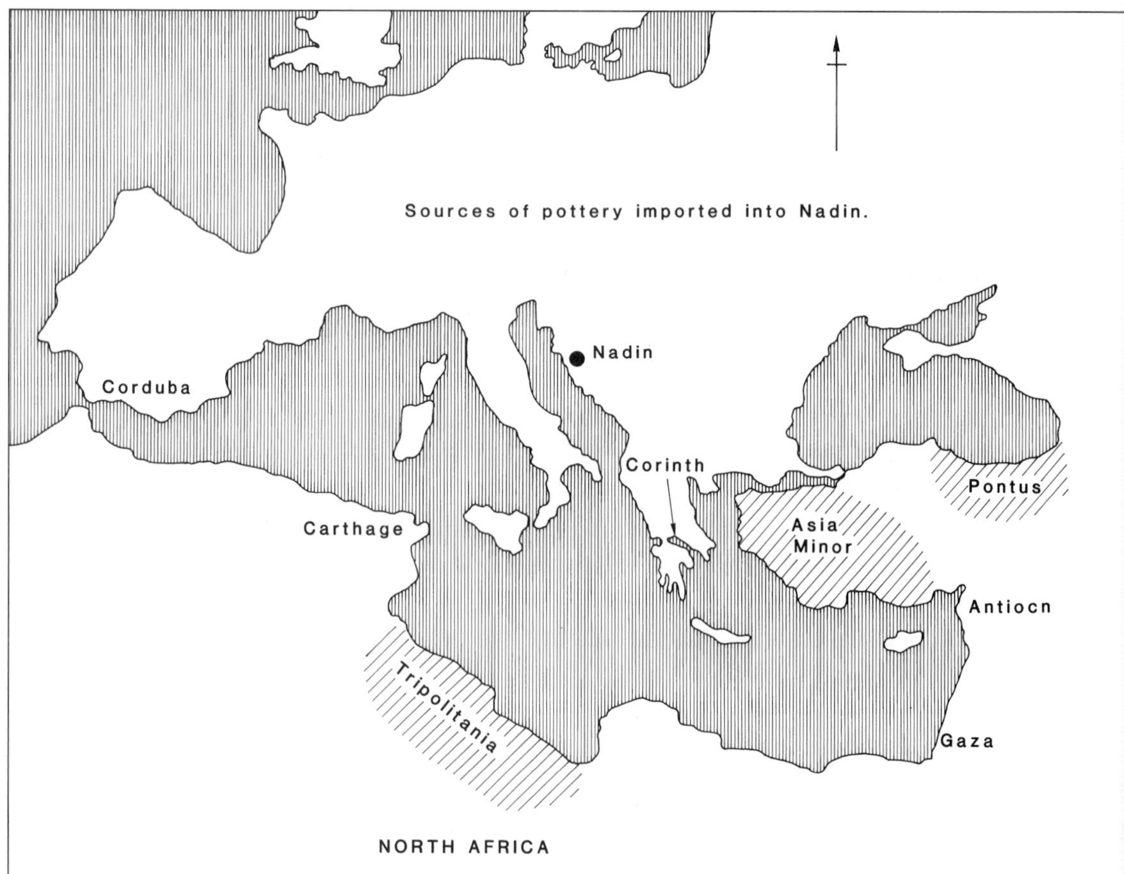

172. Sources of imported fine wares, Nadin

Republican Black Gloss ware. Late Italian *terra sigillata* of poor 'provincial' quality is gradually replaced as the standard table ware during the first century AD by the African red slip wares, although there is a fall-off in absolute percentages of 'red gloss' table wares somewhere in the second and third centuries AD.

In conclusion, the most valuable information to come from the Nadin-Gradina pottery is the demonstration of substantial overlap between previously rigorously compartmentalized coarse ware potting traditions. The necessity of imposing an historical framework should not prevent archaeologists from recognizing continuity within the Dalmatian ceramic assemblage as well as the changes imposed by alterations in economic patterns and local rises in socio-economic status.

The small finds

Small finds from Trenches 2, 4, 5 and 6 were recorded individually by context and using three-dimensional plotting. A total of 201 items was discovered, most of which were made of iron. Artefacts of glass, bronze, stone and bone were also found; their distribution by trench is shown below (table 29).

Glass

Five classes of glass finds are known from the extra-mural trenches at Nadin – beads, decorated fragments, curved glass, flat glass (?window glass) and lumps. This contrasts strongly with the remains of glass vessels found in Trenches 1 and 3 (fig. 173:1–6).

Bronze

Nine classes of bronze finds are known from Trenches 2, 4–6. These are six brooch fragments, eight fragments of sheet bronze, six pins and needles, one spiral wire, one u-shaped section, one bronze strip and one hook (fig. 173:7–9, 11, 14, 17, 19–21).

Lead

One single lead small find has been made: a bent-over fragment of lead sheet, possibly a curse (fig. 173:13).

Table 29 Distribution of small finds by trench, Nadin-Gradina

Trench	Glass	Iron	(slag)	Bronze	Stone	Bone	Total
2	12	117	(86)	29	1	2	161
4	0	35	(30)	2	0	0	37
5	1	0	(0)	0	0	0	1
6	1	1	(0)	0	0	0	2
TOTAL	14	153	(116)	31	1	2	201

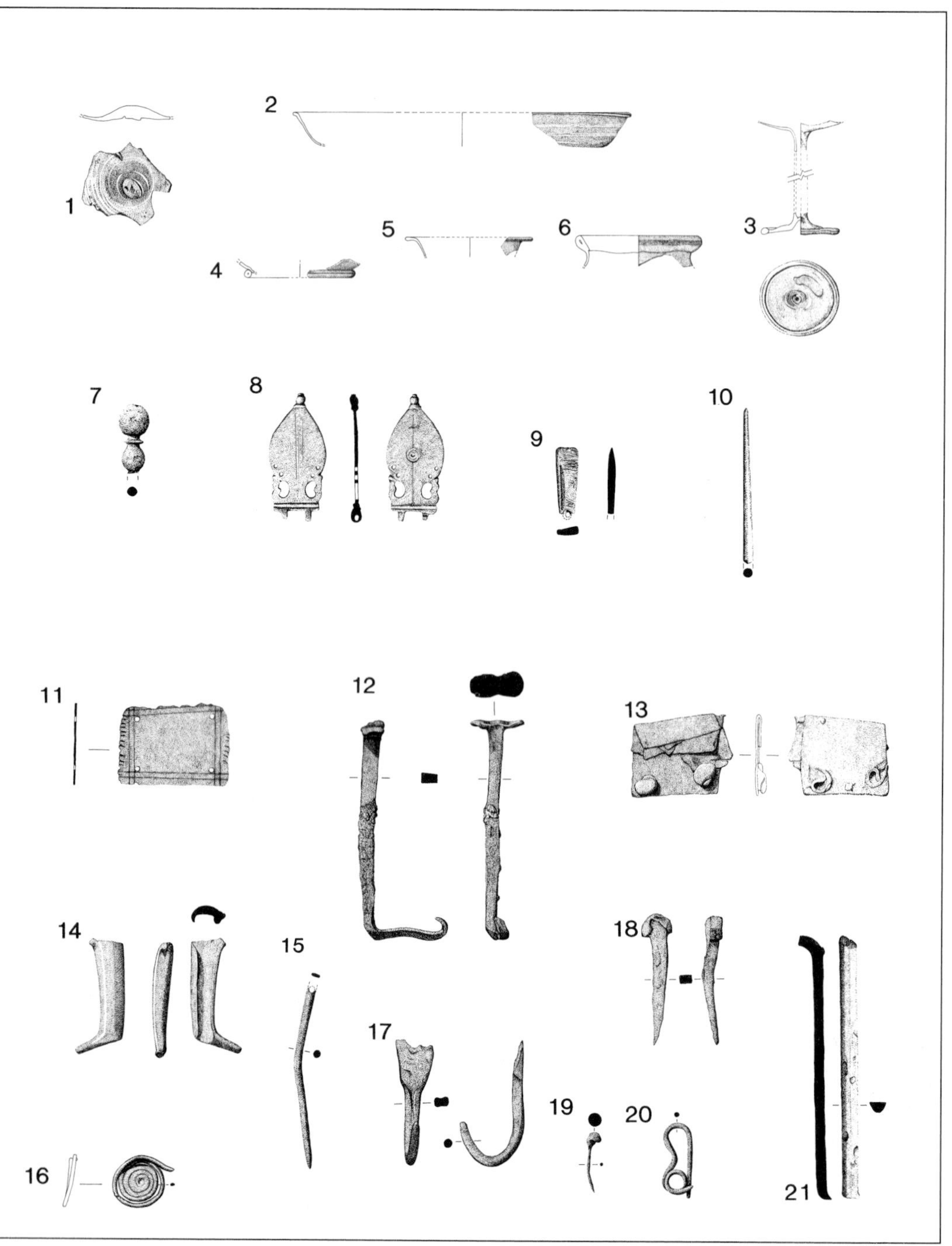

173. Small finds, Nadin. 1–6: glass; 7–9, 11, 14, 16–17, 19–21: bronze; 12, 15, 18: iron; 13: lead; 10: bone. 1: Trench 3/60–80cm depth; 2: 1/30–45; 3: 3/60–80; 4: 1/15–30; 5–6: 3/100–110; 7: surface find; 8: 1/95–110; 9: 1/60–80; 10: 3/80–100; 11: 4/Context 3; 12: 4/C. 9; 13: 4/C. 9; 14–16: 4/C. 8; 17: 4/C. 23; 2/ C. 24; 19: 2/C. 23; 20: 2/C. 24–25; 21: 2/C. 24

Iron
The majority of iron artefacts from Nadin comprise lumps of iron slag, attesting local if small-scale production of iron. Apart from the slag, six classes of iron artefacts are known: twenty-four nails, ten fragments of sheets or strips, one pin, one buckle fragment, one clamp and one irregular lump (fig. 173:12, 15, 18).

Stone
A single stone artefact was found in the extramural trenches at Nadin: fragment of a polished stone andesite axe resembling a Neolithic axe (?talisman).

Bone
Two artefacts were found at Nadin in the extramural trenches: a spatula and a fragment of polished bone (fig. 173:10).

Small finds patterning
All the main materials for artefact manufacture were present in the Iron Age as well as in the Roman period, with the possible exception of glass. The Iron Age/Roman transition period (50 BC–AD 50) was particularly rich in small finds and artefact diversity.

There are concentrations of certain classes of finds in some areas, as well as low densities of other classes in certain areas. Iron nails tend to be equally represented everywhere except outside the building. The main pattern is the concentration of iron objects (especially slag) in the terrace fill and bronze artefacts under Building 037. This may indicate small-scale iron production for household use.

An analysis by functional class produces patterns essentially similar to those found in the distribution by context group: high densities of ornaments under Building 037, with low densities of other finds, and the reverse in the terrace fill. The domination of the assemblage by iron slag (*c.* 60 per cent) is suggestive of local production of small tools such as nails and pins. The greatest diversity of finds occurs under Building 037, with the lowest diversity coming from finds in the terrace fill. This suggests that, before the construction of the building, there was a wider range of local activities which generated generalized refuse while, after the construction of Building 037, more specialized refuse was discarded relating to a narrower range of activities. The high quality of some of the small finds in the intramural zone (especially the glasswork) is suggestive of status differences between intramural and extramural occupation. This material will be the object of a separate publication by the Arheolški Muzej Zadar.

Summary

On the basis of the analytical survey and trial excavations, it is possible to propose a tentative outline of the occupational sequence of Nadin. Prior to human occupation of Nadin, woodland probably covered the entire hill. The soils at Nadin were largely terra rossa originally but human occupation has caused a change in colour. Terra rossa on artificial terraces may have covered more of Nadin hill and may have been of a finer texture than those seen in agricultural use.

No evidence was found to support the assertion of Late Bronze Age occupation on the top or slopes of the Nadin hill. The current conclusion is therefore that Late Bronze Age use of the Nadin area was minimal.

In all the trenches located outside the main hill-fort circuit, there was evidence for the deposition of Pre-Roman Iron Age pottery in garden soils. The earliest known focus of Iron Age settlement on the Nadin hill dates to the fifth and fourth centuries BC and comes from the area of Enclosure 908. The nature of this early settlement focus is not clear from our investigations. Some of the forest cover would have been removed from the Nadin hill in the middle of the first millennium BC and this is likely to have led to erosion of the A-horizon of some of the hilltop soils.

With the construction of the main hill-fort rampart, an increased rate of deforestation would have been imperative, both as a security measure and to allow quarrying. Continued erosion of extant A-horizons would lead to soil loss on the upper slopes but not necessarily from the hill-top, now encircled by a rampart. In the NDP excavations, no direct attempt was made to date the main rampart. Faber (1976, 244) dates it on stylistic grounds to the first century AD but this date seems too late in view of the third–first centuries BC pottery found at the base of Trench 3, as well as in secondary contexts in Trenches 2 and 4. The extent of *in situ* Iron Age occupation outside the main rampart is an as yet poorly defined question, although there was extensive Iron Age quarrying of the Senonian limestone needed for the main rampart and domestic buildings. It is conceivable that Iron Age buildings could have been built on the hillslopes with rubble-infill wall techniques, using surplus quarried material.

The earliest structure for which there is an unambiguous construction date is Building 037, built in the century 50 BC–AD 50. The establishment of a *municipium* in the early first century AD at Nadin appears to precede new construction activities, such as the building of Enclosures 907 and 908. The first century AD is also the period when we first have evidence for the construction of terrace walls (Terrace 220) on a modest scale. Continued occupation inside the ramparts is attested by the proliferation of early Roman inscriptions (Wilkes 1969); the wealth indicated by the epigraphic data is matched by that of the imported fine wares. The integrated road plan covering the entire east and south-east hillslopes is suggestive of a major expansion of occupation in the early Roman period.

The latest extramural finds (third century AD) can be dated earlier than the latest intramural artefacts (fifth–seventh centuries AD); intramural occupation continued later and in a more intensive manner than that on the hillslopes, where different patterns of deposition or perhaps even abandonment of terraces and enclosures had already begun in the mid-Roman period.

There is as yet no archaeological evidence to match the documentary references to Nadin in the medieval period (AD 1240–1539). Occupation of the Nadin hill by the Ottoman army from 1539 to 1669 is indicated by the remains of a tower and rampart on the highest part of the hill.

The most recent occupation of Nadin consists of a further military presence, in which a JNA tank regiment dug a position into the hill-fort with the aim of the shelling of Zadar (AD 1991–4). Much, as yet unspecified, damage of the heritage monument has been recorded (pers. comm., S. Čače, 1993).

Hence the hypothesis proposed by Batović of a continuous occupation of the Nadin hilltop from the Late Bronze Age until the departure of the Ottoman forces can be replaced by the notion of discontinuous occupation, with full-scale occupation of the hilltop in the Iron Age, expansion over the hillslopes in the Roman period with particular growth in the Early Roman occupation, abandonment of the whole site in the early medieval period, hilltop reoccupation in the late medieval period, limited hilltop defensive works during the Ottoman occupation and major offensive reoccupation by the Serbian JNA in the Serbian–Croatian–Bosnian War of 1989–95.

7 Explanatory models

Strategy of explanation

One of the main aims of the NDP is to explain the changes in physical environment, settlement patterns and social structure in north Dalmatia, many of which have been described in previous chapters. While the controversy over what is a 'good' explanation in archaeology still rages (Feyerabend 1975; Bhaskar 1982; Gibbon 1989), the three prerequisites of a convincing explanation remain consistency, parsimony and clarity. Logical consistency is required at a number of different levels in the argument and at each level of the research procedure; consistency between *explanans* and *explanandum* is also a critical issue. Parsimony concerns the minimum complexity which yet remains sufficient to formulate a proposed explanation, guided by frequent use of Occam's razor. Clarity is essential in specifying the key variables in question and their inter-relationships through time and space. The following discussion summarizes the logical basis of the strategy of explanation utilized here.

Four models are utilized to provide concrete explanations of the wide variety of ecological, artefactual and symbolic data presented above in the NDP. These are the land use capability model (LUC); the cyclic intensification–deintensification model (CID); the communal ownership of property model (COP); and the arenas of social power model (ASP).

The LUC model relates to the long time-scale and is based on expectations of land use change in the Neothermal period consequent upon changing land area and soil quality, on climatic fluctuations, and on the technology, crops and animals available. In this model, an attempt is made to define the range of environmental factors which have changed and to assess their interaction with each other and their impact on land use in a non-deterministic way. The main nexus of intervening variables concerns land use categories and their distribution, settlement pattern and contemporary land use at the millennial time-scale.

Two models are juxtaposed for an analysis of medium-term processes of change. The CID model is an elaboration of Bintliff's (1982c) cyclic model of Aegean settlement nucleation and dispersion, in which private land-holding is assumed to be the key variable. By contrast, the COP model is a development of Fleming's (1985) model of communal land-holding, as refined through the course of the Dartmoor Reaves Project (see also Fleming 1988).

Finally, the ASP model is used as a framework for understanding the short to medium time-scale of annual and inter-annual events. This approach relies on the notion that human communities create their own place-based landscapes full not only of meaning but of the opportunities for the development of arenas of social power.

In the case of the first three models, the settlement patterns predicted on the basis of the main assumptions of the model are compared and contrasted with the actual settlement data in an attempt to assess the degree of congruence between the two. 'Residuals' comprise those aspects of the data 'unexplained' by the model in question and provide a starting point for further investigation. In the ASP model, the settlement sequence is taken as the basis for interpretation of changes in the form and frequency of monuments, sites and settlement foci in the light of the creation, maintenance and/or modification of arenas of social power.

The land use classification model

Land Use Capability

Assessment of the impact of climate change, sea level and erosion or deposition on the agricultural potential of the various land classes is dependent on a method of evaluating their relative potential in values per unit area. The most convenient way of doing this is by adapting Klingebiel and Montgomery's (1961) Land Use Capability classification (LUCC) and applying it to the five land classes described earlier (see p.28) (fig. 14). As LUCC produces a generalized suitability, a threefold classification for annual crops (cereals and vegetables), perennials (trees and vines) and forage will be proposed which takes account of variable crop responses to soil conditions and climate. The relative value of the land as seen today can be placed on this threefold system and then relative values in the past can be predicted using the data presented on climate, soil, crop requirements, soil erosion and deposition (tables 30–6). This model makes uniformitarian assumptions about the socio-economic strategies underpinning land use; to the extent that these assumptions are false, the actual data may well deviate from the predictions. The fit between expected and actual use can be assessed by comparing the model data with those obtained from NDP survey and excavations. The most likely reasons for preferring certain land classes is detailed below.

Predictions: past and present land quality

In deciding how to use the landscape as a whole decisions must be made as to how to use the more 'capable' land, such as Arable. With low intensity of use Arable land may be used for all crops for which it is suited. As intensity of use increases, the

Table 30 Land Use Class Capability estimates for the modern period

	Forage	Tree crops	Cereals and vegetables	Overall ranking
Arable	1*	4	1	2**
Stony	2	1	2	1.7
Terrace	4	2	4	3.3
Karst	4	3	5	4
Reclaimed Bottomland	2	2	2	2
Natural Bottomland	3	5	5	4.3

* Numbers 1 (best) to 5 (worst) indicate the relative capability of the land for producing that group of crops under the environmental conditions of the period. For earlier periods, the land is ranked in relative position after allowing for contemporary environmental conditions.

** Average of the three crop types.

Table 31 Land Use Class Capability estimates for the Neolithic and Copper Age

	Forage	Tree crops	Cereals and vegetables	Overall ranking
Arable	1	2	1	1.3
Stony	3	1	2	2
Terrace	5	4	5	4.7
Karst	4	2	4	3.3
Bottomland	2	4	3	3

crops which can be grown on less capable land may be directed to that land, with Arable producing the crops that only it can produce easily and efficiently. Thus one might expect the more capable land to be used preferentially, but if a society preferred animal or tree crops which grow on all land classes, then they might either draw no distinction between classes or prefer land which is in our terms 'less capable'. Bearing in mind these caveats, we may use an arithmetic mean land class in the expectation that communities will use the most capable land most intensively. If the population is small or very specialized in its cropping this might not be a valid assumption. The mean LUCC (table 30) suggests that Arable, Stony and Reclaimed Bottomland are 'best' and will be used most intensively. The other three types – Terrace, Karst and Natural Bottomland – are much poorer although Karst and Terrace are quite good for tree crops, and Natural Bottomland is reasonably good as a summer grazing resource.

In the Neolithic and Copper Age (table 31) the probably drier climate and much reduced runoff due to deeper more extensive soil and greater forest cover gave Arable a relative advantage over Stony, with the other three types much less satisfactory. Terrace suffered from drought, as did Karst, although the thicker soil on Karst (much of what is today Karst was rather thin Stony land (see p. 32)) meant that it was better than Terrace. The risk of flooding on Bottomland was small, and with a dry summer both grazing and short-season cereal or vegetable crops could be grown. Clearly the expectation is that Stony and Arable land would be used most intensively. As the sea level was much lower in the early Neolithic there would have been a much larger resource of Arable land available than today. Hence it is expected that this land would have been used to the exclusion of other types.

During the Bronze Age (table 32), weather variation from warm-dry to cool-moist must have made management decisions difficult. In the wetter phases the increased rainfall, and some soil thinning on the Karst, would have increased runoff and hence flood risk on the lower lying land, while the increased moisture made sandy soils somewhat more productive. The wetness would have made Arable land less attractive than in the Neolithic, while Stony land, particularly if already cleared of stones, was as good or better overall than Arable and much better for tree crops. Terrace would have been better because of the moister conditions, and would have formed an intermediate group along with Karst. Bottomland would have been less useful because of increased risk of flooding. This all suggests that the best land would have been now further up the valley sides, with Karst not far behind Arable in overall quality. Certainly, tree crops would have prospered away from the valley floor. In the drier phases the relative usefulness of land would have been similar to that in the Neolithic, but with increased drought risk on the thinning soils of the Karst, and increased flood-wetness risk on the Bottomland and Arable.

In the Iron Age (table 33), Arable would have slipped in position because of increasing wetness making soil difficult to cultivate and threatening crops with waterlogging. Stony land would have retained pre-eminent position, but be joined

Table 32 Land Use Class Capability estimates for the Bronze Age

	Forage	Tree crops	Cereals and vegetables	Overall ranking
Arable	1	4	2	2.3
Stony	2	1	2	1.7
Terrace	4	2	4	3.3
Karst	4	2	3	3
Bottomland	4	5	4	4.7

Table 33 Land Use Class Capability estimates for the Iron Age

	Forage	Tree crops	Cereals and vegetables	Overall ranking
Arable	2	5	3	3.3
Stony	1	2	2	1.7
Terrace	3	1	1	1.7
Karst	2	2	4	2.7
Bottomland	5	5	5	5

Table 34 Land Use Class Capability estimates for the Roman period

	Forage	Tree crops	Cereals and vegetables	Overall ranking
Arable	1	3	1	1.7
Stony	2	1	1	1.3
Terrace	5	3	5	4.3
Karst	4	3	5	4
Bottomland	2	5	4	3.7

Table 35 Land Use Class Capability estimates for the medieval period

	Forage	Tree crops	Cereals and vegetables	Overall ranking
Arable	1	4	1	2
Stony	2	1	2	1.7
Terrace	5	2	4	3.7
Karst	4	2	4	3.3
Bottomland	2	5	5	4

by Terrace land, on which the coarse soil would have been advantaged by the cool wet conditions. Karst would have now been potentially better than Arable, though cereal and vegetable crops would have become increasingly difficult to manage as the soil thinned due to erosion. The effect of soil loss would be to some extent offset by the increased wetness, which provided sufficient water for growth. Bottomland would have been almost useless because of flood risk, and even the valuable summer grazing was of less value in the wetter conditions. Optimum land use would now have moved completely out of the valleys onto the slopes and ridges.

During the Roman period (table 34), the effect of the climate and soil changes would have meant that Arable improved relative to Stony land, but would still have been less suitable than Stony for tree crops. Terrace land and Karst would have been less attractive for crops other than trees because of the increased droughtiness. Bottomland would have been marginally better than these two types, but unsuitable for tree crops because of flood risk. The best sites would have now moved back downslope into the lower valley positions and the suitability of the land types would have been somewhat similar to that in the Neolithic and modern. Compared with the Neolithic, the Bottomland would have had a higher flood risk in the Roman period, due to greater runoff from the largely deforested and thinning Karst. The slightly moister climate in the Roman period would have made Terrace and Stony relatively more attractive; erosion on the Karst would have more than offset the effects of the moister conditions. Relative to the modern period, the drier conditions in the Roman period meant that Terrace would have been more drought-prone, but due to the presence of deeper soil on Karst and Stony land these would be at least as useful as at the present.

In the medieval period (table 35), the warm dry conditions during much of the early medieval would have resulted in classificational similarities to the Roman period. In the later medieval, and in some earlier phases, the cool wet conditions would have resulted in classificational similarities to the Iron Age – though there was a continuing loss of soil from the Karst and Stony land, together with increased risk of flooding on the Bottomland. Drainage of some of the Bottomland reduced this risk late in the medieval.

In the post-medieval and early modern period (table 36), the Little Ice Age constituted a notably variable period, in which, rather like in the Bronze Age and Iron Age, the climate swung wildly between drought, flood and periods of extreme cold. This period did not end until the nineteenth century AD. The impact on local land use would have been to make olives a very uncertain crop: the trees would be killed only by extremes of cold or drought but their crop would be destroyed more easily. Vines would be affected similarly, more in terms of productivity than survival; their crop is somewhat less demanding of weather than olives. Other crops and grass would be most severely affected by drought, though a long, cold winter would seriously weaken stock if there was a shortage of fodder.

The best land class in this period would have been Stony land, giving air and water drainage and holding an adequate amount of water. Arable would have supported cereals well but, in frosty or wet conditions, would have been unsuitable for anything but forage. Bottomland could be used only for seasonal grazing unless it had been improved. Karst gave only poor grazing and horticultural cropping in desperation! Terrace was satisfactory for grapes and olives but of limited use for anything else in the dry episodes. In this period, as in the Bronze Age, land selection would have been difficult.

At the present day (table 30), Arable land is undoubtedly best as far as cereal and vegetable growing is concerned because of its level situation, high water table for irrigation and stone-free soil. Fine texture is not a serious problem with machinery available for cultivation. Forage crops would also grow well, but these can be grown on land which is less well suited to cereal and vegetable growing.

Table 36 Land Use Class Capability estimates for the post-medieval and early modern periods (Little Ice Age)

	Forage	Tree crops	Cereals and vegetables	Overall ranking
Arable	1	5	2	2.7
Stony	2	1	1	1.3
Terrace	4	1	3	2.7
Karst	3	2	4	3
Natural Bottomland	3	5	5	4.3
Reclaimed Bottomland	2	4	1	2.3

Arable land is not well suited to tree and vine crops because of the risks of high winter water tables damaging the crop roots and of cold air accumulating and causing frost damage. Stony land tends to be more sloping and does not have water conveniently available for irrigation. However, it is water-retentive, and once cleared of rock is suitable for tillage, provided there are no landfast rocks in the ploughzone. Hence it is less good than Arable for cereal and vegetable crops and forage but because of the low risk of flooding and good air drainage it is excellent for trees and vines. When not improved it would provide some of the best grazing available. Unless irrigated, Terrace land is too droughty to produce good cereals, vegetable or forage but is excellent, second to Stony land, for trees and vines. Karst is unsuitable for tillage and the soil-available water is small enough to give drought problems. As the only cash crops which grow at all successfully are trees and vines, and these only on the better areas which have more extensive soil cover, this land is used for extensive grazing. Bottomland unless improved is only suitable for summer grazing because of flood risk. After improvement it provides level freely drained land which may, as a result of excessive drainage, be droughty in summer. It can produce most crops, although there may be problems with frost damage, and hence, like Arable land, it will tend to be used for those crops which cannot be grown on other land classes.

The predictions of the Land Use Capability model will now be examined against the settlement data from the NDP archaeological survey and the subsistence evidence from trial excavations.

The settlement and subsistence evidence

Mesolithic–Neolithic–Copper Age (7000–2400 Cal. BC)

Settlement evidence (figs. 33–4)

The absence of closely datable Mesolithic lithics in the survey block makes concrete discussion of the transition from foragers to farmers almost impossible. As in other periods of low sea level (e.g. the Upper Palaeolithic), it is likely that the main areas of Mesolithic settlement would have been the coastal plains, now submerged beneath the Adriatic. Some early Neolithic settlements may also have been submerged, especially in what is today Pašmanski Kanal. The discovery of Mesolithic flints in the Velebit Mountains (Forenbaher and Vranjičan 1982) indicates occasional exploitation of the mountain zone. It is unlikely that the open woodlands of the Ravni Kotari with their herds of deer and aurochs, roaming bands of suids and possibly flocks of sheep would have been ignored by foraging populations. Evidence of the burial of Bottomland such as at Kula Atlagić suggests another mechanism for the loss of Mesolithic sites; lack of recognition of

Mesolithic toolkits in the generalized lithics discarded in most findspots hinders the quest still further. The hypothesis for future exploration is that foraging populations selected valley-edge and bottom areas rather than hill-slopes and karst ridges. If this notion is correct, there would be a substantial degree of settlement continuity between the last foragers and the earliest farming groups in the area.

Finds of the Neolithic period can be dated with relative ease to one of the main subdivisions of the period (Early, Middle and Late); the Copper Age or Eneolithic also has sufficiently diagnostic pottery. Although finds were made in forty-two separate collection units, the dense clustering of finds suggests only six main settlement foci in the entire three millennia. The most dispersed focus lies in the neighbourhood of Miljovići, with fourteen separate collection units yielding Late Neolithic and Copper Age material. This appears to represent a series of shorter-term occupations with periodic relocation of settlement or, conceivably, an Extended Village pattern of the type identified in northern France (Howell 1983). A similar group of low-density Early Neolithic finds occurs near Jagodnja, although the finds are more widely spaced than at Miljovići. The other four sites represent more nucleated remains covering, in the case of Tinj, not more than 1.25ha (Chapman and Batović 1985).

Three general points can be made about the Neolithic/Copper Age distributions: all the Neolithic/Copper Age settlement foci except one – Prtenjača – lie on Arable land, with easy access to Bottomland; material remains from this period are relatively scanty, with no sign of population increase consequent upon the adoption of farming; and there are far more Early Neolithic sites and findspots than for any other phase of the Neolithic or Copper Age.

The subsistence evidence

The excavated remains of Early Neolithic Tinj-Podlivade (see p. 186) yielded a reasonable sample of subsistence data which demonstrate that, contrary to current orthodoxy (Tringham 1971, 103; Whittle 1985, 98), the earliest farmers cultivated a wide range of cereals and domesticated the five main farmyard animals from as early as the sixth millennium Cal. BC. A high percentage of domestic animals, predominantly ovicaprines, was recovered in a sample of nearly 4,000 bones. In a wide range of crop remains, three forms of wheat (?wild einkorn, domestic einkorn and emmer), plus barley and oats were identified along with a range of crop weeds and several legumes. The molluscan data from Tinj indicate use of several contrasting ecological zones; such use of coastal resources perhaps explains the evidence for short-term occupation in coastal caves such as the Buta Jama (Ilakovac 1965). If Tinj is typical of Neolithic subsistence in the Zadar lowlands, it is no surprise to find a strong correlation between Neolithic locations and the Arable land class. Almost all Neolithic clusters are located on the land which is not only the most fertile for cultivated crops but also produces the highest-quality pasture.

The subsistence evidence from the only excavated open air Eneolithic site in the Ravni Kotari – Buković-Lastvine (Batović and Chapman 1986) confirms the importance of mixed farming to the inhabitants. The dominance of domesticated animals in the faunal spectrum rivals that at Tinj, while an increase in the importance of cattle relative to ovicaprines may signal the impact of secondary products innovations (Sherratt 1979). The range of plant remains recovered was narrower than at Tinj. Local cultivation of wheat (probably einkorn and emmer) is attested and the same is probably true for oats, millet and barley. Charcoal from juniper, olive and oak was also found at Buković. Use of local and marine molluscs indicates the use of a narrower range of ecological zones and species than at Tinj.

Summary

Population levels in the Neolithic and Copper Age appear so low that all subsistence activities could be concentrated on the remaining Arable land above sea level. This suggests a small-scale economy, with specialized site location combined with generalized land use. The land occupied during the Neolithic appears to have been the 'best' for the farming system in use at that time on the basis of environmental information. The location of the settlement appears to be accurately predicted in this period from environmental data. Population levels may have been underestimated owing to flooding and burial of sites, yet much unaffected Arable land remains with no evidence of use in the Neolithic. The environmental data, however, fail to offer any explanation of this underutilization. The period for which there is least settlement evidence is the Copper Age, coeval with cooler, wetter Piora conditions.

Bronze Age (2400–1000 Cal. BC*)*

Settlement evidence (figs. 39–40)

The pattern of Bronze Age sites and monuments presents a dramatic increase in the quantity of discard and the proportion of the total area exploited compared with the previous period. The highest upper octile and quartile values for the whole survey define Bronze Age discard and finds recovery.

The major characteristic of the Bronze Age in Dalmatia is the first recorded use of dry-stone walls for the construction of linear features, field systems, cairns, enclosures and hill-forts. Twenty-three settlement foci can be detected in this period, twelve of which are defined by higher-than-average densities of finds. The remaining eleven are dry-stone walled monuments: eight enclosures/hill-forts, two field systems and a cairnfield. The sites range from a single artefact scatter with one or two single finds within a 0.5km radius to scatters with partially surviving linear features, cairns and up to a dozen single finds within a 0.5km radius. Similar variation occurs within the 'territories' of the monuments; there are no visible finds in the 0.5km radius around the small hill-fort of Muvača, over twenty cairns and scatters in the area surrounding Kruglas and Strkovača.

The location of most major Bronze Age settlement foci on what is now Karst land should be put in perspective. On each excavated Bronze Age site, evidence has been found for soil erosion beginning in, and continuing after, the Bronze Age occupation (see pp. 126–8, 133, 138, 143, 213–16, 222–5, 227–9). On this basis, much of what is now Karst had a deeper soil profile in the third millennium Cal. BC, and would have been classed as 'Stony'. On this redefinition of past land use classes, most of the Bronze Age sites would occur on Arable or Stony land, with the onset of Karst conditions on flat limestone ridges representing a degradation of the soil cover partly caused by putative Bronze Age agriculture. Away from the ridges, seven of the twelve sites are located on, or on the edge of, Arable land, indicating continuity in valley settlement in this period.

Between the areas of major occupation lie large areas of often fertile land, with low densities of finds and monuments. Higher-than-average density pottery scatters may indicate short-term residence or the cumulative use of short-term rural huts. There is, however, no question of a full use of the landscape in this period, rather a moderate degree of settlement nucleation.

Subsistence evidence

Palaeobotanical information from the three test excavations at Bronze Age sites (Mataci, Čauševica and Polača: see pp. 218, 225, 230) is limited to juniper pips, olive stones and seeds of millet from Čauševica. Whether this represents evidence of absence or the converse remains unclear.

It should be noted that there are severe criteria for accepting the domestication of tree crops like the olive and other fruit, not to mention the vine (Runnels and Hansen 1986); hence, there is little chance of determining the question of local domestication from such small botanical samples. Nevertheless, increased interest in even wild vines and olives may well have prompted the establishment of settlements on more suitable land off the Arable.

Summary

The preferred location of Bronze Age settlement in both valley and ridge locations is successfully predicted on the basis of environmental information. Again, the relative under-use of the landscape is unexplained, though variability in weather may have set limits to output and constrained further expansion. It is conceivable that the upper, level, parts of ridges may have provided an environment with a smaller variability of yield than valley sites. The adoption and possible diversification of mixed farming practices is predicated upon the wide range of stone field remains, not only field systems but also linear features and clearances as well as mortuary cairns.

Iron Age (1000–100 Cal. BC)

Settlement evidence (figs. 45–6)

The Iron Age in Dalmatia has traditionally been viewed as the 'time of the hill-forts', a period when all settlement was concentrated into the large number of hilltop defended sites (Suić 1974; Batović 1977). However, a number of 'lowland' scatters may be interpreted as dispersed farmsteads. Hence, the Iron Age distribution displays the first clear indications of settlement hierarchy in Dalmatia. A two-level system of hill-forts and farmsteads in the earlier Iron Age was replaced at some time in the last three hundred years Cal. BC by a three-level hierarchy, with the addition of an extra level of major hill-forts.

A total of twenty settlement foci is known for the Iron Age – fourteen monument-based and six site-based. Iron Age off-site discard is much reduced, with more than five scatters within a 0.5km radius around only one site (Nadin-Gradina). Similarly, off-site discard between the settlement foci is very low indeed; this decline may reflect a shrinking use of the landscape or merely a different set of discard practices in the Iron Age. The absence of field systems datable to the Iron Age is a curious anomaly.

Almost all the enclosures and hill-forts of the Iron Age are located on what are today Karst land. Despite the occurrence of post-Iron Age soil erosion on the Karst, steeply sloping sites would always have had thin, discontinuous soils, and on these sites land use potential can never have been much better than at present. Several valley sites are, however, located on, or on the edge of, Arable land. It seems likely that a smaller proportion of the productive potential of the survey area was exploited in this period than in the Bronze Age.

In the Iron Age, a strong preference for hilltop and ridge sites indicates settlement in just those areas which have been, or are in the process of being, degraded, at least partly through human intervention. The construction of terraces and subsidiary enclosures at Nadin-Gradina indicates labour-intensive land management in the late Pre-Roman Iron Age. However, since no Early Iron Age enclosures have been excavated, it is difficult to judge whether degradation of the Karst was continuing into the first millennium Cal. BC or constituted a primarily Bronze Age phenomenon. The current hypothesis is that, given the scale of Iron Age use of the Karst, vegetation and soil loss would continue to have been an important factor throughout this period.

Subsistence evidence

The only direct palaeoeconomic evidence from the Iron Age derives from the NDP excavations at Nadin-Gradina (Batović and Chapman 1987). The faunal sample from the late Iron Age indicates a predominance of caprines over cattle, pigs and horses in a sample dominated by domestic animals. Botanical identifications document the local cultivation of emmer and spelt wheat, six-row barley and millet and the use of the olive and the vine. The charcoal samples imply the proximity of broad-leaved associations (oak, hazel, willow) as well as some Mediterranean evergreen vegetation (*Quercus ilex*). These data indicate the use of local land, probably Terrace or Stony for the exploitation of vines and olives, with the possibility of cereal cultivation on what is now, and may have been then, Karst land on the main Nadin Ridge.

Summary

A higher proportion of Iron Age than Bronze Age settlement clusters are located on the Karst land on ridges. In view of the unpleasant, and perhaps even risky, conditions in the regularly flooded valleys, this is not surprising and fits well with the model's expectation of 'best' land type. Also, cropping would now have shifted to the ridges, with the valleys used more for grazing. As more labour is needed for cropping than for stock, the advantages of living on the ridges appear to be quite clear. Environmental factors again appear to play a major role in influencing the land use pattern, but the concentration of population is not explained.

The Roman period (150 BC–AD 500)

Settlement evidence (figs. 53–4)

The incorporation of the Ravni Kotari into the province of Dalmatia in the late first century Cal. BC stimulated many changes in the settlement pattern and land use strategies of the region, especially in the cultivation of vine and olive on Terrace and Stony land. These latter changes were probably facilitated by the warming and drying of the climate. Nevertheless, while the innovations introduced by the Roman authorities were important, the elements of continuity with what went before are particularly striking in settlement, social structure and land use (Chapman and Shiel 1991).

The most striking change in the settlement pattern is the expansion of the extensive use of the lowland landscape that had not previously been matched. What may be important about the Roman economy is that settled areas were more widely occupied than before, not that the Roman economy was more efficient or more intensive than anything prior (pers. comm., K. Griffiths, 1987). This more extensive exploitation was achieved within the framework of a hierarchical settlement pattern which, in the Zadar lowlands at least, resembled the three tiers of the late Pre-Roman Iron Age structure with the addition of *Iader* (Zadar) as an administrative and market centre, or *colonia*, on the highest hierarchical level.

The major Roman settlement expansion was in the low-lying areas, where the number of lowland farms increased from six in the Pre-Roman Iron Age to at least sixteen in the Roman Iron Age. In addition to these major farm occupations, there is artefactual or structural evidence for farming activity at a further twenty-two lowland sites in the Roman period. There is abundant evidence of artefact discard between settlement foci, suggesting either widespread manuring practices and/or frequent short-term/seasonal use of rural structures. The sizeable number of clearance cairns dated to the Roman period can be interpreted as evidence for the deliberate improvement of soil resources in the area. The Roman period is distinctive in the use of all major land classes, including Bottomland. Centres of rural administration (*municipia*) were still located on karst ridges, but the vast majority of productive farms were situated in lowland valley or hill-slope locations, many with access to both Stony and Arable land.

In summary, the Roman occupation of the Ravni Kotari displays a combination of increasing nucleation of administration with the highest level of dispersal of rural land use seen at any period in the survey area. The on- and off-site totals of artefacts indicate the highest absolute discard rates over the whole survey area in the last ten millennia.

Subsistence evidence

Without excavation of several Roman farms, it would be difficult to test the hypothesis that generalized site location is the counterpart of specialized land use. The subsistence data from Nadin-Gradina are the only direct subsistence evidence for the region. The clear predominance of domestic caprines over any other food animal shows continuity from Iron Age husbandry. The list of locally cultivated plant species includes spelt, six-row barley, two species of millet, legumes, the grape and the olive. Charcoal identifications reveal a similar balance of broad-leaved and evergreen species to that found in the pre-Roman Iron Age. Given that the 1km territory of Nadin includes land of all classes except Bottomland, there is considerable potential for specialized cultivation. The construction of an enclosure facing Nadinsko Blato, the largest area of summer grazing in the plain, reinforces the importance of stock-raising at Roman Nadin. The stimulus of market goods such as woollen textiles, sheep's cheese, olives and grapes to the regional economy is one reason for the expanded areas of land in classes best suited to these products taken into cultivation or used for pasture. The ready availability of Zadar as a harbour both for Italy and, later, for Greece and Byzantium ensured that transport facilities kept pace with economic growth.

Summary

Now that specialist crops such as olive and vine were available uses could be found for all the land types under the prevailing conditions. The expected expansion onto all land classes, facilitated and perhaps driven by climatic fluctuations and soil erosion, is found, with lowland farms integrated with ridge-top administrative centres.

The medieval period (AD 500–1400)

Settlement evidence (*figs.* 57–8)

The medieval pattern of settlement indicates a severe contraction from the dispersed Roman pattern, with a concentration in the lowland valleys and a preference for a balanced mix of Land Use Classes. The selection of Arable and Bottomland locations fits in well with the predicted choice in a relatively warm period. The choice of generalized village locations with the potential for diverse production strategies indicates a trend well advanced towards the modern pattern.

Subsistence evidence

The current position is that the subsistence picture for this period is documented by neither the archaeological nor the written records.

Summary

The continuation of warm, dry conditions up to the start of the Little Ice Age implies that there is a high potential for cultivation of lowland Arable land and Bottomland. The limited archaeological data on settlement pattern provide some support for this hypothesis; the LUC model provides a reasonable fit to the limited amount of data.

The post-medieval and early modern period (AD 1400–1850)

Settlement and subsistence evidence

The primary data for this evaluation are presented in full by Bracewell (see below pp. 308–36); a brief assessment of land use and territorial settlement is presented here.

In the era of Ottoman domination, the land used by the local Dalmatians appears to have been selected on the basis of security as much as quality. On the offshore islands, with their periodic population expansion, the shortage of Arable and Stony land would have led to garden-style cultivation of the Karst. Stock were the best option, not only because they could be moved into a secure location but also in view of the uncertain weather. The large population of Vlachs who settled the area probably shifted the balance towards pastoral farming and may have been responsible for building the large stanovi mentioned earlier (see p. 31–2). The large number of 'stanovi' toponyms indicates the widespread presence of these stock shelters all over the Ravni Kotari and the Velebit Mountains (see also Nandris 1988).

During the Little Ice Age, the under-utilization of the mainland was probably matched by an over-exploitation of the islands of the Zadar archipelago. The spread of pastoralism would have led to a reduction in soil erosion and an improvement in soil quality. Under grass and woodland, a soil's structure and nutrient content improved fairly quickly (Shiel 1991) but these advantages can be lost over a relatively short time by cropping. This period can therefore be viewed as one of soil recuperation, when considerable stock restriction could have led to forest regeneration. In the period of political and social stabilization after the Ottoman withdrawal, the woodland and the fertile soil could have been intensively exploited, leading to a major increase in soil erosion on the Karst due to a growth in sheep density, particularly where cropping was reintroduced on the sloping Stony land.

Evaluation of the model

The LUC model provides a sound framework for relating changes in the physical environment to differing land use capabilities and subsistence strategies in the Neothermal period. An internally consistent set of predictions about settlement locations for each period in the study region has been derived from the model, given climatic fluctuations and the availability of specific plants and animals. How accurate is the interpretation of the regional implications of the broader climatic trends and how close a fit is found between the actual and the predicted settlement distributions?

Of the climatic reconstructions there is a greater degree of agreement within the literature over temperature than over precipitation, though even in the case of glacial temperature depression estimates vary from 2 to 5 °C (Bottema 1974) to 20 °C (Peterson *et al.* 1979) for the Mediterranean area. There is little dispute over the timing of the major global warming at the end of the last Glacial period, nor is it contested that all subsequent changes in temperature were of lesser amplitude than that of the Terminal Pleistocene (Roberts 1989). However, the proxy record of a cooler Piora Oscillation and a cooler Medithermal period has been interpreted in terms of the effects as much of anthropogenic factors as of climatic variations (Dimbleby 1985). Nevertheless, the changing distributions of cool-tolerant species such as *Fagus* do confirm the existence of cooler oscillations (Huntley 1988).

The regional significance of variations in precipitation is perhaps greater for the 'Wet Littoral' of the Balkan Peninsula than for other parts of the Eastern Mediterranean. An increase in evaporation (mostly during the summer) would reduce growth on soils on the hillsides, while an increase in winter rain would lead to a greater incidence of erosion and flooding. Hence, low-lying areas of north Dalmatia are likely to have suffered from even marginal increases in rainfall and/or slight decreases in evapo-transpiration rates. Until arterial drainage work was carried out, from the Ottoman period, the ongoing soil erosion would have tended to cause a progressive increase in flood risk in the valleys.

There are some grounds for confidence in the basic parameters of the LUC model. The settlement distributions defined for the survey zone show broad agreement with the model's predictions. The main settlement trends of a concentration on valley locations in the Neolithic and Copper Age and ridge and valley locations in the Bronze Age and ridge sites in the Iron Age are all successfully predicted by the LUC model. With the trend towards increasing plough agriculture, Arable land is favoured, although level or terrace-improved Stony land is also good. The model predicts the shift in land use downslope in the Roman period but not the generalized use of land nor the continued interest in hilltop locations, which must have been inconveniently dry. The high density of Iron Age hill-forts in the Velebit Mountains was not predicted by the LUC model because of the lower temperature, greater precipitation and lower productivity in the first millennium Cal. BC. The purpose of such hill-forts is, however, unknown, but the most feasible use for sites located up to 1400m elevation would have been for summer grazing.

What the LUC model cannot successfully predict is the size of the regional population, the actual, rather than the relative, amount of land used in any given land-use class and the degree of nucleation or dispersal defining the settlement patterns through time. Nor can the LUC model predict settlement form and the likelihood, if any, of land boundaries and/or field systems. These variables require discussion of the social structure of north Dalmatian populations and are the object of the second phase of model-building.

The cyclic intensification–deintensification model

Introduction

In a stimulating model of long-term social and settlement change, Bintliff (1982c, 1984, Chapters 3 and 7) defines the basis of settlement pattern cycles as the intensification and deintensification of land use, with intensification defined as an expansion of the intensively cultivated infield with large nucleated central sites and a hierarchy of peripheral villages and farms, while deintensification is characterized by the inward expansion of the outfield component of the territory, with no central places but, instead, a largely dispersed network of hamlets and farmsteads (fig. 174). The dispersed phase is related to small, independent communities with a tribal leader or 'king' with limited powers but the achieved status of these leaders changes to the ascribed, hereditary status of landed élites dominating both land and peasants from central places in the intensification phase. This model is applied to a wide range of periods and places in Europe, from the Aegean Neolithic and Bronze Age to medieval Atlantic Europe.

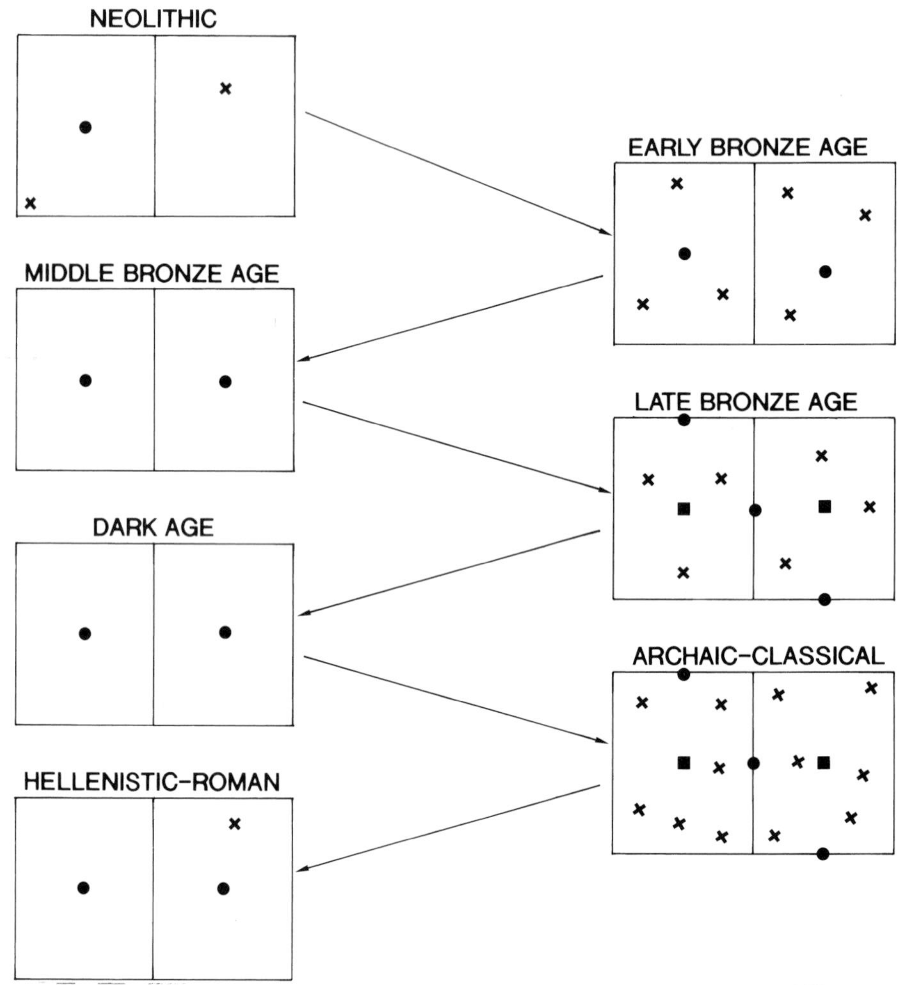

174. The cyclic intensification and deintensification model. *Source: Bintliff* 1982c

Although the model is refreshingly wide-ranging in time and spatial cover, its internal dynamic rests on two untested assumptions: the 'seemingly inevitable process of social differentiation in land-holding and agricultural wealth' and a great surge of population and associated land intake, a 'colonization' nourished by the élites for the concentration of surpluses and manpower (1982a, 110, n. 5). The apparent 'inevitability' of social differentiation is belied by its manifest lack of inevitability in many parts of Europe; there is no 'natural trend of increasingly dense populations' which is 'accentuated in the Copper, Bronze and Iron Ages' (1984, 83). Since social differentiation cannot be taken as a given, Bintliff's explanation of the shift from intensification to its converse is weakened. The congruence of forces 'demographic, economic and individual opportunism', which are held to account for social élites in Neolithic Europe (1984, 102) indicates the essentially asocial tenor of the argument. The references to prehistoric élites as 'squirearchies' seem to project a vision of the medieval era onto the more distant past without the recognition of very different modes of production in the two periods.

It is more useful to stress another factor in this cyclical process – the competition between families or lineages based on differential reproductive success (Chagnon 1990; cf. references to dynastic families and aristocratic households in the Iron Age in Bintliff 1984, 166 and 174). Those household heads with larger families can call on a larger workforce for agricultural and construction tasks, in turn leading to larger surpluses recycled to kinsfolk through increased feasting and ceremonial. The differential production of household surpluses can lead to a wider chain of alliance networks through surplus exchange. Because of the widespread checks and balances against excessive accumulation, such expansion of family power is unlikely to last for more than two or three generations unless institutionalization of such structures is achieved. While Bintliff (1982c) hypothesizes patron–client relations leading to hereditary élites and, later, dynasties, an alternative more appropriate to the emergence of social differentiation is increased ideological control over ritual in nucleated settlements or the development of formalized landscapes in dispersed settlement conditions. In the latter, the construction of public monuments can be explained by the desire for an impressive arena of social power controlled by the leading lineage; in the former, central meeting-places would reinforce the power of central residents by their continued association with the structures of power, providing a stronger rationale for the change to a form of institutionalized control, perhaps a hereditary leadership. In this way, the cyclic dynamic is maintained through the success or failure to maintain institutionalized structures, in turn related to subsistence production rooted in differential reproductive success.

Predictions

Four predictions derived from the modified CID Model of Cyclic Intensification and Deintensification will be examined relative to survey and subsistence data from the study area for the period from the Neolithic to the Roman.

> Prediction 1: Cyclical patterning. The long-term settlement record consists of alternating phases of settlement expansion and contraction.

In so far as surface scatters indicate general use of a locale for settlement, there is strong cyclic patterning in the survey data. Phases of expansion (Bronze Age, Roman) alternate with phases characterized by the under-use of large areas of fertile land (Neolithic-Eneolithic, Iron Age, medieval). In the phases of expansion, a greater portion of land is utilized and greater attempts are made at land improvement and agrarian management.

> Prediction 2: Intensification. The phases of settlement expansion reflect land use intensification, while contracting settlement networks are associated with agricultural deintensification.

Bintliff (1982c) attempts to measure intensity of land use by the size, density and degree of hierarchy of settlement remains: a series of rather more objective measures is used here, relying on the concept of settlement foci consisting of occupation sites and their 0.5km radius territory. Six measures are used:

1. Discard patterns within settlement foci – this measures the intensity of discard near the occupation zone.
2. Discard patterns between settlement foci – this assesses the amount of activity between occupation zones.

3–4. The incidence of land improvement features (cairns and linear features).

5. The level of vine and olive production.
6. The type of plough in use. The largely qualitative results are presented below (table 37).

Four of the measures indicate a positive correlation with the CID model: the discard data and the incidence of land improvement features peak in the Bronze Age and Roman periods, with alternate lows in the Neolithic, Iron Age and medieval periods. The high incidence of Bronze Age cairns can be related to a new

Table 37 Measures of agricultural intensification

	Neolithic–Eneolithic	Bronze Age	Iron Age	Roman
Discard within foci	low	variable	low	high
Discard between foci	low	moderate	very low	high
No. of cairns	–	137	10	27
No. of linear features	–	6	2	8
Olive/vine production	none	none	low	high
Type of plough	none	bronze ard	iron plough	iron plough

agrarian strategy of cultivating land on ridges, often classed as 'Stony', as well as to the need to lay claim to such intake through highly visible landscape markers. A relatively low proportion of all known linear features is dated and these fall mostly in the Bronze Age and Roman period. However, the class of plough and the incidence of olive and vine cultivation show a pattern of cumulative development into the medieval period.

> Prediction 3: Nucleation. In the expansionist phases, increased use of infield areas for cultivation is associated with nucleated settlements, often with high-status buildings which house a land-holding élite. In phases of contraction, increased use of outfield areas, held communally for pasture, are associated with dispersed settlements with few, low-level central places occupied by household heads.

In north Dalmatia, the whole prehistoric sequence is characterized by a predominance of small-scale, dispersed settlement units. It is only in the Roman period that urban centres occur, whether a *colonia* such as *Iader* (Zadar) (58ha) or *municipium* such as *Nedinum* (Nadin) – the largest site in the survey block at 32.6ha. Other measures of settlement pattern growth include the number of levels in any existing settlement hierarchy and the degree of focused land use as measured by the proportion of surface remains within distinct dated settlement foci. The results are presented below (table 38).

With the exception of the site size statistic, measures of settlement nucleation fit a cumulative trend towards increasing growth in settlement hierarchies, at least until the end of the Roman period. These trends are not matched by the cyclical variation in the proportion of landscape with traces of settlements. But a cumulative pattern is found in the changes apparent in high status architecture. The adoption at the largest Late Iron Age hill-forts of dressed, drystone 'megalithic' walls (Faber 1976) precedes the development of monumental Roman architectural styles in *colonia* and *municipia*. The construction of churches in the early medieval period indicates a new arena of high status architecture.

> Prediction 4: Private land-holding. The expansionist phases are associated with an increase in private land-holding by élites who control surplus production. The phases of contraction indicate a higher proportion of land under communal ownership.

Table 38 Evaluation of settlement hierarchies

	Neolithic–Eneolithic	Bronze Age	Iron Age	Roman
Degree of nucleation	very low	low	moderate	high
No. of levels in settlement hierarchy	1	1	2–3	4
Size of largest settlement (in ha)	2.8	11.1	7.1	32.6

The only data pertaining to the question of land-holding are the epigraphic data from the Late Iron Age and Early Roman periods (400 Cal. BC–AD 200). Despite differing views on the kinship structures of the Iron Age period (Alföldy 1965; Wilkes 1969; Suić 1974; Čače 1982, 1985; Chapman and Shiel 1991), there is general agreement on the existence of kin-based hill-fort communities with a village council and communal land. If reduced cognatic descent were the dominant kinship principle in Liburnia (Chapman and Shiel 1991), communal land-ownership, settlement and ritual obligations would have been fundamental to Liburnian social life. Indeed, in the Zadar lowlands, communal ownership of pastures and forests continued on well into the Roman period (Suić 1981, 271); what is in doubt is the degree of private ownership of cultivable land in the Late Iron Age. The fact that both Suić (1981) and Čače (1985) stress the importance of a land-owning aristocracy among the Late Liburnian élites suggests that there is a role for private accumulation of land inside the larger and more important *cognationes* up to the imperial incorporation of north Dalmatia, which may be indicative of an incipient patron–client network.

Whether Suić' or Čače's views are more accurate, the differences between them are as much in emphasis as substance; the general trend is for cumulative increases in the expansion of private-sector land holdings, with Roman accumulation clearly on a far greater extent than in the Iron Age. The extent of Roman private land-holding is dramatically symbolized in the establishment of a centuriated field system on the mainland near *Iader* and on the first row of offshore islands (Bradford 1957; Zaninović 1977).

Evaluation of the model

The predictions of the CID Model in respect of cyclical patterning, intensification, nucleation and private ownership have been strongly confirmed for cyclical trends in land use, modestly supported for some measures of intensification and private land-holding, and not proved for settlement nucleation. The alternative pattern of cumulative growth in technological and agrarian innovations, settlement hierarchies and size and private ownership provides a counterbalance to the cyclical model and permits the incorporation of changes in mode of production into the diachronic dynamic. Hence, the CID Model is partially disconfirmed for the Study Region. The Iron Age becomes a pivotal period, in which low discard and apparently modest usage of a small portion of the total landscape sit uneasily with the growth of land-owning élites and economic take-off.

The communal ownership of property model

Introduction

Through his model of collective land-holding and co-operative labour relations, Fleming (1982, 1984, 1985) attempts to explain the origins of prehistoric field systems in north-west Europe in later prehistory. Three levels of social grouping are defined for dispersed settlement configurations: the household, the territorial group and the socio-political group (fig. 175). Since the labour force of the household is ill-matched to seasonal agricultural work, pooling of labour and resources is essential to social reproduction in second-order territorial groups based on ramifying kinship links. The social centres of dispersed communities were the hearths of each house; thus, social integration was direct, from home to home, rather than via a central place such as a village. The advantages of communal land-holdings organized by the territorial group are summarized as a plentiful labour supply, economies of scale, the reduction of intra-group disputes and labour on boundary-building and the furtherance of group cohesion. Importantly, the compatibility of collective property-holding and decision-making with private wealth maximization and, indeed, inter-group competition, is stressed. Fleming suggests that the increased importance of boundaries lay in the attempt by communities organized on segmentary principles to maintain

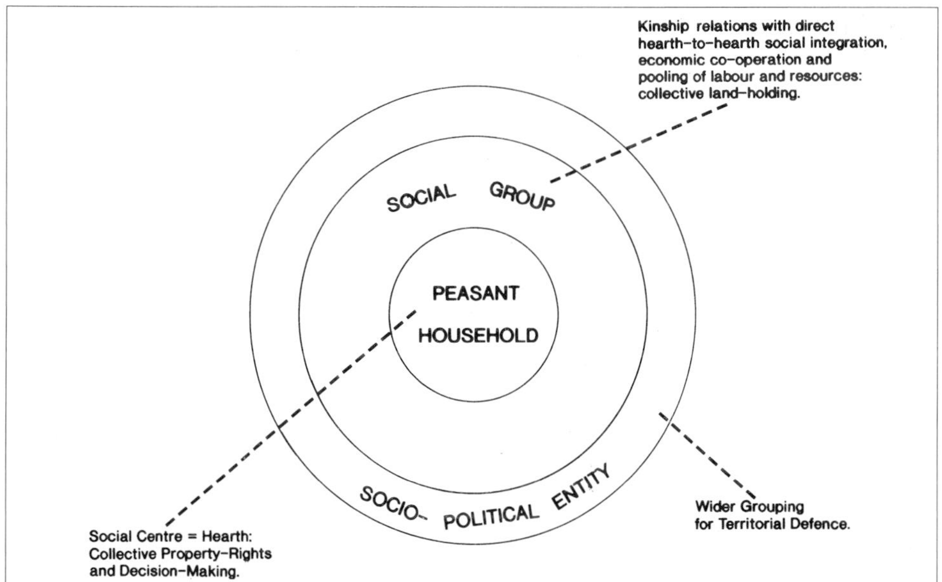

175. The communal ownership of property model. *Source: Fleming* 1984

collective economies under the strain of increasing internal competition for access to communal land.

The main point of contrast with Bintliff's model relates to the possibility of competition between élites based on control of bronze exchange networks and between polities within a system of collectively held land, supported by pooling of labour and resources. Interestingly, the internal dynamic of Fleming's model also relies on 'general prosperity accompanied by population increase' (1985, 141), without attempting to explain how or why these significant changes occurred. Yet Fleming's model contains the elements of an explanation for these changes, based on the kinship networks which are so important in co-operative labour forces. This model can be tested through examination of four hypotheses related to the communal ownership of property.

Predictions

> Prediction 1: Communal land-holding. In areas with a long-term tendency to settlement dispersion in farmsteads and hamlets, the economy will be based on communal land-holding and the co-operative pooling of labour and resources.

The predominance of small, dispersed settlement units well into the first millennium Cal. BC and beyond (especially in the early medieval period) and the absence of evidence for private ownership of property before the Late Iron Age indicate that the basic tenet of this model is modestly supported. Indeed, communal ownership and use of vital summer grazing resources is documented well into the early twentieth century AD, both in the lowland zone (the seasonal marsh of Nadinsko Blato, shared by the flocks of up to a dozen villages: pers. comm., J. Lulić, 1985) and in the mountain pastures of the Velebit range (Nandris 1988). However, there is epigraphic evidence for a struggle lasting fifty years between the Neditii of Nadin and the Corinii of Corinium for karstic pasture on the Malo Brdo ridge north of Benkovac (Čače 1985) and for an attempt to control much of the Velebit upland pasture from the town of Vegium (the inscription at the source of the river Begovača: Čače 1985). In the Roman period at least, 'common' pasture was the source of inter-group rivalry. The evidence for a significant area of communal pasture in the high medieval period is presented below (see p. 329–30).

The closeness of kinship links between most members of dispersed population groups in north Dalmatian prehistory is confirmed by Wobst's (1974, 1976) modelling of breeding networks (cf. also Chapman 1988, 1989). In the Neolithic and Eneolithic, breeding networks of 400–500 people would have required the participation of most, if not all, of the settlements in the Zadar lowlands; the same was likely in the Bronze Age. Breeding networks would have spanned two or more hill-forts and their surrounding lowland farmsteads for much of the Iron Age. Indeed, it is doubtful whether endogamy would have been desirable even in the larger hill-forts of the Later Iron Age.

The existence of kinship networks between dispersed settlements indicates the likelihood of the co-operative pooling of labour and resources in the study region; but is there any positive evidence in favour of this proposition? The main evidence comes from the work study of stone-built monuments (see Chapter 5).

The results of the work study reveal a pattern of consistent increase in the largest mobilization of labour during the second and first millennia Cal. BC. Given the availability of 40–45 days per annum for communal building tasks (Hogbin 1939; Erasmus 1965, 281), there seems no problem for a local breeding network to complete a small Bronze Age hill-fort within one or at most two seasons. For the medium-size hill-fort of Vinculja, an estimated 6,500 people-days could have been provided by sixty-five people with construction work spread over two years.

The question arises whether the larger works required the use of slave or corvée labour or whether these prestige defences could be built using local labour. Nadin has a labour requirement far higher than for any other site. The labour input of 65,000 people-days would have required full-time contributions for five years from an estimated twenty-four stonemasons and quarrymen and twenty unskilled local workers. The existence of a redistributive centre at Nadin explains the means of payment for such hired labour; elsewhere, organization of local labour over one to three years would have been sufficient for monument construction.

Hence, the Dalmatian evidence supports the association between dispersed settlement, a strong tendency to communal land-holding and the pooling of labour for public building, at least until the Late Iron Age; in that phase, the extraction of at least client labour is attested.

> Prediction 2: Proliferation of land boundaries. There is a tendency for the proliferation of land divisions with time, especially with increased internal competition for access to communal resources.

Since fewer than 20 per cent of the linear features discovered during survey are datable, the large quantity of missing data complicates evaluation of this prediction. The dated examples are as follows: Neolithic/Eneolithic, 0; Bronze Age, 6; Iron Age, 2; Roman, 8; medieval, 0; cf. undated, 61. The tendency for an increase in land boundaries with time is not apparent. This is true even if all the linear features found within dated settlement foci are contemporary with the adjoining settlement; these loosely associated linear features peak in the Bronze Age and Roman periods, with steep declines in the Iron Age and the medieval period. If this hypothesis is correct, a decline in field boundaries indicates lessened internal competition for access to resources. This explanation does not fit well with the picture of expanding Iron Age élites.

> Prediction 3: Location of land boundaries. The creation of small-scale management boundaries, often running along boundaries between land use zones, is likely to precede the definition of socio-political boundaries running across land use zones (as defined above, see p. 24).

There is no evidence in Dalmatia for any systems of land boundaries on the scale of the large co-axial field systems of north-west Europe (Fleming 1984, 1987). None of the Roman boundaries exceeds 100m in length, while there are only two Bronze Age boundaries which are significantly longer. The first is the 1.8km linear boundary running along the Karst–Stony junction at Polača-Dražice, as a main feature in an 11ha field system. The other long Bronze Age wall crosses the Stony and Karst slopes of the Pridraga cemetery at right-angles, dividing the same land use classes into two unequal parts (Chapman *et al.* 1987, 127 and fig. 4). It is arguable that all the linear features hitherto mentioned are small-scale land management boundaries. In most cases, they run along the grain of environmental zonation.

With one exception, the data on which to base socio-political boundaries are epigraphic; it is rare to find field corroboration of such divisions. Such data is limited to the Iron Age and Roman periods. The distribution of major Late Iron Age hill-forts can be used to construct a map of their territories, assuming contemporaneity and based on the technique of unweighted Thiessen polygons (fig. 176). The more extensive Roman epigraphic data permit a reconstruction of approximate administrative boundaries (fig. 177). Analysis of the boundaries in respect of regional environmental zonation produces the following results (table 39).

An almost identical picture is presented for both the Iron Age and the Roman period. For the most part, Roman jural frontiers simply took over putative Iron Age socio-political boundaries. Excluding maritime demarcation (six cases), land divisions which cross environmental zones are in a clear majority of 3:1 over boundaries which follow ecological divisions. Most socio-political boundaries in north Dalmatia cut across environmental zones, while smaller-scale land management boundaries generally respect ecological zones. The only clear case of a definable boundary in the early medieval period is the city territory of Zadar, defined by the boundary of the Roman centuriation system (Suić 1955). This boundary runs along the grain of the ecological boundary between ridge and valley before cutting across it.

> Prediction 4: Decline of communal ownership. Communally-based economies include the potential for differential accumulation of private property: the impact of urban networks on such communities prompts a decline in communally-held resources in favour of private ownership.

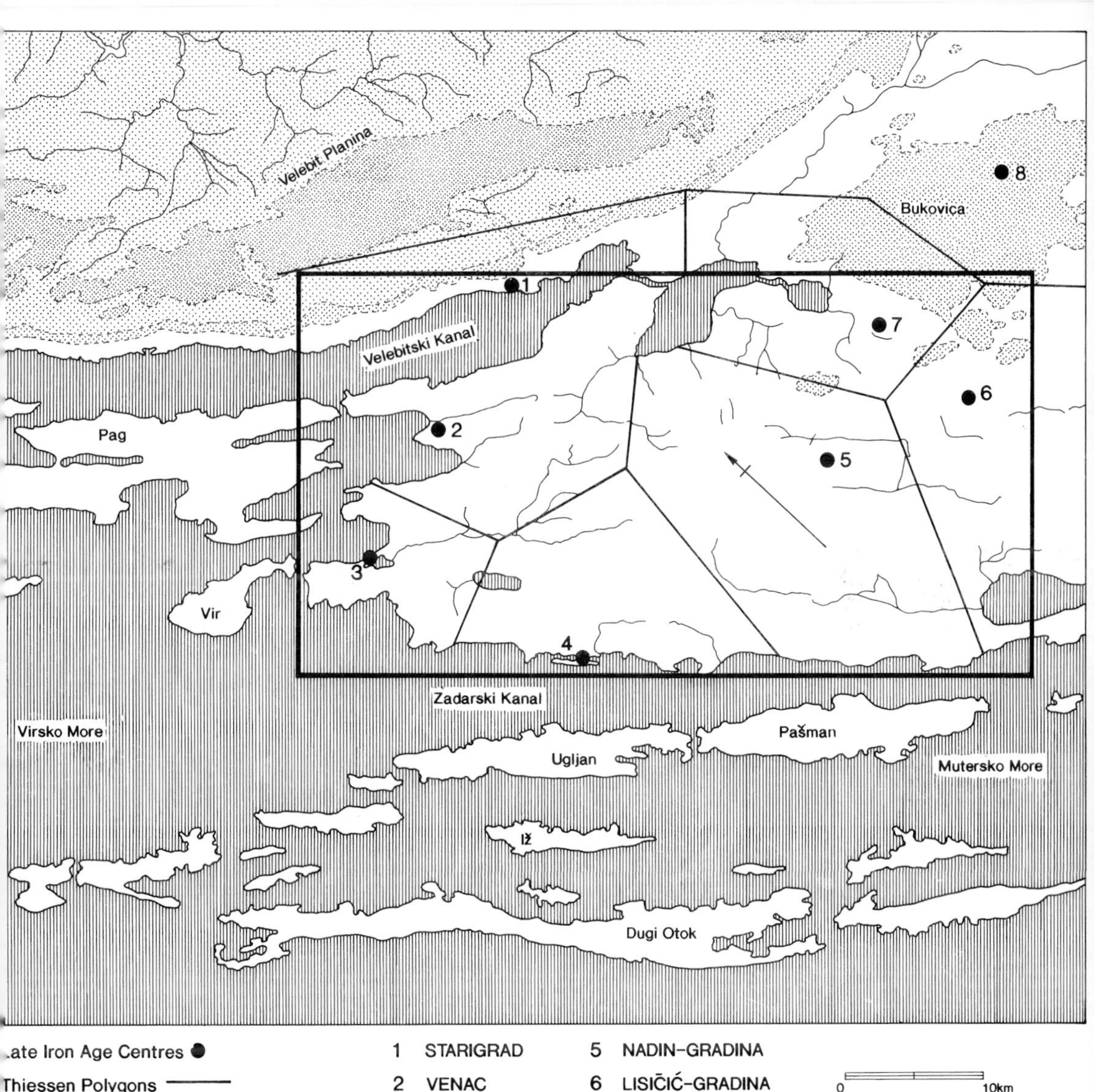

176. Reconstructed Late Iron Age hill-fort territories, based on Thiessen polygons

A two-stage hypothesis can be tested here. A decline in communal ideology and ownership is unlikely until the impact of state or urban networks is felt in dispersed communities. Prior to this, private accumulation may develop within the overall communal framework.

The Later Bronze Age in north Dalmatia can be characterized as the first period of major economic growth since the inception of food production. As in adjoining parts of Europe (Clarke 1979), the Adriatic zone witnesses a quantum

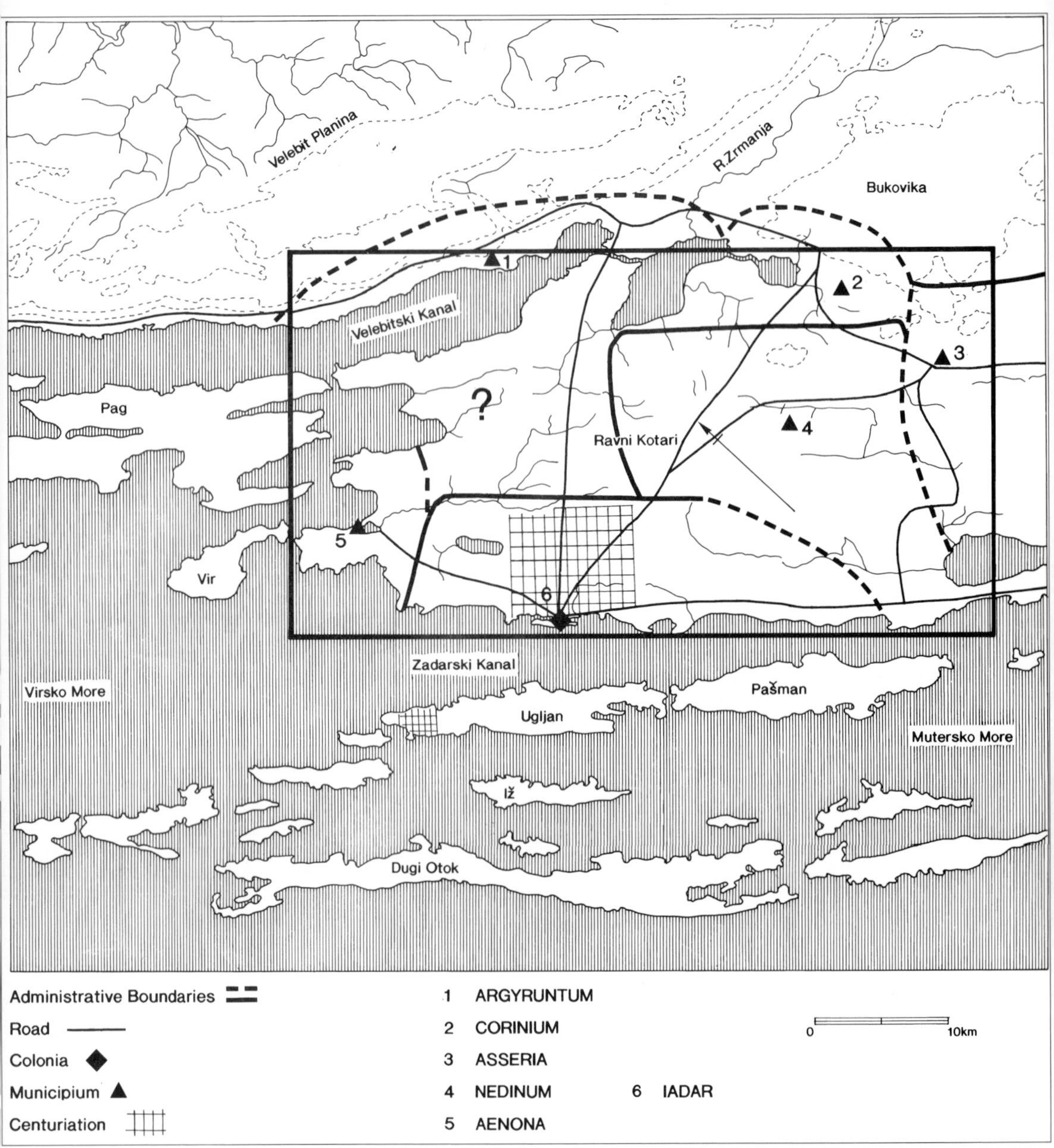

177. Reconstructed administrative boundaries, Early Roman period, based on epigraphic data

leap in the quantity, quality and diversity of metal artefacts (Harding 1972; Peroni 1979). This industrial development coincides with the expansion of settlement networks, with a major development of enclosed and fortified sites in much of the Adriatic coastal zone (Batović 1983). There is burial evidence for the creation, manipulation and maintenance of new status positions, whose holders had the

Table 39 Location of Roman socio-political boundaries in relation to environmental zones

Site Name	Direction or boundary	Configuration of boundary	
		Iron Age	Roman
Aenona/Nin	south–sea		
	west–sea		
	north–Ljubljana	across karst	sea
	east–Zadar	across zones	across zones
Iader/Zadar	south–sea		
	west–Aenona	across zones	across zones
	north–?	along ridge	along ridge
	east–Nedinum	across zones	across zones
Nedinum/Nadin	south–sea/Iader	–	across zones
	west–Iader	across zones	across zones
	north–Corinium	between ridge/valley	along ridge
	east–Asseria	across zones	across zones
Asseria	south–Lake Vrana		
	west–Nedinum	across zones	across zones
	north–?	across karst	across karst
	east–Varvaria	across zones	across zones
Corinium/Karin	south–Nedinum	between ridge/valley	along ridge
	west–Novigrad Sea		
	north–?	across karst	across karst
	east–Asseria	across karst	across karst

potential for private accumulation such as was not available in the Copper Age or the Cetina phase of the Early Bronze Age. These heightened contrasts in grave goods and mortuary ritual continued in the Early Iron Age – marked by construction of large cairns and the deposition of even richer grave goods. After 600 Cal. BC, the extension of regional into inter-regional alliances previously used to procure bronze facilitated the contacts necessary for the acquisition of high quality iron (Čović 1980). Such alliances were another factor stimulating the development of élites with the redistributive potential for differential accumulation of prestige goods.

The first evidence for Liburnian contact with Greek or Hellenistic merchants takes the form of Liburnian imports of Apulian Geometric Painted Wares, dolia and wine amphorae dated to the fifth and fourth centuries Cal. BC (Čače 1985, 568), along with the first scattered and rare coinage, mostly from Metapontum (Wilkes 1969; Batović 1974, 1987). It is surely not a coincidence that the start of the Late Iron Age, with its postulated economic growth and élite land-holding has been dated to exactly the fourth century Cal. BC (Čače 1985). The extent of commercial bow-wave contact increases steadily until full incorporation into the Roman Empire some three hundred years later (Chapman and Shiel 1991; cf. Haselgrove 1987).

Hence, the final hypothesis is also not disconfirmed; the final phase of communal ownership was one of increasing private accumulation, in which contacts with Greek, Hellenistic and, later, Roman commercial sectors widened the horizons of acquisition for the emergent Liburnian élites.

Evaluation of the model

There is a long-term nexus of dispersed settlement, communal land holding and pooling of labour and resources in prehistoric north Dalmatia. Non-proliferation of land divisions with time is not found but the gradual development of both socio-political boundaries and small-scale land management boundaries is attested. Private accumulation during periods of essentially communal ownership occurs in the Late Bronze Age and Early Iron Age, before the increase in private ownership generated by the onset of commercial contacts with state economic networks. In general, the COP Model receives strong support for the basic assumption of a developmental path, expressed not so much by the idea of progress as by a notion of cumulative growth based on past trajectories.

The arenas of social power model

Introduction

The examination of the LUC, the CID and the COP models indicates that each model makes a partial contribution to the explanation of the total phenomena under study. While the LUC model 'postdicts' gross patterns of settlement according to the relative merits of various landscape segments at different periods, this model cannot explain population curves or settlement nucleation and dispersion. The CID model provides support for cyclical trends in land use and subsistence intensification but falls down on settlement nucleation. The COP model helps to focus attention on the relation between land boundaries and private accumulation in times of communal land-holding, without explaining the logic of this developmental path. Each of these models lacks a fine-grained view of social change which may be able to account for these apparent correlations rather than simply identify them. For this reason, it is necessary to turn to an explicit model of social power in the landscape.

The differentiation of physical space from neutral environment into a varied landscape replete with social meaning marks a process which interacts with social change itself (Chapman 1988, 1989). Arenas of social power mark a conjunction of a specific place, with its functions and meanings, and the social actors who have the power (including knowledge) to perform the activities in that place. The notion of social power used here relies on Michael Mann's (1986, 1993) distinction between

POWER IN THE ARCHAEOLOGICAL RECORD		
Type of power	**Control over**	**Dimensions of arcaeological record**
I	Ritual knowledge	Differential distributions of figurines, symbols, temples
	Practical knowledge	Differential spread of innovations (pottery, metal)
	Structuring knowledge	Cognitive data
E	Land	Type & extent of land division
	Labour	Location of production
	Tools & facilities	Extent of spread of innovations
	Raw materials	Type of exploitation of mines & quarries
	Exchange products	Differential artifact
	'Surplus' resources	Discard (hoards, houses, graves)
M	Others' territory	Extent & differentiation of offensive-defensive capabilities
	Others' possessions	
	Others' manpower	Evidence for slavery
P	Labour	Form of urban settlement pattern
	Residence	
	Landscapes	Formalization of landscape

178. Relationships of IEMP power to the archaeological record

four types of social power – ideological, economic, military and political (for their application to prehistoric data, see fig. 178). However, since Mann's model is applied only to the leading edge of world historical development, social power must be spatialized to relate the model to other regions where changes of global significance did not occur.

The reasons for the creation of a new arena of social power are often related to the development of contradictions in the social order, where new developments are incompatible with the traditional social structure. Thus, household or individual wealth accumulation may be impossible within the social framework of communal ownership of land and herds, yet opportunities arise for private accumulation based on either exchange or local production. Alternatively, major changes in gender relations may lead to the elaboration of new arenas where the social power of one gender may be reinforced at the expense of the other. Thirdly, the colonization of new landscapes may lead to the creation of new arenas which legitimize the social claims of leaders to the newly settled land. Hence, the identification of new arenas of social power is always a sign of fundamental social change which demands explanation in terms of the local landscape and the regional setting (Chapman 1991a, 1991b, 1992, 1993, 1994a: Chapman and Shiel 1993).

Cosgrove (1984) has defined the landscape as a 'visual ideology'. In the sense that their object is the representation of the exercise of power over space, landscape studies become an inherently ideological research field. The greater the sources of social power, the more widespread the interpenetration between culture and nature in the landscape. Three important extensions of social power into the north Dalmatian landscape will be examined: the origins of agriculture, the intensification of farming in the Bronze Age and the incorporation of Dalmatia into the Roman Empire.

The origins of farming in Dalmatia

The emergence of farming comprises a complex set of changes in human behaviour, both economic and cognitive, which led to a way of perceiving time and space, period and place strikingly different from that of the preceding foragers (Hodder 1990).

The foragers' time-world was based on the seasonal round in the narrow sense of an annual cycle but the repeated longer cycles of inter-annual periods were alien to them. The thick Palaeolithic deposits at the trans-Velebit cave of Ćerovačka pećina (Malez 1965) indicate repeated occupations, with the likelihood of similar seasonal routines and possibly routes to the hills over long periods. Such a regular movement may have been the first patterned activity in which the time-world of the hunting group was shaped. A similar pattern may have existed in the Mesolithic, with the evidence from Vaganačka pećina for contact between the Ravni Kotari and the Velebit Mountains. The long-term associations of the cave, with its insistent seasonal rhythms and migratory routes, are an indication of a patterned time-world where humans and domestic animals, wild animals and the natural 'home' of a cave were closely juxtaposed.

The primary contrast between foragers and farmers may therefore relate to the way in which different social groups imprint their identities on the landscape. The cyclical nature of the farming year remained but there was a tendency to replace movements with occupations. Instead of the more broadly-based, extensive use of the landscape which characterized the latest foragers in the Altithermal period, the earliest farmers created a series of place-based communities centred on their hamlet or village and with radiating rings of decreasing familiarity: from home to hamlet to fields and pastures to wildwood. Often, these socio-spatial categories are assimilated to a homologous series of animal classes, tending to refer to increasing degrees of inedibility (Tapper 1988). Subsistence production entailed a classification of the landscape which became the setting for farmers' everyday lives: in Bourdieu's (1977) term, their 'habitus'. The nucleated settlement enshrined a mono-focal concept, where the people created a single dominant, central place out of the natural space which they colonized. The centrality may have been defined by an open space or by a structure or by the concept of a centre itself. By contrast, dispersed villages were based on the plurality of foci, perhaps of equal importance, perhaps of varying significance in the landscape, with the social core more likely to be defined by a structure since the concept of centrality is otherwise lacking or weakened.

According to available evidence, the early farmers practised single burial in shallow pits within the settlement area (Batović 1966, 1979). There is at present no evidence for the differentiation of mortuary areas separate from living sites. Whatever mortuary ritual took place on the living sites was limited but open and public. In a study of the ideology of foragers and farmers, Criado (1989) demonstrates that the world-view of the former relies on the denial of the new dead through the absence of formal burial, in an attempt to portray a timeless world in which the living maintain significant relations only with the ancestors. By contrast, farmers are vitally concerned with kinship reckoning and time, so their burial rites are dominated by classifications concerned with the new dead (Criado 1989). In the north Dalmatian Neolithic, a very small percentage of the dead received any formal burial, so the foraging ideology continued to exert a strong influence. Those new dead formally buried within the settlement contribute to the emergence of household clusters, ritually constituting their home space and underpinning their investment of labour.

Agricultural intensification in Bronze Age Dalmatia

It is significant that, after some three millennia of farming, the 'habitus' of most farmers in north Dalmatia seems to have changed little from that of the earliest agriculturalists. Until the very end of the Copper Age, there is no dated evidence for monuments in the landscape, just as there was little stone on cultivated land. This picture of minimal socio-spatial differentiation changes in the Bronze Age with the construction of the first clearance cairns and field boundaries, and the more explicit and visible definition of domestic space by stone-walled enclosures. The extension of the domesticated segment of the landscape was achieved by deliberate strategies of monument construction, both in the domestic and the mortuary spheres.

The Bronze Age foci differed from the Neolithic and Copper Age sites in that their place-centred quality was far more manifest, through the construction of permanent drystone features. The construction of enclosed spaces serves to unify those within from those without and is suggestive of the emergence of new social groupings at this time (pers. comm. G. Ferrell, 1989). Thus there is already a differentiation of domestic place between hill-forts, enclosures, open sites and caves. Within occupation sites, a further distinction is between those which incorporate cairns, usually in prominent locations, and those which do not. In other words, there is a blurring of domestic and mortuary arenas, suggestive of the requirements of the living to incorporate monuments to the dead into the very centre of their social space. Those more dispersed foci share combinations of similar features yet they are as multi-centred as their Neolithic counterparts, perhaps emphasizing kinship distance rather than community integration.

The Bronze Age expansion onto the ridges led to the use of Stony land, in turn leading to stone clearance from the fields. This intensification through higher labour inputs prompted a tendency for longer site occupation, in turn leading to the generation of more stones through continued ploughing of the same cultivated areas. There are obvious practical reasons for a consistent policy for the 'storage' of stones removed from the earth. Yet there must have been something mysterious about the continued appearance of fresh stones from areas of 'soil', especially when the last stones had apparently just been removed! The consistent production of stones may well have been interpreted not as a labour-intensive nuisance (the modern utilitarian view) but as a sign of the fecundity of the earth, which yields up part of its 'harvest' to the farmers who plough it. If this were the case, the 'harvest' of stones would have had a ritual significance just as great as the practical issue of disposal. The annual removal of stones from degrading Stony land would have become part of the farming groups' 'habitus', a regular ceremony in which a monument was created through communal labour to celebrate the renewal of nature. In this sense, the decision whether to store the stones in one area, creating a cairn, or in linear fashion, creating a linear feature, was of ideological as well as practical import. A similar phenomenon is noted in Late Neolithic Denmark by Kristiansen (1984, 79–80), who notes that monuments built with the stones cleared from fields symbolized the creation of agricultural land and reflected the same type of social mobilization and leadership as was needed for clearing the forest.

The Bronze Age in the Ravni Kotari was notable not only for its agricultural intensification but for the concomitant creation of new arenas of social power. This differentiation occurred in three arenas: the domestic, the agricultural and the mortuary, as well as in combinations of the same. First, domestic space was divided into unenclosed and enclosed sites. Secondly, some of the pastures and fields were enclosed with stone walls or stone-and-earth banks. Thirdly, a new custom was initiated – the burial of the dead under clearance cairns.

All of the enclosed sites and hill-forts of the Bronze Age examined by the NDP could have been built by small teams of kinship relatives in one or two seasons (see pp. 172–3). This level of social mobilization entailed either stone clearance over several hectares of cultivated land (e.g. Mataci) or the use of limestone scree from the immediate vicinity (e.g. Kutlovica, Kruglas). In each of the three enclosures excavated by the NDP (Mataci, Čauševica and Polača), the walls have been found to contain earth with worn sherds indicating a pre-enclosure use of the nearby land. The incorporation of earth tilled by previous generations into a current wall may have embodied ideological links to the ancestors which could have been used in strategies of social reproduction. In this way, living in an enclosed site provided a stronger link to the ancestors than was available to anyone living in an open site. The act of enclosure magnified the identity of the group living within through stressing their relations with the ancestors.

The importance of clearance cairns in the annual calendar of Dalmatian farmers is reinforced by their dispersed ubiquity and their ease of construction. The decision to link into their stored nexus of past–present/living–fertility relationships the dimension of death must have been an extraordinarily powerful combination of symbolic messages. The burial cairn is the first example in Dalmatian prehistory of a bounded mortuary space, at once separated from the living space yet inextricably joined to it. As with Neolithic burials within a settlement, cairn burial ritual was open and public but available to only a small proportion of the community – perhaps family heads. In comparison with Neolithic burials in a shallow grave-pit, cairns allowed wider participation by kinsfolk and other acquaintances by the placing of earth and/or stones or broken vessels on the surface of the cairn. The significance of the cairn lies in the permeation of the mortuary space with the 'harvest' of the soil which would contribute to future fertility. Animal bones, plant remains and lithic debitage are found not only on the old land surface where burial takes place but also scattered through the fill of well-excavated cairns (e.g. Batović and Kukoš 1986). Here, the principle of incorporation of ancestral soil as found with enclosure walls is transposed into the mortuary sphere; the deceased is reincorporated into the soil of his once-fellows to provide a kinship classification for the living (Criado 1989). The symbolic significance of this integration of the newly dead, the ancestors and future soil fertility is reinforced by the location of burial cairns in the landscape. Three common locations can be distinguished: prominent locations within enclosed sites or hill-forts, prominent ridge-top locations, and prominent locations within a group of clearance cairns. In each of these contexts, the juxtaposition of burial cairn with other monuments or with landmarks emphasizes the significance of the place to the newly dead and hence to future occupation of the land. In comparison with clearance cairns, burial cairns are sufficiently infrequent that they may have been endowed with social power for those who deposited the often rich grave goods (e.g. the Privlaka gold finds: Vinski 1959).

In the Velebit Mountains, the rarity of Bronze Age monuments gives the impression of less intensive use and therefore less elaborated ancestral relations. The discovery of burials in each of the few Velebit cairns does, however, indicate that the nexus of living and dead first developed in the plains was transposed into the uplands. The idea of ancestral relations in the mountain zone was as much perpetuated by the long-term use of caves such as Vaganačka pećina as by the more recent construction of cairns. The location of the cairns and hill-forts may, however, define an expansion of the viable pastureland available on Velebit. This may represent another kind of land colonization process, one common enough in the Dinaric Mountains, where the construction of cairns 'fixes' the identity of the transhumant group on a newly settled area of summer pasture.

In north Dalmatia, the social opportunities offered by the incorporation of the region into an inter-regional network of metals exchange (Harding 1972; Maran 1987; Batović 1983) stimulated not only local production but also the possibility of the unequal distribution of the social surplus. Much of the newly acquired prestige goods was deposited in burial cairns. Variation in deposition of grave goods is related to many factors, principally the relationship of the newly dead and the living to positions of lineage power and authority. In this way, the living not only used the occasion of burial in a cairn to exploit the power residing in this new arena of social action but also used/withheld the quality and quantity of grave goods available to them in an active strategy of social reproduction. The incorporation of north Dalmatia into the inter-regional exchange networks of the Bronze Age may be one of the causes of the parallel development of a place-based, ancestor-focused strategy for the fixing of local identities in the landscape. The novel contacts with distant communities necessitated the maintenance of firm local roots.

The management of land is intimately connected to the symbolism of place in the Bronze Age. Social groups colonizing new land as well as strengthening their ties to previously farmed Arable and Bottomland used the strategy of 'fixing' their cultural identity onto the landscape more visibly than ever before. The new strategy did not depend on large labour forces; indeed, such small monuments would not have been beyond the capabilities of Neolithic and Copper Age groups. But the creation of a large number of small monuments is an indication of extensive settlement based on the relations of the living to local ancestors. The strategy was developed initially out of local agricultural practices, in which field clearance led to the accumulation of stone piles or linear features. At a later stage, the burial potential of these monuments linked to the fertility of the land and thus the living became evident and a new ideological nexus of living and dead was created. The construction of land divisions in stone led to greater sedentism and even closer relations with the local ancestors.

The meaning of different combinations and recombinations of similar stone features can be related to several factors. Monuments on the simplest scale – either cairns, or linear features or both – relate most probably to small-scale agricultural clearance of ancestral land: sacred and profane cannot be separated at even this basic level. More complex monuments may reflect the length of occupation (fields compared with field systems) or the scale of the project (grouped cairns compared with linear cairnfields). While a scale of social complexity cannot be read off the diversity of features in a single settlement focus, the range of symbolic and practical reasons are in some way a function of local social organization.

In this interpretation, Bronze Age societies developed new arenas of social power as a result of their colonization of ridges and hillslopes, first through the creation of annual ceremonies relating to field clearance and the construction of clearance cairns or linear features, and later by the integration of burial of the newly dead into cairns constituting monuments to the fertility of the land. The development of bounded mortuary arenas within yet outside domestic places supported an ancestor-based strategy of social reproduction. The integration of prestige goods often obtained through inter-regional exchange networks into the mortuary arena lent further symbolic significance to these monuments as the loci of social power, since successful participation in such exchanges was in turn dependent on local productive expansion as the basis for local power. The continued expansion or new creation of clearance cairns maintained the impetus of the very agricultural intensification which provided the initial stimulus for clearance. The decision to occupy some sites longer than others led in some cases to a second occupation phase of enclosed settlement, often using ancestral soil and artefacts as construction material. The enclosed sites thereby increased the strength of their inhabitants' relations with the ancestors over those of the inhabitants of unenclosed sites. This strategy of 'tethering' may have been problematic in the face of increased soil erosion or climatic fluctuations in the first millennium Cal BC. This ideological distinction is the first evidence for differentiation of the domestic arena and forms the basis for the further evolution of hill-forts in the Iron Age.

The Liburnians and the Roman Empire

The Late Iron Age was a period of steadily increasing interaction between the Romans and the Liburnians across the Adriatic. This relationship became steadily less balanced until the absorption of Liburnian territory into the Roman Empire in the late first century Cal. BC.

In the Late Iron Age, the concentration of the majority of the population into hill-forts and enclosed settlements, often on limestone ridges (Batović 1977), led to a heightened distinction between these monuments and lowland open sites. The domestic arena was further sub-divided into large and small hill-forts, with a continuation of drystone wall building on the smaller sites and the construction of shaped 'megalithic' walls on the larger, more impressive monuments. The main change in the domestic arena was in the size and scope of the internal, enclosed areas. At *Iader*, the interior of the Iron Age site covered an area of 18ha (cf. *Aenona*, 16ha; Budim, 11ha; Vrčevo, 8.5ha, Nadin, 7.1ha and *Varvaria*, 7.2ha: data from Čače 1985, Tab.1.IV). One important feature of Liburnian hill-forts is the lack of internal sub-division of space (an exception is Vijenac) by drystone wall. Nevertheless, the excavation of the hill-fort of Radovin revealed a regular layout of rows of rectangular houses Batović 1968b). The partitioning of interior settlement space is as important as the increased permanence of the stone-footed structures in the latest Iron Age period (e.g. Nin: Batović 1968a).

The construction of monumental buildings in hilltop enclosures is a sign of the concentration of social surplus in nucleated sites, for the first time in Dalmatian prehistory. The rest of the social surplus in the Ravni Kotari remained dispersed, whether in small farmsteads or minor hill-forts, just as it had done in the Bronze Age. The large areas of fertile lowland in the Ravni Kotari without Iron Age settlements are testimony to a rather different type of land use and control of land, partly developed in response to the changes in productive potential of the early Medithermal period. The prediction based on the LUC model focuses on a major expansion of the pastoral component in the valleys and the mountains, with cultivation of arable and tree crops on medium-altitude ridge and hillslope locations. Political boundaries were established, for the first time, in the Late Iron Age to define the territories of groups occupying the major hill-forts (fig. 176). In this way, political authority was concentrated in the hill-fort residents in the form of descent groups termed *cognationes* (Chapman and Shiel 1991). By the Late Iron Age, settlement nucleation on major hill-forts meant the consolidation of several cognatic groups as one of the few ways to expand the amount of land under group control. It is noticeable that the first evidence for hill-fort nucleation occurred at a time when increasing commercial contact with *Magna Graecia* and Apulia widened the possibility for overseas disposal of surplus goods. The commercial bow-wave in advance of the Roman Imperial army had a significant impact on Late Iron Age social formations in north Dalmatia.

The differentiation of the domestic sphere in the Iron Age was matched by similar developments in the mortuary arena. While Iron Age groups continued the practice of cairn burial, flat individual burials also occur in the Late Iron Age, often with rich grave goods (e.g. Nadin: Batović 1987). This distinction between rich flat graves near hill-forts and often poor cairn burials away from hill-forts indicates that different ideological principles governed the relationship between the living, the newly dead and the ancestors in the Late Iron Age. The significance of imported exotica increased with time through the last four centuries Cal. BC. In addition, a new form of monument was the mortuary enclosure, such as that opposite the Venac hill-fort on the Mataci-Stojići ridge. There, a drystone wall enclosing sixteen large stone cairns lay adjacent to a large flat grave cemetery of the Late Iron Age. The social differentiation of hill-fort élite from flat grave population is important; through its claim to longer-term ancestry than in the flat cemetery, the Venac enclosure constitutes a new type of arena expressing social power in relation to status and inheritance.

The central paradox of the Iron Age of north Dalmatia is that, at a time of increasing accumulation of wealth, a larger portion of the landscape appears to be devoid of artefact discard than at any phase of the Bronze Age. Various solutions to the problem of the 'empty areas' can be proposed: increasing wetness reducing the value of lowland soils for cropping, a switch to pastoralism outside the settlement foci, the development of infield/outfield systems with little need for off-site discard, or a preference for a place-based settlement where central domestic areas became critical for social reproduction. In the sense that the monuments of the local ancestors are still visible as significant landscape features, there is no need to fix the cultural identity of the group onto an untamed environment, rather to ensure continuity by respecting the pre-existing monuments and constructing more impressive hill-forts as a mark of the differentiation of domestic space. The pre-existence of highly visible monuments permits a modification in the way the living related to the dead; since living in proximity to older monuments suffices, there is less need to construct a multiplicity of small monuments.

Given the 'empty areas' and the abandonment of other Bronze Age settlement foci, the question arises as to the significance of the Iron Age settlement clusters. One possible reason for their emergence is that the Iron Age marks a period of socio-political integration, in which new place-based statuses are emerging centred on stronger polities. The increasing differentiation of grave goods in this period is another indication of changing social structure at a time when new arenas of social power are being created.

In the Iron Age, the main contradictions in the social structure arose out of the tensions between two opposed principles of land ownership – the traditional communal versus the more recent private. The creation of novel arenas of social power permitted élite monopoly over social reproduction channelled through bounded mortuary spaces. At Nin, the use of traditional mortuary space supported legitimation of the emergent principle of private accumulation of land, while at Venac this was supported by the traditional form of cairn burial inside an enclosure type mimicking the domestic sphere.

Incorporation of Liburnia into the Roman Empire led to the conversion of major hill-forts into the *colonia* of *Iader* and several *municipia* and the construction of Roman farms on the coast, inland and in the Zadar archipelago. In the countryside, the construction of monuments similar to those pre-existing the Roman reuse of the landscape creates links to traditional land use and reinforces the relationships of the living with the ancestors. In terms of the total surplus product, construction of cairns and linear features in the Roman period was never as significant as the building of such monuments in the Bronze Age, yet such Roman new 'antique' structures helped to imprint the Roman identity on the landscape much as happened in the distant past. This extensive land management increased the value of the land cultivated from local farms, as did the building of field huts, enclosures and platform huts. The use of minor hill-forts as consolidations of several individual farms led to rather different links with the ancestors – namely the focus on traditional domestic space occupied in the Pre-Roman Iron Age.

None the less, there is striking continuity of settlement forms from the Iron Age into the Roman period, in which Romanization can be seen as an overlay upon an essentially indigenous pattern. The Iron Age focus on domestic space is magnified to even greater proportions in the Roman period, when a large part of the surplus product is concentrated in the *colonia*, the *municipia* and rich coastal villas. The lavishness of the conspicuous consumption in monumental structures, inscriptions and tombstones is in direct proportion to the extent of changes in social structure in the early Roman period; much of the epigraphic material and some of the monuments are far more scarce in the late Roman phase in Dalmatia.

The formation of a four-level settlement hierarchy enabled concentration of much social surplus in *Iader* and the *municipia*, while still allowing the accumulation of private wealth in dispersed farms. The complexities of private land ownership and the sale and purchase of multiple estates meant that, for the first time in the Dalmatian sequence, residence and land ownership were not necessarily closely related. At the same time, the empire's enormous demand for goods, provisions and labour sustained appropriate, small-scale technological developments, not least in agriculture, as well as the creation of a distribution system based on monetized market activity (Greene 1990). The change from reciprocal to redistributive and market exchange is intimately connected to the process of urbanization and the creation of ever greater social surplus (Harvey 1973). As Harvey puts it (1973, 228), the city acted as a locus for disposing of the surplus product, whether in monumental architecture, lavish and conspicuous consumption or in need-creation. In this way, Roman centres not only generated effective demand, they also used part of the surplus to create new means of production to increase productivity (the technological changes outlined by Greene 1990). By the end of the period of imperial expansion (end of second century AD), the Roman provinces were generating massive wealth for both export and local consumption.

It is in the context of conspicuous consumption that the growth of arenas of social power can be traced in the Roman period. Three aspects of the Roman presence are particularly revealing about the impact of Rome on the regional landscape: roads, aqueducts and centuriated fields. In each case, the variation on pre-existing linear features carried with it a notion of formal power related to the imposition of geometric order on the landscape.

The imposition of essentially straight Roman roads across a largely domesticated landscape must have had an impact on local residents similar to that of a modern motorway construction across a valley in the Green Belt. The utter indifference of Roman road builders to local place-values and traditional landscape patterns is a sign of raw, social power only later mitigated by the utilitarian opportunities of better access to markets and the like.

A second class of Roman construction is the aqueduct. The conspicuous consumption of that most precious of Mediterranean resources – water – through the medium of 'roads of water' up to 40km in length was another ecological revolution of enormous impact on local residents. Aqueducts were, in one sense, different from roads, in that they had to take account of the subtlest altitudinal changes in topography to ensure constant water flow along the total length of their route (Ilakovac 1982). Nevertheless, their routes were not designed to respect the social geography of the region, merely the narrow topographical constraints; thus aqueducts were as ideologically devastating as Roman roads.

The third class of Roman imposition of grid frameworks on the landscape related to the rewarding of veterans for their military service in the campaigns of the first centuries BC and AD. The granting of parcels of land, regularly made in areas adjoining major Roman centres, was inherited from the Greek colonization of the Adriatic in the fourth century BC (e.g. Pharos on Hvar: Stančić and Slapšak 1988). The block of centuriated land near *Iader* is only one of a series found in every large fertile plain in Dalmatia (Bradford 1957). The centuriated system is based on the division of land into small square or rectangular parcels. The *Iader* system was laid out over Stony and Karst land on the mainland and on the offshore island of Ugljan, using land currently ideal for the cultivation of vines, olives and almonds, though formerly useful for vegetables and cereals as well as these.

A basic characteristic of the Roman countryside is differentiation on all fronts, whether in town walls, civic buildings and private villas, the level of interior and exterior decoration or the materials used in construction. In north Dalmatia, the socio-spatial differentiation created in the Iron Age between major and minor hill-forts, hilltop versus lowland sites and enclosed versus unenclosed sites is adopted largely unchanged as the basis for social reproduction, with these differences magnified through the use of exotic materials and monumentality. The term 'differentiation' masks the extraction of surplus through élite redistribution by means of exploitation of both urban poor and rural workers on the land. Individual variation in social power increased dramatically in the Roman period in Dalmatia.

Evaluation of the model

A sequence of social action can be traced from the early 'domestication' of the landscape by the first farmers, through the development of greater intensification of agriculture and a wider range of arenas of social power in the Bronze Age, to a period when social power emanating from the centre of the Roman Empire created a range of new social arenas in the Late Iron Age and Roman period. This sequence was neither necessary nor inevitable but relied on small-scale, often cumulative changes in short-term social action as well as the structural constraints of the medium-term and long-term (cf. Bintliff 1991). These short-term changes are particularly significant in the creation of new arenas of social power.

8 Historical studies

Introduction

The following chapter covers a short time from a prehistoric perspective but resembles *la longue durée* from the perspective of the historian. At the outset, it is important to stress that the differences in the classes of evidence utilized in the medieval period in comparison with earlier periods in fact mask certain continuities in the general picture of land use and subsistence in the study region. But we can never forget that modes of social production and reproduction in the medieval period are sharply distinguished from those of prehistory or indeed the Roman Empire. Perhaps the most important general observation about the medieval period is that its unique history negates the notion of a social evolution of ever-growing complexity. Indeed, a quite different picture emerges of a long period of cyclical rise and fall in social, economic and technological complexity, often related to the vagaries of the balance of military power.

In the first part of the chapter, Huw Evans offers a synthesis of the early medieval period (AD 600–1000), with a coda on the developments of the late medieval period (AD 1000–1400). Wendy Bracewell follows this with a detailed study of the period of Venetian and Ottoman struggles over the fate of the Zadar Lowlands and its rich population and resources (AD 1409–1797).

The baseline of Evans' research is the careful deconstruction of the foundation myths of the Croatian state – no easy task at any time and not a task for the faint-hearted. The questions of ethnicity and ethnogenesis which Evans raises are issues that have marked the mature phase of Croatian medieval history, yet there are still sufficient ambiguities in the (mainly Byzantine) documentary sources for variations of 160 years – from 630 to 790 – for the date of any possible Croatian migration. Evans has been the first to utilize the military logistics of Michael Mann as an analytical tool in this field of study. As for the field record, the archaeological evidence for the mortuary domain is stronger than for the domestic arena. The paucity of excavated early medieval settlements limits the scope for subsistence or economic reconstructions, yet there is some potential for the reconstruction of socio-political organization. The emergence of a late medieval mode of feudalism based on the Frankish model marks a baseline for the developments treated by Bracewell.

Wendy Bracewell relies entirely on the documentary sources – Venetian rather than Ottoman – for her narrative of the inter-relationships between land use, military power and population in the early modern period. The archaeological sources for these four centuries are so weak that this is almost inevitable. For almost four hundred years, the Zadar Lowlands became one of the principal battlegrounds and border zones between two mighty empires. Not surprisingly, demographic pressures were largely of the Malthusian kind. Bracewell paints a picture of the juxtaposition of landlord-stimulated tax incentives for the recolonization of abandoned land in times of greater hostility with poorer landlord–peasant relations in longer interludes of peace. Unlike the medieval period, the early modern centuries provide relatively good documentation for subsistence, even though cadastral surveys quoting areas of land under specific crops are restricted to the eighteenth century. These data show that the classic 'modern' basis of Mediterranean mixed farming – wheat, olives and vine, with sheep and goat – has a long ancestry from at least the Bronze Age.

It is the changing balance between arable farming and stock-raising that provides much interest, not least when linked to variations in war-induced mobility or to ethnicity. The emergence of an important group of Vlach ('Morlak' or 'Istrians' (or 'Čiči')) pastoralists organizing their year around inverse transhumance – the moving of flocks to the lowlands in winter from upland bases – was complementary, at least for part of the period, with lowland groups moving their stock to upland summer pastures. The significance of Velebit and trans-Velebit pastures in the early modern period may well shed light on possibilities of extensive pastoralism in the Iron Age and Roman periods.

The two historical accounts which comprise this chapter make it abundantly clear that the study region is an area with a distinctive personality – definable in particular historical records as much as through its landscape changes found through archaeological fieldwork. But it is the merit of these accounts that they define the personality of north Dalmatia through differences from, as much as through similarities with, the Roman and prehistoric periods. A basic point is the check on regional development provided by long-term imperial warfare. By confronting structural differences as well as parallel developments, we may learn about a wider range of Dalmatian 'pasts'.

The medieval Ravni Kotari: a synthesis

By H. M. A. Evans

The collapse of Rome

The end of Roman rule in Dalmatia was a complex phenomenon, with the province being lost by the Western empire to what became the Ostrogothic kingdom, only to be regained by the Eastern empire during the Justinianic recovery. However, at the same time as the Gothic territory was being retaken, the Danubian frontier of the empire was being breached regularly by small armies of raiding Slavs, Antes and nomadic horsemen, such as the Bulgars. From the 560s, matters worsened as a new force became involved in events. The Avars, a nomadic people who fled the Steppes as a result of Turkish attacks, established themselves in the Carpathian Basin. From that base they dominated the Danubian Slavs and their allies, and began to conquer and hold Byzantine territory. The threat of the Avars and Slavs was not constant and the Byzantines managed to stem or reverse their advance on several occasions, but the first half of the seventh century saw a dramatic loss of territory, leading to the siege of Constantinople in 626. The siege failed, and Avar power in the Balkans eventually decreased until the second Khanate was destroyed by the Franks in the eighth century (for Slav and Avar attacks on the Balkans: Lemerle 1954).

There is no direct documentary evidence for the Avar and Slav advance on the Ravni Kotari, so the situation must be inferred from indirect sources, most notably the tenth-century document *De Administrando Imperio* (hereafter *DAI*). In chapters 29 and 30, two similar accounts are given for the fall of nearby *Salona* to the Avars and Slavs, but the numerous improbabilities of the account betray a lack of understanding of the seventh-century situation (Evans 1989, 66 and 71). What can be accepted is that Salona fell some time between 630 and 640 (Marović 1984), and that the decade that saw the fall of Salona almost certainly saw Avar forces on the Ravni Kotari. It is not known why *Diadora* (Zadar) did not fall to the Avars, and speculation on failed sieges or negotiations cannot provide answers. What is more certain is that about this time Diadora lost its hinterland to the Avars and their Slavic allies and subjects.

Although the success of the Avars marked the end of Roman/Byzantine control of the greater part of the Ravni Kotari, it still remains to establish how exactly the Slavic settlement took place, taking into account the problematical 'Arrival of the Croats'.

The Slavs and the arrival of Croats

In areas away from the borders of the Byzantine empire, the territorial expansion of Slavic groups displayed much of the character of seeping treacle, not moving with any specific goal, but relentlessly spreading under the pressure of its own weight. That this was an acephalous movement is, in part, demonstrated by the inability of the Slavs to make any substantial gains in the Balkan provinces on their own. They raided but they did not conquer. The advent of the Bulgars and the Avars changed this pattern, providing the organizational capacity to take and hold territory. What the nomads were not capable of doing was settling the territory taken; that was left to the Slavs. So, with the restraint of the borders removed, Slavic seepage was able to continue, modified now with the possibility of reaching distant areas very rapidly. To change the metaphor, the Avar assaults on the Byzantine empire were tides, which advanced and receded, never maintaining all gains made, but leaving behind, in the times of withdrawal, rock pool communities of Slavs all over the Balkans, from the Danube to the Peloponnese. There were, of course, areas which the Avars permanently controlled, mainly closer to the Carpathian Basin core of their territory, and here the development of Slavic groups was different. The Ravni Kotari, along with other parts of coastal Dalmatia and the hinterland, did not remain under Avar control, a phenomenon which demands explanation.

The failure of the Avars to maintain control was recorded by Constantine Porphyrogenitus (*DAI* chapters 29 and 31) as being brought about by the arrival of the Croats and Serbs at the invitation of the emperor Heraclius, and their subsequent wars with the Avars. Once the Avars had been defeated, the Croats and Serbs were set by Heraclius to rule the Slavs in the liberated areas under Byzantine overlordship. This simple account has been the cause of one of the longest and most creative debates in early medieval historiography. There is not space to rehearse it here, and this author refers those interested to Barada (1952) and Evans (1989) for detailed treatments. All that will be presented here are the main load-bearing structures. The question of the Croats' arrival must be resolved, as the development of the Ravni Kotari throughout the following period can only be understood properly if the original situation is accurately defined.

The chapters of *De Administrando Imperio* which mention the arrival of the Croats are 29–31. However, these do not give a continuous narrative, for 30 is an interpolation containing a different account from 29 and 31. The authorship of 30 has been variously attributed but the chapter should probably be regarded as the work of an unknown Byzantine official. According to 29 and 31, the Croats arrived at the invitation of the emperor Heraclius and set about defeating the Avars. With this achieved, the Croats established themselves in Dalmatia, including the Ravni Kotari. The dating of this event depends upon the invitation of Heraclius and it has generally been taken to have occurred between 626 and 640, during the decline of Avar power. The consequence of this for the Ravni Kotari is that the initial Avar domination would have quite quickly come to an end, to be replaced by a mixed community of Croats and Slavs.

In chapter 30, no mention is made of Heraclius or the Byzantines. Rather, the migration is led by five brothers and two sisters, who come with 'their folk' from 'White Croatia', a land set somewhere beyond the Carpathians. This group defeats the Avars in a seven-year war before settling in Dalmatia and other parts of Croatia. No datable point is given in this account and it has been generally regarded as an authentic, internal tradition recorded from the Croats.

The authenticity of one or the other or both of these accounts has varied over the years since Lucius published his *De Regno Dalmatiae et Croatiae* in 1666.

Although they had both been rejected at the end of the nineteenth century, by the middle years of this century the accounts in 29/31 and 30 were taken to be of the same basic event but seen from two viewpoints. The Croats had arrived from White Croatia at the invitation of the Byzantines, had raised a revolt against the Avars and succeeded in establishing their own state. There were dissenters from this position, including Barada, who did not accept the separate Croat migration. However, in 1952, Grafenauer analysed the account in 29/31 and decided it was untrustworthy, being largely an attempt at justifying Byzantine claims to overlordship over the Croats. Rejection of the 29/31 account did not lead to the redating of the migration as it was accepted that the first half of the seventh century was reasonable.

No one seriously challenged the dating until 1977 when Margetić published his reassessment. He stated that, if the 29/31 account was rejected, then the Heraclian date for the migration had also to be rejected. However, Margetić did not leave the migration of chapter 30 chronologically adrift but concentrated upon internal statements of chronological value. These statements were that the Croats were subject to the Franks in their own home (i.e. White Croatia) and that they arrived and fought the Avars for some years, later rebelling against the Franks for their eventual liberation. Margetić tied in these events, to which he allowed a span of some twenty to thirty years, to the rebellion of Ljudevit Posavski, which broke out in 822. On that dating, the Croats arrived around 795, at the end of the eighth century shortly before the Avaro-Frankish war. Klaić has accepted Margetić's redating of the migration whilst disagreeing with some of his secondary conclusions, in particular the extent of the Avaro-Frankish war, the existence of an Avaro-Croatian war and the association of the rebellion in chapter 30 with that of Ljudevit Posavski (Klaić 1986).

The implications of a late eighth-century date for the social and political developments of the Croats and also of the now nameless Slavs on the Ravni Kotari are immense. The establishment of the state would not have taken centuries but decades and the material culture referred to as '*starohrvatska*' (early Croatian) can be nothing of the kind. In fact, a total reassessment of the situation would have to be undertaken. Is it then worth attempting to save the seventh-century date, as Suić has attempted (Klaić 1986, 44)? I do not think so. I believe that the level of uncertainty surrounding these chapters of *DAI* means that their testimony cannot be accepted without consideration of the broader aspects of the migration. It is these questions that will now be addressed.

Three basic models for the situation in Dalmatia have been constructed:

1. The Croats arrive in Dalmatia shortly after 630, either at the request of Heraclius or not, defeat the Avars and establish their own rule over the Slavs already present.

2. Slavs occupy Dalmatia, possibly under the domination of the Avars. Towards the end of the eighth century, the Croats arrive, fleeing from the Franks, and establish themselves in Dalmatia. The Franks defeat the Avars and the Croats are briefly subjected to the Franks before liberating themselves.
3. The Croats are only one among a number of groups of Slavs and nomads making up the Avar forces during their assaults on the Balkans. Taking the opportunity of Avar weakness and disorder following the failed siege of Constantinople and the fringe position of Croatia, the Slavs in the central portion of Dalmatia, including the Ravni Kotari, revolt and free themselves from Avar domination.

To distinguish correctly between the models, it becomes necessary to consider both the logistics of such migrations and the archaeological evidence. Given that predictions of archaeological patterns resulting from any of the above scenarios will depend upon the migration logistics, these will be briefly considered first.

Early medieval sources in their accounts of migrations do not deal with the logistics of the troop or population movements. Procopius merely gives the number of Slavs who descend upon the Balkan provinces, whilst Jordanes and Paul the Deacon give only the names of kings and nobles. Any logistical details will have to come from other sources. In his discussion of Mesopotamian empires, Mann (1986, 137–42) gives details of the limits of supply for ancient armies. There is an absolute limit on the time that an army can carry water, food and fodder – namely a four-day operation. Given the speed of these armies, the maximum unsupported range becomes 80–90km. In order to go beyond this, there must be a measure of foraging and living off the land which will slow down movement and reduce efficiency. Modifications have to be made to these figures when dealing with migrant groups, but these tend to reduce the rate of travel rather than increase it. At these speeds, it would take somewhere in the region of three to four months for any sizeable group to travel from White Croatia (assuming it for the moment to be North of the Carpathians) to Dalmatia. The size of the migrating group is again unknown but, for it to have any chance of defeating the Avars and whatever other opposition existed, it may be supposed to be of the order of 10,000 individuals. The logistical nightmare of supplying such a group for such a period is such that, if feasibility were the only decisive criterion of whether there was a migration, the conclusion would have to be that one did not take place.

The arrival of such a group into an area will have two effects upon the archaeological material. First, it will result in the introduction of new items and, secondly, the disruption of the material reflections of social, economic, ideological and political systems. The more significant the arrival, that is, the larger the migrating group compared to the original population, and the greater the domination one has over the other, the more obvious the disruption will be. In the case of the Croats, the migration should be visible in the cemeteries, both in the objects buried and the organization of the burials.

I have detailed elsewhere (Evans 1989, 152–8) the implications and potential observability of the three models and it must be said that, although conditions for viewing the early and late migrations are far from perfect, there is little archaeological trace of them. Considering this beside the untenable nature of the Heraclian invitation, and questions about the late migration, it seems most probable that there was no separate migration of the Croats from White Croatia.

The consequences of a non-migration are that there is no outside agency to invoke, but rather an internal development upon the lines sketched by Barada (1952). Establishment of a Croatian state, or better, an area free from Avar domination can be seen as being the result of the collapse and contraction of the first Avar khanate, coupled with the rebellion of an allied or subject Slavic group. The alleged connection with white Croatia is little more than a link made by an individual keen on ethnogenesis upon hearing that two peoples have the same name. All that remains is one of the splendidly named seven siblings who led their folk from White Croatia: Chrobatos. Who is he but the legendary eponymic founder of the Croat *ethnos*? An individual of significance, and as real as Old Father Czech.

Social systems

Having laid the historical foundation for consideration of the early medieval period, it is now possible to proceed to a detailed consideration of the social and other systems among the population of the Ravni Kotari from the seventh century onward. There is little that need detain us in the documentary sources, so we may pass on to the archaeological material, and the two main routes for reaching social systems. The first, examination of housing patterns and structures can be rapidly exhausted for, whilst there are Slavic settlements that have been excavated elsewhere, notably in Bosnia, they are missing on the Ravni Kotari, as has already been noted. The second route – the examination of funerary material – has greater potential and it is to that we must proceed.

The cemeteries of Stankovci, Razbojine, Maklinovo Brdo, Materiza and Ždrijac present the best standard of information for the Ravni Kotari. Other sites such as Biljane Donje, Glavčurak and Sv Križ are of use for some analyses. The cremation cemetery at Maklinovo Brdo was not sufficiently excavated to be of anything but general use. Investigations concern the representation of parts of the original population in the cemeteries, focusing upon male and female and adult and child divisions. This may be followed by a consideration of different treatment of individuals in terms of grave goods, both in quantity and type. Finally, the relational aspects of the cemeteries can be dealt with by more complex means.

Table 40 Male:female ratios in the early medieval cemeteries, Croatia

Cemetery	Male:female ratio
Maklinovo Brdo	1.15:1
Materiza	1.57:1
Razbojine	2.00:1
Stankovci	1.20:1
Sv Križ	approx. 1.00:1
Ždrijac	1.20:1
Veli Dol	0.30:1
Čelega	1.30:1
Francini	0.30:1
Vrh	1.00:1
Žminj	0.63:1
Bajer	1.20:1
Brodski D/Vac	0.80:1

The ratio of males to females in cemeteries ranges from approximately 1:1 at Sv Križ to 2:1 at Razbojine (table 40). Such a range must call into question whether the cemeteries reflect viable original populations; it is not one that can be subject to detailed demographic analysis. To establish if whole populations were buried in the cemeteries comparison can be made with male:female ratios of known modern populations. A complicating factor is the proportion of individuals of indeterminable gender, which in some of the cemeteries is as high as 25 per cent. When this, and the size of the cemeteries, is taken into account, it is clear that most could represent an original balanced male–female population. The only exception is Razbojine but this is obviously only the remnant of a much larger cemetery. In general, it seems unlikely that gender-based selection took place.

It is useful to attempt an evaluation of the position and status of children in these cemeteries. The most striking fact is the comparatively low number of child burials in the cemeteries. At Biljane Donje, Maklinovo Brdo and Sv Križ, there were no children buried and only a few at Materiza and Stankovci, whilst at Ždrijac child burials formed 20 per cent of the cemetery. Now, although demographic reconstruction of the population from the cemeteries is not possible, some idea of the under-representation of children can be gained from considering the outcomes of various birth and death ratios. Given two assumptions – namely monogamy and a 50 per cent death rate for children – maintenance of a steady population would require a ratio of adult to child burials of 1:1. If either the death rate is increased or the population is growing, then the percentage of the dead that children form can be well over 60 per cent. In Slavic cemeteries of comparable date in Istria, the percentage of children approaches 50 per cent more frequently. Given the quoted figures, it is clear that, even for cemeteries with some child burials, children are still grossly under-represented in their ratio of deaths:discovered burials.

The under-representation of children is a physical indication of a perceived difference between adults and children which affects an individual's right to be buried in the cemetery. Two possible explanations exist, both arising from a similar origin. The first is that the right of burial in a cemetery depends upon the individual having undergone a particular rite of passage into adulthood. Such a rite would, in transforming the child into the adult, bring full benefits of adulthood. The second explanation depends upon the general incorporation of the individual into society. Death brings about a disruption of the social order in the form of an individual's removal. The severity of disruption will depend upon the deceased's degree of involvement. If funerary ritual endeavours to deal with such disruption, then the requirement for children will be less than that for adults, with the consequence that children will not be buried in the same manner as adults.

If Ravni Kotari and Istrian cemeteries are considered together, it seems that neither explanation on its own is sufficient. However, the total absence of child burials in some cemeteries suggests that, originally at least, there is some rite of passage at work. Interestingly, the later cemeteries in Dalmatia (tenth century onwards) have percentages of children that are generally higher and nearer the Istrian levels. Some change in perception has obviously taken place. Whether this is the result of conversion to Christianity is difficult to say, but that must remain a possibility. Overall, the fundamental perceptual division is between adult and child, with the possibility of further differentiation being displayed in different ways.

Differentiation in treatment between individuals occurs in the selection and deposition of grave goods, in terms of quantities of goods found with different individuals as well as variation between goods deposited with males and females (see fig. 179). The cemeteries present a range from unaccompanied burial to the deposition of a sword, spurs and glass vessels in Ždrijac grave 322. For most cemeteries, the modal number of objects included in a grave is one or two and graves rarely have more than five or six items. It might be possible to attempt to assess the relative wealth of individuals from such figures but, as there is no agreed standard of worth with which to grade such diverse items as firesteels and necklaces, such an attempt is not worth making. More valuable is the comparison of individual cemetery ranges, which demonstrate the existence of considerable differences between sites such as Materiza and Ždrijac.

When objects are considered on the basis of gender associations, five categories may be defined:

Male exclusive: weapon, horse gear, razor, sickle, whetstone, horn items
High male: firesteel and flint, awl, buckle
Mixed: knife, pot, key, nail, coin
High female: ring, necklace
Female exclusive: ear-ring, comb, needle-holder, bracelet, spindle whorl.

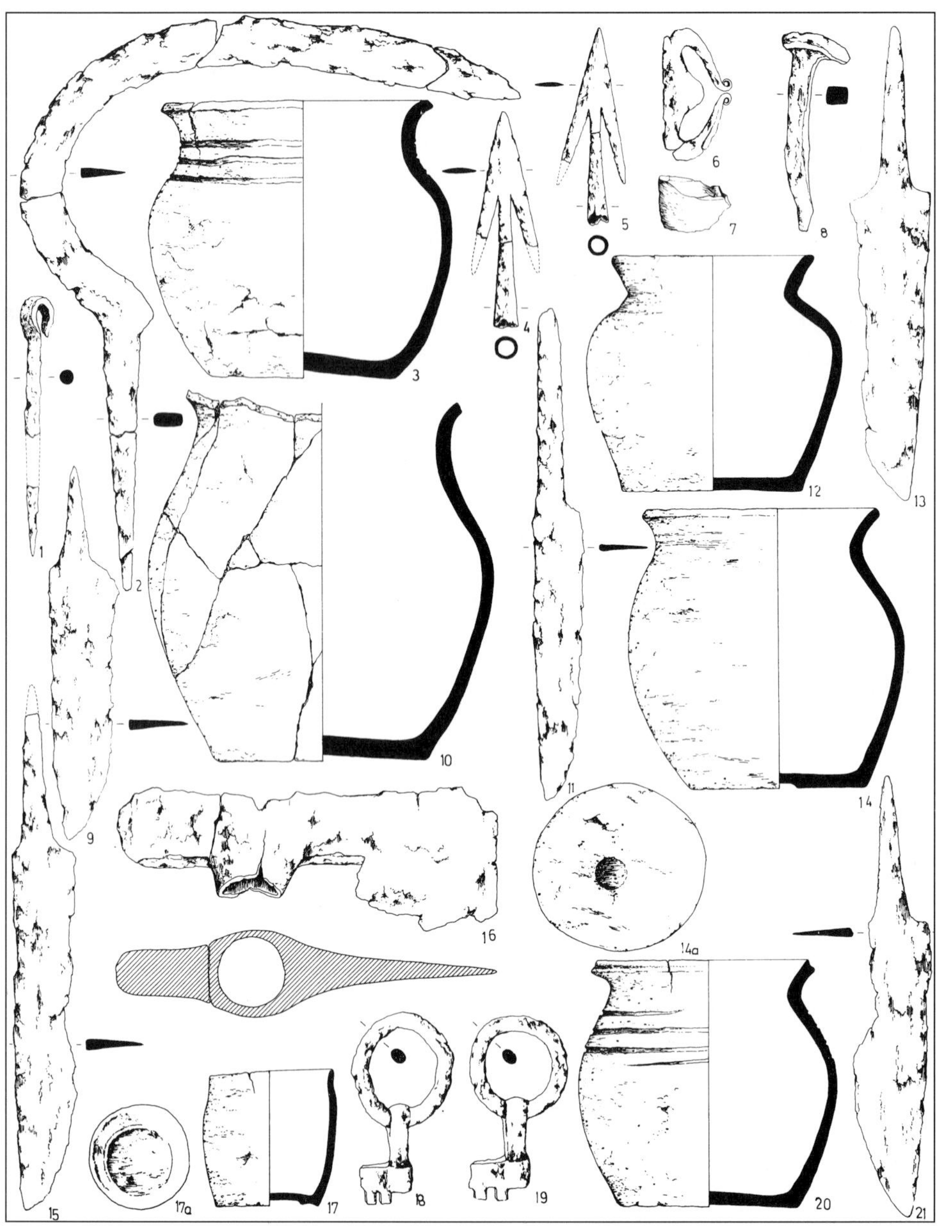

179. From Belošević 1980, table xxxi: 1. iron awl, Kašić – Maklinovo Brdo grave 20; 2. iron sickle, Kašić – Maklinovo Brdo grave 20; 3. pot, Kašić – Maklinovo Brdo grave 20; 4. iron arrow head, Nin – Ždrijac grave 99; 5. iron arrow head, Nin – Ždrijac grave 99; 6. fire steel, Nin – Ždrijac grave 99; 7. flint, Nin – Ždrijac grave 99; 8. iron nail, Nin – Ždrijac grave 99; 9. iron knife, Kašić – Maklinovo Brdo grave 20; 10. pot, Kašić – Maklinovo Brdo grave 20; 11. iron knife, Biljane Donje – Trljuge grave 1; 12. pot, Biljane Donje – Trljuge grave 1; 13. iron knife, Nin – Ždrijac grave 99; 14. pot, Nin – Ždrijac grave 160; 15. iron knife, Kašić – Maklinovo Brdo grave 20; 16. iron axe head, Kašić – Maklinovo Brdo grave 20; 17. pot, Nin – Ždrijac grave 160; 18. iron key, Nin – Ždrijac grave 160; 19. iron key, Nin – Ždrijac grave 160; 20. pot, Nin – Ždrijac grave 160; 21. iron knife, Nin – Ždrijac grave 160

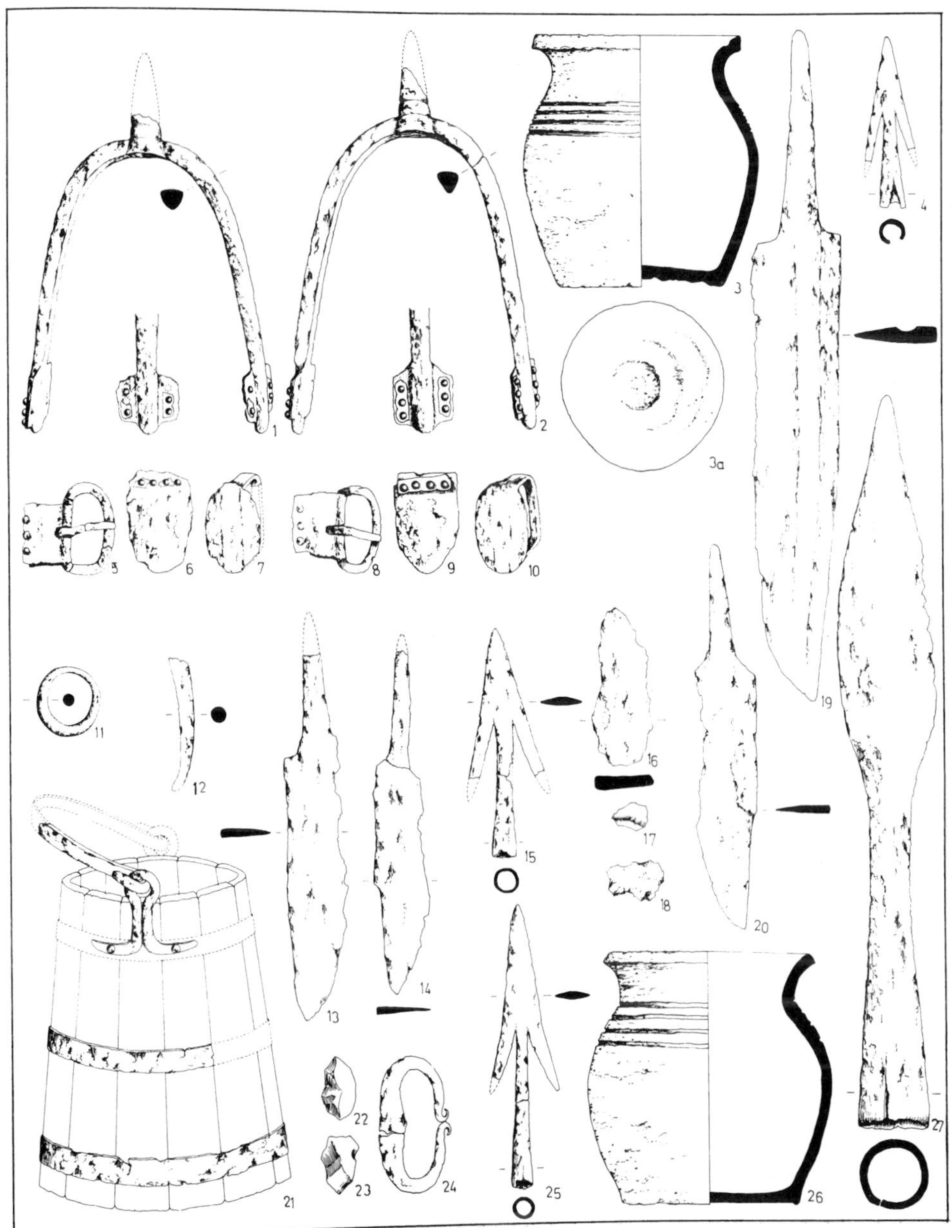

180. From Belošević 1980, table XXVII. All graves at Nin – Ždrijac: 1. iron spurs, grave 167; 2. iron spurs, grave 167; 3. pot, grave 167; 4. iron arrow head, grave 195; 5. iron spur fittings, grave 167; 6. iron spur fittings, grave 167; 7. iron spur fittings, grave 167; 8. iron spur fittings, grave 167; 9. iron spur fittings, grave 167; 10. iron spur fittings, grave 167; 11. bronze belt buckle, grave 167; 12. unidentifiable metal fragment, grave 167; 13. iron knife, grave 167; 14. iron knife, grave 167; 15. iron arrowhead, grave 167; 16. unidentifiable metal fragment, grave 167; 17. flint, grave 175; 18. unidentifiable metal fragment, grave 175; 19. iron knife, grave 195; 20. iron knife, grave 175; 21. iron bucket fixtures, grave 167; 22. flint, grave 167; 23. flint, grave 167; 24. fire steel, grave 167; 25. iron arrowhead, grave 167; 26. pot, grave 175; 27. iron spearhead, grave 175

In most cases, the reason for particular associations can be determined: male exclusives tend to be activity-defined, whilst the female exclusive is determined partly by activity and also by costume (fig. 180). Some items in the intermediate categories would probably, upon more detailed examination, be divided more completely. Although burials took place with objects generally associated with appropriate roles and dress, there was no significant difference of treatment beyond that. Locational analysis of goods within graves, which might have indicated more subtle differences, was not feasible with the information available.

The cemeteries do not display a formal system of stratification. Razbojine, Materiza and Stankovci do not have a range, rather fluctuations on a scale; they represent communities of agriculturalists at much the same social level. Maklinovo Brdo has one or two graves that stand out, whilst Ždrijac has a number of graves without goods as well as those that have been characterized as noble (Belošević 1980, Tab. xxv). In these two cemeteries at least, there are signs of more than one social group. At Ždrijac, which was associated with the settlement of Nin, the ruling class certainly seems to be present in some numbers.

It is difficult, from the archaeological data, to follow the development of the social system into the full-blown medieval as the deposition of grave goods ceases in the ninth and tenth centuries, with the exception of female jewellery. However, one or two trends can be suggested. It is known that at Solin the royal family of Croatia was buried in its own funerary church and that some individuals of princely or noble status were buried within other churches, whilst the rest of the population was interred outside. This spatial separation is not remarkable and mirrors developments in other countries. Greater social complexity is to be expected in later centuries and the attempt to trace it in detail will not be made here.

Economy

Because of the lack of any excavated settlement in Croatia or medieval settlement contexts, the examination of the economic systems is bound to be fragmentary and any conclusions drawn will be incomplete. Virtually the only hints towards the agricultural base are to be gleaned from the funerary remains, and whilst these could be fleshed out by reference to parallel situations in places such as the Czech Republic, there is little point in offering such conjectures. A little more can be said on trade and manufacture, but there can be little movement towards a full understanding of the organization and supply of trade. *DAI* mentions that the Croats traded along the Adriatic coast as far as Venice but there is no evidence beyond the mere knowledge that it existed and a few of the traded objects from the cemeteries. Moreover, if any area of early medieval archaeology deserves greater study, it is surely this.

Conversion

Although, at the beginning and end of the medieval period, the Ravni Kotari was ideologically dominated by Christianity, the period was marked by severe ideological disruption, with the late antique church being largely destroyed and supplanted by the paganism of the Slavic migrants. This pagan belief was in its own turn destroyed by the reintroduction of Christianity.

Slavic paganism has been a difficult cult to deal with, both because of the lack of its own written beliefs and because of the hostile attitude of those writers who noted details in passing. As a result, paganism is only known in general terms and not specifically for Croatia. Studying the replacement of such a poorly defined ideology by Christianity is problematic, particularly when it is asserted by most modern authors that conversion was largely a political act and did not impinge upon the beliefs of the majority of the population. The only way is to examine attributes of burial and other cultural remains which may be predicted to be influenced by ideology. If written sources are to be believed, cremation was originally practised among the Slavs to ensure the release of the spirit from the body (Evans 1989, 229–30), and resources would be expended very soon after death to secure this release. In contrast to this, contemporary Catholic doctrine led to the expenditure of resources following death to speed the soul's passage from Purgatory to Heaven (Bede v 12; Evans 1989, 238–9). Similar and more observable changes can also be predicted and their occurrence or non-occurrence examined. In this case, the abandonment of cremation, the orientation of burials, the deposition of grave goods and provision of a funeral feast were all possible physical manifestations of conversion. An examination of these four indicators rapidly reveals that the situation on the Ravni Kotari is not uniform. Some cemeteries such as Materiza and Stankovci scored positively on two pagan traits whilst others only scored one, with the alignment of graves being in the end inconclusive either way. According to the written sources, the date of the conversion – and this is only to give a range to a broad process – is the first half of the ninth century but a lessening of pagan ritual can be observed well before that.

Political organization

The origins of the political systems which developed on the Ravni Kotari lie in the dynamic of interaction which occurred between the Avars, their Slavic subjects and allies, the Romano-Illyrian inhabitants of the area and the population of *Diadora* (Zadar). The first significant account we have of the political organization is in *DAI* chapters 30 and 31. Here, Dalmatian Croatia is spoken of as being divided into '*županias*', political territories held by a '*župan*' under the authority of the *Ban* or the king. Three *županias* divided the Ravni Kotari between them – the *županias* of Nin, Bribir and Sidraga, with their centres at Nin, Bribir and Biograd – with some remaining territory staying under the control of *Diadora*. Quite how the *županias* came into being is unclear, but the term is regarded by many as non-Slavic, and possibly of Avar origin. Whether this is the case or not, such political units, which are also attested from ninth-century inscriptions (for example on the church of Sv Križ at Nin), as well as possibly in Greek sources (Theophanes speaks of the Slavs as having 'exarchs, archons and stewards' (Klaić 1975, 146)), differ considerably from the egalitarian democracy Procopius describes as existing among the Danubian Slavs, and which has been frequently taken as characteristic.

The period of Avar domination, as well as earlier contact with other nomadic groups, played a significant part in creating more complex and politically mature institutions among the Slavs in Dalmatia. One possible scenario would be that, having gained control over large tracts of territory, the Avars set up governors of some description to control areas and populations for them. At times of stress, such as when the Avars suffered military defeats, it would be feasible for such governors to revolt and free themselves from overlordship. The revolt of Kouvrat represents one such event. Once independent from the Avars, such individuals or the ruling groups they represented would set about maintaining their position and extending it wherever possible. The set of *županias* on the Adriatic coast and inland may well be the result of such revolts, with Croatia representing the amalgamation of units under one ruler. Indeed, the *Ban* with his three *županias* may be the remnant of an earlier event.

The Ravni Kotari was influenced politically as well as culturally by the Byzantines and the Franks, with both empires claiming authority at some point. However, although the treaty of Aachen placed the Ravni Kotari in Frankish hands, along with the rest of Dalmatia, the effective level of governmental control exercised by the Franks was nominal, given that the territory was at the maximum limit of their military range (unlike Pannonia, which was able to be more completely controlled). Byzantine influence was more indirect, though still significant, with one monarch moving the royal residence to be nearer the chief city of the Byzantine theme of Dalmatia. At another level, the presence of *Diadora* on the Ravni Kotari must have increased the development of the institutions necessary for negotiation, treaty and the receipt of tribute (*DAI* chap. 31, lines 119–42). Finally, it is worth mentioning the remnant of the Romano-Illyrian population, which should not be regarded as having been totally destroyed by the incoming Slavs. The presence of such a group, accustomed as it was to different ways of government, would have had some influence – however slight – upon Slavic institutions, as it did upon the material culture.

Consolidation and development

Having established in some detail the situation on the Ravni Kotari in the early part of the medieval period, as far as the tenth century, it is now necessary to examine the later developments. The main evidential difference between the later and earlier period is the substantially greater number of documentary sources for the later one. The documents have been treated in detail by Klaić (1975) and Antoljak (1978) and it is not intended to treat them here. In fact, the political situation and its analysis is far too complex to be narrated in all its twists and turns. Rather than attempt what would necessarily be a sketchy account, only the main trends will be dealt with.

Politically, the most significant events were the unification of Pannonian and Dalmatian Croatia under Tomislav (910–30) and the annexation of Croatia by Hungary following a period of dynastic problems, whilst the most startling was the sack of Zadar during the Fourth Crusade. However, parallel to these events were considerable changes in the government and administration of the Ravni Kotari, as a fully feudal system developed from the Frankish systems of noble land tenure. The main effect of this was to subjugate even further the agricultural classes and demote most of them from the status of free peasants that their ancestors enjoyed. The increase of stratification this represents can to an extent be seen in the archaeological remains in the separate burial of noble and royal families from the rest of the population, as well as in the construction of considerable palaces and residences. It is unfortunate that the lack of early settlements means that comparisons which might illuminate the development cannot be carried out.

The economic development of the Ravni Kotari continued, with Zadar flourishing to a fatal extent (it was commercial rivalry which led Venice to set her destruction as the price for aiding the Crusaders). Trades and crafts improved and Zadar was fully incorporated into Adriatic and European trade networks.

The church also flourished, but not without considerable controversy, particularly over the status of the bishoprics of Nin and Spalato. Essentially the matter was one of ecclesiastical nationalism, with the new Croatian bishopric of Nin being challenged for supremacy by the ancient (and allegedly apostolic) foundation of Salona. In the end, after two synods, the question was decided in Spalato's favour. The struggle gives an insight into the transnational character of the medieval church and the importance of such a body in maintaining the character of medieval Europe. The wide distribution of churches on the Ravni Kotari is another evidence of this.

Generally, the later medieval period was marked by a consolidation of the power groups that were established by the tenth century. Both the military upper classes and the church held and expanded the power they had attained, whilst the rural classes lost in comparison. Only in cities such as Zadar were the artisan and merchant classes flourishing. By the end of the period, population levels had probably reached, and maybe surpassed, those of the Roman period, although the observed density of sites is certainly not as great. The late medieval period as a whole was one of great change and considerable development, the consequences of which are still present in the Ravni Kotari.

Economy and society in the Zadar lowlands under Venetian and Ottoman rule, 1409–1797

By W. Bracewell

Introduction

After Venetian rule over Zadar was established in 1409, its mainland territory enjoyed a brief period of gradual economic development. However, between the end of the fifteenth century and the beginning of the eighteenth, six Venetian–Ottoman wars were fought across the territory of Zadar (1499–1502; 1537–40; 1570–3 [Cyprian War]; 1645–69 [Candian War]; 1684–99 [Morean War]; 1714–18). The two centuries of conflict had a severe effect on the Zadar lowlands, bringing about drastic changes in administration, population, economy and social structure. During this period, control over a large part of Zadar's district passed first into Ottoman hands, and then was recovered for Venice. In the sixteenth century, Venetian Zadar suffered a severe diminution of its hinterland territory as a result of losses and treaties following the wars of 1537–40 and 1570–3. Some territory was recovered during the war of 1645–69 (though not all was retained with the treaty of 1671), and from 1699 the lowlands were once again completely under Venetian administration, but it was not until 1718 that all Ottomans were completely removed from Ravni Kotari and Bukovica. Zadar would pass out of Venetian control only in 1797, with the fall of the Republic (fig. 181).

These political changes have important implications for a historical study of the Zadar lowlands in the period under consideration. The most extensive archival sources are Venetian, but they refer almost exclusively to that part of the territory which remained under Venetian control. Thus for the sixteenth and seventeenth centuries only a very small section of the Zadar hinterland is documented (though the documentation is quite rich), while the Ottoman territories (including the settlements of Nadin and Vrana) are much less fully covered.

Demographic patterns

Venetian administrative records give quite detailed demographic figures for the Zadar area in the sixteenth and seventeenth centuries, a result of the Republic's preoccupation with the human resources needed to defend Venetian territory – not only in fighting but also in providing for economic needs by working the land.

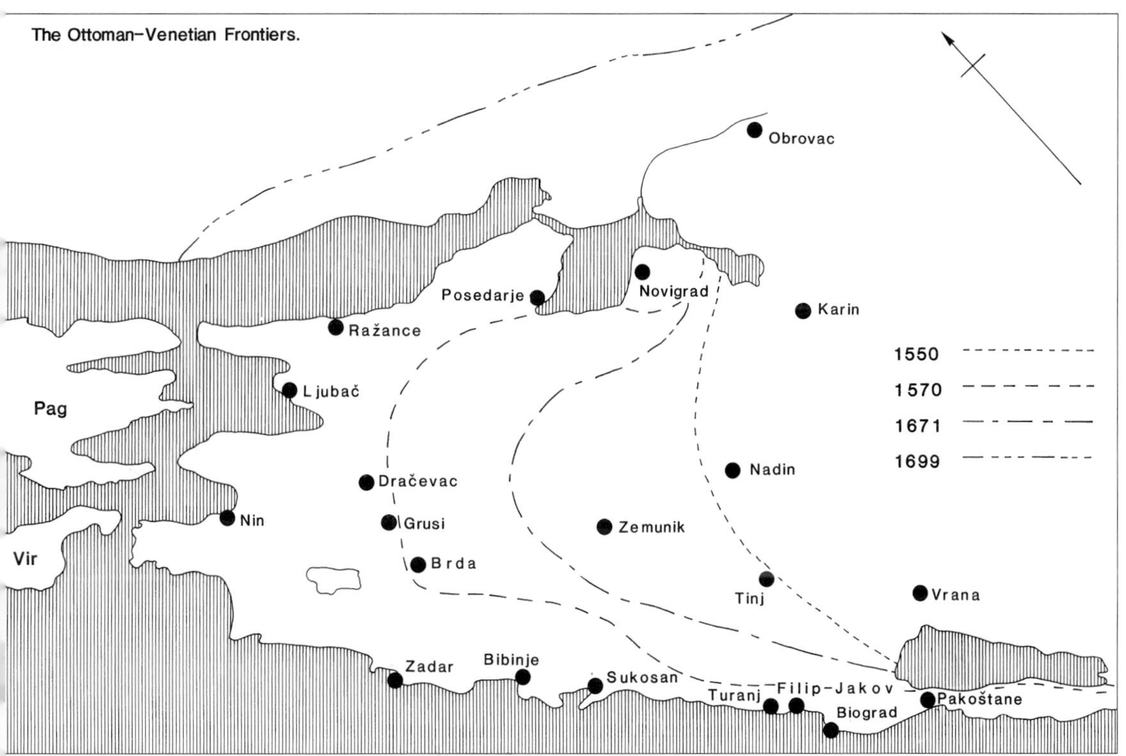

181. Boundaries of the Zadar territory at the time of Venetian rule

Table 41 Population in the Ravni Kotari in the 1603 visitation record

	Biograd & Pakostane	Vrsi	Zaton & Zlosane	Novigrad	Ražanac
Hearths	89	16	30	160	22
Total population	600	100	120	400	150
Average family size	6.7	6.23	4	2.5	6.8
	Poljica	Privlaka	Vir	Posedarje	Sukosan
Hearths	20	20	27	35	57
Total population	60	200	130	100	350
Average family size	3	10	4.8	2.8	6.7
	Bibinje	Turanj	Filipjakov		
Hearths	22	40	9		
Total population	175	290	40		
Average family size	7.9	7.25	4.4		

Population density and distribution fluctuated drastically over the course of this period (table 41). The first reliable statistics for Zadar and its territory date from 1527 (*Commissiones*, I, 203–23).[1] These figures reflect the demographic situation that followed almost a half-century of Ottoman pressure, culminating in the raids of 1499–1502 and the death or enslavement of large numbers of the inhabitants of Zadar's territory. Just after the 1527 census, the Rector reported that Zadar has:

> a most beautiful district and a large number of possessions, all uncultivated and derelict, because of the great fear of the Turks and the Morlaks who have recently come to settle in the lands of the Turk, so that all our poor subjects are forced to abandon their houses and possessions, and have gone (and continue to go) to live in foreign lands, some of them in the places belonging to the Turk, in order that they not be made slaves in perpetuity together with their families.

Thus, despite a certain improvement in the first two decades of the sixteenth century, data given in the 1527 census must be regarded as representing a drop in the population since the mid-fifteenth century (largely concentrated in the mainland territory, with the islands and the city less affected) (cf. T. Raukar 1977, 22–5).

Reports such as those quoted, emphasizing the loss of population in the territory, would be characteristic of the next century. The total population continued to decline, with sudden sharp drops in response to the disasters of war, epidemic and famine. The decline was more gradual on the islands and in the city, which absorbed large numbers of immigrants from the district, but in the hinterland territory, the area most exposed to Ottoman attack (and most reduced in area by Ottoman conquest),[2] it was drastic. The population of Zadar's district dropped from about 9,000 in the early wars of the sixteenth century, recovering briefly and then plummeting again from mid-century. Only towards the end of the seventeenth century did the population begin to return to the levels of the early sixteenth century. This decline had been offset to some extent by immigration from the Ottoman hinterland but it was not until late in the seventeenth century, with massive waves of immigration of Ottoman subjects to the Zadar territory in the course of the Ottoman wars, that the Zadar territory began to recover its population and its former economic importance. Statistics covering the much increased Venetian territory in the eighteenth century make direct comparison with earlier years difficult but the slowness of the district's demographic recovery can be seen in frequent Venetian complaints of underpopulation and administrative efforts to encourage further immigration. By the eighteenth century, immigration had virtually halted and even though the territory may have been seen as underpopulated, groups of settlers were beginning to leave for Ottoman or Austrian lands, driven out by economic disaster, agrarian abuses or religious intolerance (Raukar *et al.* 1987 have demographic summaries for the sixteenth to eighteenth centuries).

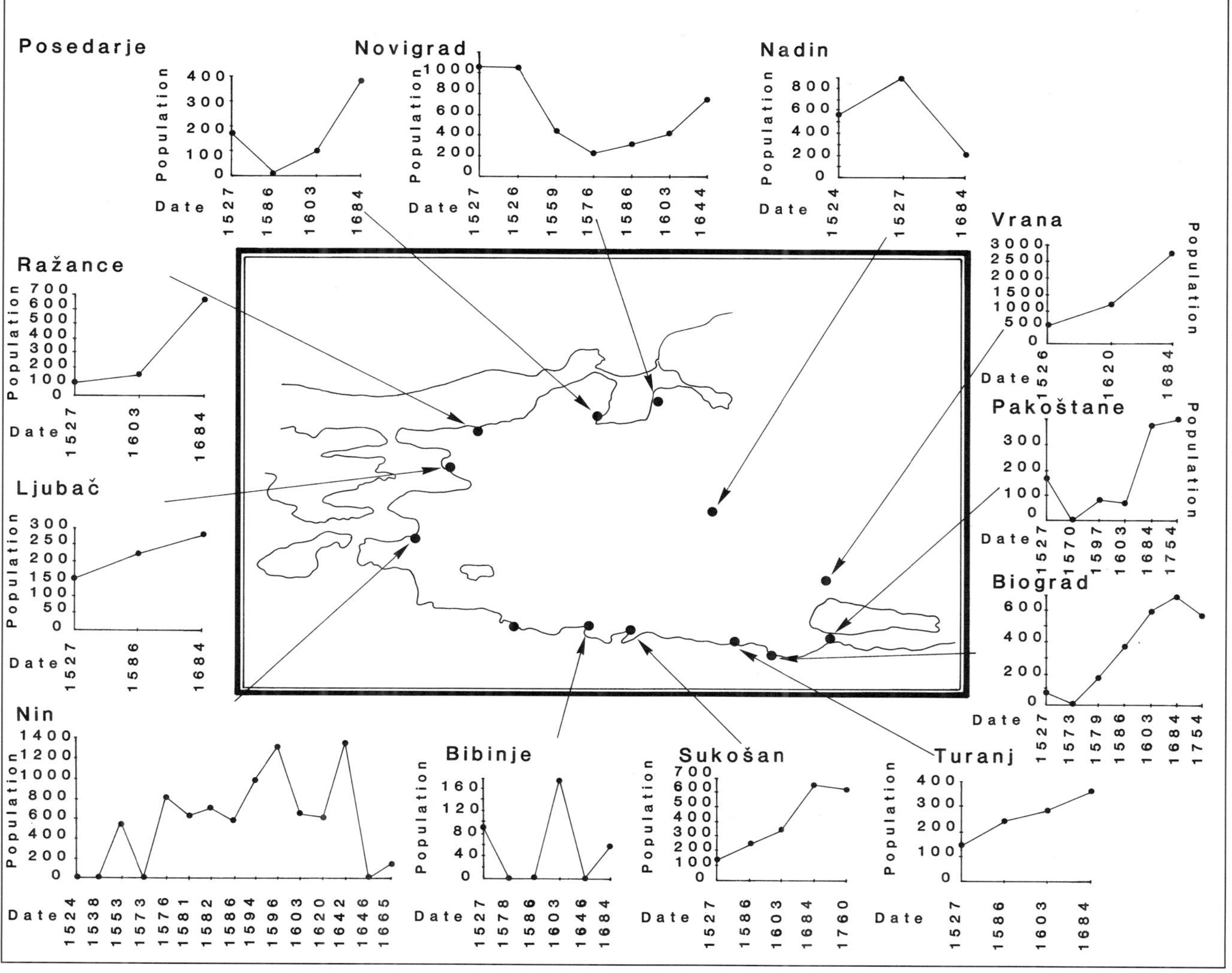

182. Population changes in villages in the sixteenth and seventeenth centuries AD, Ravni Kotari

The primary cause of population decline in the Zadar territory from the late fifteenth century was the conflict brought on by the Ottoman wars. Other causes to a large extent derived from this. Open warfare was obviously detrimental, particularly as Ottoman military strategy emphasized continual small debilitating raids, which seized captives and livestock and pillaged the countryside, before troops were brought in to besiege and take the towns. It is difficult to estimate the total numbers of victims of such warfare, particularly as the reports in Venetian archives are usually based on rough estimates. Nevertheless, these reports give an idea of the impression made by these Ottoman attacks. In 1499, for example, Zadar officials reported that Skender-paša of Bosnia had carried off 37,987 head of large and small livestock, and that the district had lost 674 men and 1,314 women and children (Marin Sanuto, *I Diarii*, quoted in Raukar *et al.* 1987, 181). It was not only strictly in wartime that Ottoman raids posed a threat – even in times of official peace the population was subject to smaller raids, for it was generally agreed on both sides that such actions were an everyday occurrence on the border, and that a peace was not broken until artillery was brought in to attack the towns. It can be assumed that the population of both sides of the border was equally affected by these patterns of conflict.

Warfare took a particularly heavy toll of the adult male population, not just because of death or capture, but because of the demands of recruitment. As a consequence of the Venetian interest in the military and economic potential of the population, the censuses often concentrate on this aspect of population structure. The total figures are accompanied by the numbers of those '*da fatti*' or '*da fatione*' – essentially able-bodied men between the ages of 13–16 and 60. This proportion in general hovers at about 25 per cent of the population, but, not surprisingly, drops after periods of open war (fig. 182). In the Zadar mainland territory, the percentage dropped to 22 per cent after the war of 1537–40. In contrast, on the islands, where recruitment for sailors and oarsmen for the Venetian galleys was very extensive, the percentage of able-bodied men dropped as low as 16 per cent after the 1537–40 war, and 13 per cent after the 1570–3 war. This depletion of the male population on the islands was recognized nervously by Venetian authorities, who repeatedly proposed programmes of resettlement.

The uncertain state of the border and the constant threat of Ottoman attack sent many inhabitants of Zadar's territory into flight – first to the shelter of the city and the islands, and then further abroad. The comments of the Dalmatian syndics in 1525 would, again, be repeated throughout the century: 'All the peasants [from the district] who were left after the raids have fled, part having gone to live in Apulia and the Marches, part in Istria, and part in the Zadar archipelago' (*Commissiones*, II, 13). Ancona and other towns of the western shore of the Adriatic would develop large colonies of Dalmatian refugees in this period. The economic ruin and stagnation that resulted from this loss of population led to still greater flight – as well as contributing to repeated famine when the poor agricultural yields of the largely unworked fields of the territory failed and could not be supplemented by imports from Ottoman territory or Venice. (There were notable famines in 1500; 1525; 1559; 1570; 1596 and so on.) Epidemics, usually of the plague, also contributed to depopulation (1500; 1525; 1530; 1619; 1631; 1636 etc.). The threat of Venetian impressment also sent some into flight. In 1554 it was noted that the men of the Zadar territory were so opposed to the requirement of serving on the galleys that they preferred to cross the border to work Ottoman lands instead (*Commissiones*, III, 57).

The population decline of the sixteenth century was at first partially redressed by the return of some who had fled abroad. This reverse migration occurred primarily in the early years of the sixteenth century, when the Captain of Zadar reported (*Commissiones*, II, 172) that many of those who had fled to Apulia, Abruzzi and the Marches wished to return:

> Not knowing how to accommodate themselves to the language and customs, and not being able to bear the climate, which is very different from that here (nor can their animals, taken from one region to another, live more than two years), these poor people come back, and prefer to place themselves at the mercy of the Turks, and return to their homeland, than to remain in those places which they find disagreeable and insupportable.

The Venetian authorities not only encouraged this reverse migration by planning to provide improved conditions (by repairing the border fortresses, etc.), but were also known to carry off these potential settlers (as valuable commodities) by force from their new homes in Italy (*ibid.*, 172: (1543) '...I have sent ships to bring back the earlier villagers who had gone to Apulia and the Marches, chased away by war and famine, abducting some of them, and begging the lords of Apulia to let the others return'). Such returns helped restore population levels by the mid-sixteenth century, but occurred less often as the Ottoman presence on the border became firmly established.

Immigration from deep in the hinterland was a much more important source of new settlers for the lowland territories. There had long been a pattern of migration from the over-populated mountain regions to the coast, and Zadar was able to restore population losses due to political and natural disasters from this source through the fifteenth century. (For an analysis of overpopulation in mountain pastoral economies as a source of migration in the Balkans, see Cvijić 1922, 194–203.) With the Ottoman conquest, this flow from the mountains of the interior to the coastal lowlands continued, with the Ottoman rulers themselves recruiting new settlers, usually from the mobile stockherding population ('Vlachs') from deep in the hinterland, to repopulate their newly acquired territories. From the 1520s, the Zadar borders were settled with 'Morlaks', identified as recent immigrants.[3] In the early years of the Ottoman presence, this flow at first halted at the Venetian border or at any rate did not benefit the Zadar districts under Venetian control. Groups of Ottoman subjects which did cross into Venetian territory were regularly settled well away from the border, in Istria or on the islands (and not in Zadar and its territory), in part to protect them from Ottoman demands for repatriation, in part because of fears that they would form an Ottoman fifth column. Nevertheless, there was some hinterland immigration to Venetian territory around Zadar in the sixteenth century (particularly during the 1570–3 war). This grew to a flood tide in the seventeenth century, particularly during and after the Candian (1645–69) and Morean (1684–99) wars, when the Venetian authorities made an effort to attract immigration by the promise of land and privileges. Thus, in 1670, of the 8,722 inhabitants in the Zadar district, only about 1,000 were original inhabitants, and the rest were recent immigrants (Stanojević 1970, 268–9).

Patterns of settlement

The fluctuations in the population of the Zadar territory led to changes in the pattern of settlement (fig. 181). By the sixteenth century, many formerly populous villages were deserted.[4] Many of the abandoned villages simply disappeared (a list of vanished villages, most located geographically, based on ecclesiastical records, can be found in Bianchi 1887, II). Other villages, particularly those that had been more substantial, lay empty for a time, especially during and following periods of war, and were then resettled, as was the case with Dračevac, Pakoštane, Filip-Jakov, Bibinje and Biograd. Nin was repeatedly pillaged, burnt, abandoned and resettled in the course of the century. In smaller villages, Filip-Jakov for example, often no indigenous population remained, and they were resettled with completely new inhabitants from the hinterland. As a result, old toponyms were forgotten and disappeared, and new names appear in the records (Filip-Jakov had formerly been known as Pristan or Rogovski Pristan, as it had served as the loading dock for the Rogovo monastery). Sometimes the names remain, but attached to a new site, as was the case with Dračevac (Malpaga) – ruined in the 1570–3 war and subsequently rebuilt on Venetian orders in a more favourable position nearby (*Commissiones*, V, 27 (1596)).

What factors contributed to the survival or disappearance of individual villages? Structural factors probably had an influence. There was no need to work marginal land with many fertile fields left lying uncultivated due to the decline in the rural population. Location also affected settlement in other ways – Nin was left empty as much because of its 'unhealthy air' due to the swampy, poorly drained surroundings as for any other reason. But strategic location on the border – the ability to resist Ottoman attack – was probably decisive in the sixteenth and seventeenth centuries. Undefended villages within easy striking distance of Ottoman garrisons in Zemunik, Poličnik or Sedd-i Islam quickly fell victim to raids after 1576 and were either abandoned or refortified.

Venetian policy also played an important role in the pattern of settlement on the territory by maintaining garrisons for the defence of the local population; rebuilding or fortifying villages to make them more secure; conceding land to be worked under reduced obligations in order to attract settlers; settling immigrants from the hinterland in abandoned villages. Venetian garrisons were maintained in Novigrad, as an important strategic point between Obrovac and the sea, throughout this period. Though the suburbs were burnt in the 1570–3 war, reducing the population considerably for a few years, the presence of the fortress and garrison ensured that a growing number found it safe enough to remain there. Other villages too, such as Ljubac, Posedarje and Grusi, were periodically defended by a garrison force (usually a handful of cavalrymen).

Concerned by the loss of income and defence potential that accompanied the decline of the population in the Zadar territory, the Venetian authorities made an effort to rebuild and fortify certain badly affected villages. Regarded as one of the most important outlying towns, Nin was the subject of much concern, with some debate over the century whether it should be restored and garrisoned, or completely destroyed. The Venetian authorities had varying degrees of success with their decisions to rebuild and repopulate other villages. It was planned to make a small fortified outpost out of Radovin, between Slivnica and Ražanac. Nevertheless, ten years later it was still abandoned, its fields unworked, and the same was true in 1613, though its wood was often cut by neighbouring Ottoman subjects. The failure of this attempt seems to have been caused by Radovin's exposed position on the coast, far away from any defensive outpost, and its distance from the lands that had been parcelled out by the Venetians at reduced obligations as an inducement to settlement there. It was true that a group of Vlachs, formerly Ottoman subjects, had wanted to settle in Radovin in the early 1600s, but the authorities had been dubious about settling this unknown population in such an exposed area where they could not be kept under closer supervision, and where it was feared that they might cooperate with *uskoks* attacking across Venetian territory, or become involved in other sorts of mischief (*Commissiones*, IV, 292; V, 111–12; VI, 195, 223. Archivio di Stato, Venezia, Provveditori da terra e da mar, fol. 418 (1607–12)).

The resettlement of Dračevac (Malpaga) (and its neighbouring village Grusi) was a greater success. Like Radovin, it had been destroyed by the Ottomans in the war of 1570–3, and then damaged again in a retaliatory raid about 1582. It was rebuilt in 1585 at the order of the Rector of Zadar and, as an inducement to settle there, the lands around it owned by Venice had been offered at rates from one-eighth to one-tenth of the yields (as opposed to the customary one-quarter) for a period of eight years. By 1586, the population stood at 60 men, 53 women, and 106 children. Three years later, Dračevac was still not completely settled, due on one hand to continued Ottoman harassment, and on the other to a lack of materials and money to finish the rebuilding. Nevertheless, the fields had been cultivated and sown. By 1591, it was being noted as one of the best populated and fortified villages on the territory and in 1626 it was one of only fourteen large villages still inhabited on the Venetian part of Zadar's district. Though it was plundered by the Turks in the Candian war and left abandoned, it was resettled with recent Morlak immigrants immediately afterwards (*Commissiones*, IV, 367, 374–5, 444; V, 27. Desnica 1950–1, I, 161). The factors that had caused the Radovin project to fail were less applicable to Dračevac. Though close to the Ottoman border and under threat from the troops in Zemunik, it was closer as well to Zadar and the city's large garrison, and it was not difficult to send guards out to protect it. Lands offered on good terms were also an attractive inducement, as can be seen from the fact that they were being cultivated in 1586 even though the labourers were still not entirely installed in the village itself.

Did the turbulent events of the sixteenth century affect the patterns of settlement within the villages, the ways that people chose to live, in other ways? Villages in the Zadar territory in the fifteenth century appear to have been primarily of the compact type ('*zbijeno selo*'), consisting of a number of village houses, one next to the other, each with its garden and courtyard of farm buildings, grouped together in a relatively concentrated area and surrounded by vineyards, fields and common land – a configuration partly resulting from the fragmented and scattered character of the parcels of land worked by each family. It was usual for there to be shelters outside in the fields as well, for greater efficiency in times of intensive fieldwork, such as harvest (see Miličić 1955, 54–5 and Raukar 1977, 169–71 for descriptions of such villages).

There are some indications that the Ottoman threat had an influence on the shape of village life of this sort. Repeated references to new work on village walls and fortifications appear from the late fifteenth century.[5] As the population in the territory declined, so it too became concentrated within the walls of the largest village in an area, as all the peasants working the adjacent lands crowded within for security. In 1570, for example, at the beginning of the Cyprian War, the Karnarutićes conceded the right to live in Biograd 'with the advantage of the walls there existing' to fifteen villagers of Poskaljine for an agreed payment (Historijski Arhiv, Zadar (H.A.Z.), Spisi Zadarskih Notara: Simon Budineus, vol. 2; II/2, fol. 705 (13 January 1570)). Nor was it only the peasantry that sought the shelter of the walled villages – in the aftermath of the 1570–3 war it was reported that 'the poor villagers are becoming accustomed to come every evening with all their livestock into the city and every morning to go out into the fields to work' (*Commissiones*, IV, 176). This attempt to protect the cattle would continue in many areas, contributing to the overcrowding in the villages.

The degree of security thus obtained was offset by the 'infinity of inconveniences' caused by 'building up the villages so narrowly' in a limited space, in particular 'the constant fear of everything going up in flames if one of the houses were to be set alight, either through negligence or through malice' (*ibid.*, IV, 247). The danger of fire must have been increased by the poor materials used in hastily building or rebuilding temporary, ramshackle structures which would not be much of a loss if levelled once again. Straw roofs and huts are often mentioned as the type of sub-standard dwelling to be found in the rebuilt villages. In Nin in 1591, there were 'no more than three walled houses, quite small, the rest all farmyard hovels, unmortared, covered with straw, which could be knocked down in the shortest possible time' (*ibid.*, V, 29).

Venetian authorities were constantly pointing to the dangers of overcrowding and recommending state expenditures to expand the villages. In 1581, the Senate ordered 200 ducats spent to make Filip-Jakov a secure refuge, so that it would be possible to relieve Turanj, 'in which there are so many inhabitants that due to the straitened, crowded circumstances of the place it is hardly possible for them to take shelter there'. The newly repaired village of Filip-Jakov would provide a good retreat,

> so that the people who have abandoned this good and fertile village will return to resettle it, and those who cannot take shelter in Turanj can come here, so that with this refuge they will be safe from the depredations which often take place in this area (*ibid.*, IV, 291).[6]

Not only the physical shape, but also the social shape, of the villages changed under the impact of Ottoman aggression. All those who could afford to do so moved out of the villages for the greater security and comfort of the city. While earlier larger villages, and certainly the small city of Nin, might have had a patrician summer house, with residents including wealthier peasants and resident clergymen, in the sixteenth century this social mixture was thinned down to peasant labourers alone, possibly accompanied by a handful of soldiers. Posedarje in 1581 held only a company of cavalrymen – nine in all, with one woman and one girl; 'the rest keeping their families in the City for safety'. It had been some time since the Counts of Posedarje had actually maintained any presence there (*Commissiones*, IV, 292, 373–4). Nin is a particularly good example of the phenomenon of social levelling. It was a city in its own right with a Rector and a Bishop – both of whom, like the rest of the better-off population, preferred to live in Zadar (not surprisingly, given the condition of the houses described above). After its destruction in the wars, it was reported as having the appearance of a village more than a city, and most of its inhabitants were labourers in the fields (*ibid.*, VIII, 95).

As the danger of attack decreased with the end of the Venetian–Ottoman wars in the early eighteenth century, some of the constraints that had shaped village life were lifted. As new settlers arrived, land that had been abandoned was cleared and villages were rebuilt or founded anew, concentrating in the more fertile lands, and only then moving into less attractive areas. Nevertheless, it appears that village society remained fairly homogeneous in this century as well. Many landlords in the eighteenth century never even saw their lands, according to contemporary descriptions, preferring to remain in Zadar, often maintaining a steward in the village for part of the year to see to the collection of rents. Village architecture reflected this social homogeneity, with the villages made up primarily of peasant houses and courtyards, with a slightly grander building with a tithe barn for the accommodation of the steward, or perhaps a local chapel.

Land tenure

Throughout the period under consideration, most of the agricultural population of the Zadar district worked land belonging to someone else (usually landlords of higher social status living in the city, who had acquired ownership of the lands in the district over the course of the fifteenth century). The terms under which they worked in the fifteenth century usually amounted to one-quarter of the annual harvest (a proportion specified in the Zadar Statute), though the details varied according to type of culture. The *težak* (labourer) agreed with the landlord either to plant and raise grapevines (or olive trees) or, more rarely, to work existing ones, delivering to the landlord, at his own expense, one-quarter of the fruit (or one-third, if these were pre-existing vines or trees) and, less frequently, '*onoranze*' (usually specific items, such as a chicken, delivered on certain feast days). The vines planted by the labourer became his own property, and could be sold or otherwise disposed of, but the land remained the property of the landlord, who could not renegotiate an agreement for use of the land during the lifetime of the vines.

The *kmet* (peasant) agreed with the landlord to work arable land, usually in units (*sors, ždrijeb*) of about 7–7.5 hectares, which included common rights to pasturage, woods, water etc. shared with the rest of the village where the land was located. The peasant bound himself for an agreed period (usually five to ten years) to live on the land, to work the land according to the two-field system (ploughing half and letting half lie fallow each year – which means that he supported himself and paid his rent on the produce of about 3.5ha of land), and to give the landlord as rent one quarter of all produce in kind, specified '*onoranze*' if the peasant lived in a dwelling provided by the landlord, and usually also labour services on the landlord's own land (*zgon*). This usually amounted to the cultivation of 0.25ha of land annually, all the fruits of which went to the landlord. In other cases, where there was no labour obligation, the peasant often paid an additional one-tenth for the landowner's portion.[7]

From the late fifteenth century, contracts made in Zadar increasingly refer to Ottoman incursions as a justification for not fulfilling the terms of these agreements, but the basic pattern of land tenure obligations changed only very slowly under the impact of the Ottoman invasions. As they began to lose lands to Ottoman conquest, landlords not only attempted to retain all their old privileges, but also to impose new obligations on their peasants (increasing the amount of labour services on the *zgon*, for example, or attempting to ensure that the peasants worked only their land). In addition, landlords began to require payments for the use of pastures that had previously been used in common by those working landholdings in each village. Nevertheless, as the agricultural population in the district dropped and large areas were left uncultivated, some aspects of the land tenure arrangements began to relax in response to these pressures.

The most obvious change was the reduction in dues and obligations needed in order to bring abandoned fields back into cultivation. Venice had recommended that land be conceded under relaxed obligations shortly after the war of 1570–3, when it was feared that large tracts of abandoned land would be usurped by Ottoman subjects (as indeed would be the case in several areas, particularly around Novigrad). Noting that 'many do not wish to go and inhabit and cultivate dangerous places and then have to pay one-quarter to the landowners,' the Rector of Zadar recommended in 1578 that it be ordered that 'all those who go to settle and cultivate uncultivated areas should not have to pay any sort of *terratica* (land rent), and may work them without any permission from the owners', with the aim of repopulating the areas and bringing land once again under the plough (*Commissiones*, IV, 225). This plan, however, does not appear to have been imposed as a general Venetian policy, though the Venetian Senate made special provisions for certain areas intended for reconstruction, such as Dračevac, as noted above, or Grusi, where state-owned lands were granted for as little as one-tenth.

Both private secular and ecclesiastical landlords, however, were forced to relax some of their claims in order to ensure that their land would be worked, in particular postponing for several years the payment of the full one-quarter on uncultivated land (*terreni deri*) which was being brought under the plough (Raukar 1970–1, 240–1).[8] Pakoštane was resettled with reduced obligations in the 1590s. The agreement is given in detail as an example of this type of arrangement. The land itself had been granted to the Zadar Karnarutić family for services rendered to the Venetian Republic, though at the time it was completely uninhabited (*Commissiones*, IV, 372). In 1597, an agreement was made between Margarita Karnarutić and the representatives of twelve families, living in Biograd, Zloselo and Murter, to resettle and fortify the abandoned village of Pakoštane. At their own expense they would build a wall around the village, building a limekiln to produce the necessary lime for mortar. Margarita would give each peasant a plot of land, and in return they would pay her one good hen each year at Christmas, beginning in 1598, as long as they and their descendants lived there ('*l'honoranza*'). Their more substantial obligations to the Karnarutić landowners consisted of annual dues of one-twentieth of the increase of their flocks – a much smaller proportion than usually demanded, as the pastures of the village were largely occupied by the Turks. If these pastures were regained, then this obligation would be increased to one-tenth, still a fairly low proportion. All manure from the livestock was to be used on the fields and not sold for profit to others. Further, they were to pay one-quarter of the yield of pre-existing vineyards (slightly less than the standard amount), and one-tenth the yield of pre-existing olives and other trees. Each year, except in wartime, they were to plant a certain area in new vines while good land was available. Of all new plantings they were to pay one-fifth of the yield (less than the standard one-quarter). They were also to bring unworked land and wooded land under the plough, and to pay one-quarter of the yield of grain and forage crops from ploughed land. They were explicitly excused the '*decima del dominicale*' – a payment of one-tenth of the yield traditionally required in addition to the one-quarter in some areas (perhaps a substitute for labour services in the landlord's own fields, which are not mentioned here). All the payments in kind were to be delivered to the landlord by boat at their own expense.[9] In general this was a fairly liberal agreement, far less onerous than the standard dues of one-quarter. It had the desired effect: Pakoštane became a stable community once again, and the Karnarutić family again received payments in kind from their land, the main source of their income. But in some exposed or unattractive areas, even these concessions could not attract workers – Brda is noted in 1581 as one such place (*Commissiones*, IV, 291). As a device for resettling abandoned villages, concessions were most successful when they were backed up by the resources of the state in providing support in such areas as building materials and, most importantly, a measure of protection from Ottoman attack.

In spite of all their efforts, the landlords of Zadar (primarily the patriciate, the upper stratum of citizens, various institutions of the Church, and the Venetian fiscal chamber) found the income from their land declining in the sixteenth and seventeenth centuries, affected both by the loss of lands to Ottoman conquest and the drop in an agricultural workforce to work those lands they still held. Many of the landlords still controlled considerable resources on the islands and on the narrow coastal lands, or even farther afield in the cases of some nobles, in lands acquired through marriage contracts with Split or Trogir families. The patriciate in Zadar was perhaps better off than in many other Dalmatian cities, but they nevertheless found themselves under increasing pressure over this period, affected by demographic decline, competition from the wealthier citizenry, and above all, the loss of income from their mainland territories. Venetian observers describe them as gradually withdrawing from an active role on their estates by the seventeenth and eighteenth centuries:

> The nobles and the citizens are for the most part idlers, and lead a lazy life with the little they receive from their very slender incomes, which could be augmented, if they wished, by assisting the cultivation of their lands as is done elsewhere, or by trade in respect of the commerce which they have with the Turks...but they don't trouble themselves at all, and prefer to describe themselves as cavalrymen.

The rising ratio of land to labour affected villagers in several other ways beside the official reduction of dues and obligations. During wartime, dues were often not collected at all, especially on Ottoman lands (where dues were in any case lower, encouraging peasants on the border to work land for Ottoman *sipahis*), which had the effect of raising the expectations of the villagers, and provoking complaints against the insolence and insubordination of those who had become accustomed not to pay. Individuals were also able to acquire more land to work in a single grant – more than twice the standard land-grant of the fifteenth century – largely because only parts of this would be cultivated.[10] At the same time, villagers were able to extend their legal rights over the land they worked, as agreements were no longer concluded for a specific period of time but put in terms of 'heirs and descendants' (cf. the 1597 Pakoštane agreement cited above, pp. 319–20), a practice which would, over time, strengthen the feeling that the land in some sense belonged to them (for all these changes see especially Raukar 1977; Raukar *et al.* 1987; Garagnin (1806) gives a vivid picture (from the landlord's perspective) of the villagers' views on their rights to the land they worked).

With the acquisition of the Ottoman lowland territories after the Candian and Morean wars, the Venetian government claimed the land as state property, issuing land grants to new settlers, usually to be held in permanent possession with the right of inheritance in the male line, in exchange for a tithe of one-tenth of the harvest (originally only for wheat, but later extended to cover all agricultural products). The settlers were also expected to act as a militia, forming a Venetian military frontier against the Ottomans. This more or less paralleled the obligations that had been owed in the same territories under the Ottoman system. In time, other obligations were added, including a pasture tax, and labour on state enterprises. These terms were initially very attractive, not only to the new settlers from the hinterland, whom the Venetian authorities had hoped to attract, but also to the inhabitants of the districts that had remained under Venetian control, where customary obligations were much higher (still usually one-quarter of the harvest in the eighteenth century, though now rarely including a labour requirement).[11]

One of the intentions of this action had been to ensure a minimum landholding for peasant families (with a minimum grant of about one hectare per head proposed as standard in the early eighteenth century) that would aid in resettling the land, but the distribution was badly managed from the outset, with land grants ranging from enormous complexes to influential individuals, to little or nothing to poorer families. The land allocated in this way was supposed to be inalienable, with the right of inheritance in the male line, and could not be sold or seized for debt. Only if it was unworked for two years, or if the male line died out was it to be returned to the state for reallocation. In practice, however, there were few effective legal safeguards for the agricultural workers, whose rights to the land were only rarely recorded in cadastral surveys. With time and with extensive legal abuses, much of the land in the new territories accumulated in the hands of large landlords, who paid the tithe owed on them to the state, but who then parcelled them out to be worked by peasants under much the same conditions as were customary on privately owned land (for more details on eighteenth-century land tenure see Raukar *et al.* 1987; Berengo 1954, 469–510).

Overall, the position of the villagers in the Zadar lowlands in relation to their landlords appears to have worsened in the course of the eighteenth century. While the Zadar borders were constantly under threat of Ottoman attack and labour was scarce, the villagers had benefited from substantial concessions in the terms under which they worked the land. Warfare and raiding also offered an alternative to work on the land, one which might supplement village income when the fields lay untilled. Landlord–labourer conflict was nothing new to the Zadar area, but with the end of the Ottoman wars in the eighteenth century, however, these relations worsened. While the general character of the conditions of land tenure stayed much the same, the villagers found their rights slowly eroded (through the loss of common lands, in particular) and their obligations increased (with the imposition of new grazing fees and new dues to the state, among other changes). These changes upset the fragile equilibrium between peasant and landlord interests that the Ottoman wars had helped maintain, and drove the villagers to express in action what one Dalmatian landlord ironically called their 'irrefutable axiom': 'that since the land is the Lord's, its fruits belong to the arms that work it'.[12]

From the end of the seventeenth century the labourer's resentment at the claims of his landlord erupted more and more frequently in resistance and outright rebellion. These could take legal forms, for example litigation in the courts against new impositions for which there was no precedent nor justification (this was the case in a prolonged lawsuit carried out on behalf of Ražanac in 1787 against its landlords, for example) (Peričić 1980, 47). They could also take extra-legal forms, most usually in the shape of refusal to pay dues and obligations, a means of resistance to landlords' demands that had been common in the Zadar area even during the Ottoman wars, but which reached the dimensions of a mass movement in the eighteenth century, with entire villages jointly refusing to pay their obligations, whether to their landlords or to the state. Resentment occasionally flared into rebellion, as in 1692, when the villagers of Pakoštane and Biograd assassinated a Zadar nobleman against a background of resistance to the forcible collection of the state tithe, or in 1704, when a revolt broke out in Bukovica and Ravni Kotari, again over dues owed to the state. As the Venetian Provveditore explained, this revolt began:

> over the exactions attempted or carried out on pasturage; grew with the pretext of the state tithe [villagers objected to payments in cash, and on other products in addition to grain – W.B.]; then the most recent tax farmers and tithe collectors were accused of extortion; and finally [the villagers] turned against their commanders.

Both rebellions were put down by Venetian forces (documents in *ibid.*, II, 274–8, 379–84, 386–9, 416–19). A few years later parts of the Zadar lowlands were also affected by the agrarian revolts that swept over all of Dalmatia in 1736–40, primarily protesting the payment of dues on what the villagers saw as common pastures and woods, though this movement was largely played out on the so-called *vecchio acquisto* (the islands and the mainland territories under Venetian rule before the Candian and Morean wars). Once again the revolt was put down by the Venetian government, which affirmed the landlords' rights to pastures and woods in their possession, and made landlord–labourer conflicts a matter for state adjudication, rather than civil litigation (Grgić 1960; for other details on agrarian revolts, see Raukar *et al.* 1987, III).

Patterns of land use

The most important products of the Zadar district throughout this period were vines, olives, grain and livestock. It is very difficult to get any clear idea of the proportions of land devoted to each of these types of production, though it is clear that even in the fifteenth century much land in the district was uncultivated. In general, the area around the city bounded by the villages of Diklo, Bokanjac, Babindub and Bibinje had long been used primarily for vineyards, which were worked mainly by labourers who lived in the city, where it was possible to find the extra labour necessary at harvest. Olives, too, were predominantly grown along the coast (it was believed into the eighteenth century that they would only succeed within smell of the sea), often intermixed with vines. (The Zadar statute specifically required that olives be planted around the border of each vineyard.) Ploughed land and pasturage predominated deeper in the district, though there too the peasants also established small vineyards where they could, as these offered a much higher income for the same area than did wheat (about ten times higher in the fifteenth century) (Raukar 1977, 156–7). Most ploughed land was used for grain in the district (primarily wheat, barley and millet), though this was supplemented by other agricultural products.[13] Stockherding was the other mainstay of the district peasantry, using as pasturage those village lands which were unsuitable for ploughing.

Agriculture

The decline in available manpower in the sixteenth and seventeenth centuries had a marked effect on the pattern of land use in the Zadar territory. As already noted, large tracts of land on the borders that had previously been worked lay uncultivated. On the basis of the available sources, it would be futile to try to calculate changes in the ratio of cultivated to uncultivated land, or to measure the decline in production with any accuracy. Nevertheless, it is clear that less land was under the plough in the course of the sixteenth century, causing a drop in the production of grain (repeatedly noted as a cause for concern in the reports of the Zadar administrators, and regularly requiring imports of wheat to satisfy local needs: *Commissiones*, III, 128; IV, 256; V, 171; VIII, 89). Similarly, vineyards and olive groves on the mainland territory suffered, partly from outright destruction in the wars. In 1566 the olive trees on the Zadar territory and islands yielded only one-sixth of the total before the war of 1537–40 'as the groves have all been cut down and burned' (*Commissiones*, III, 167). Natural disasters also affected this type of production. The chronicles of the period regularly report unusually severe storms, frosts and droughts, noting their effects on the olive groves.[14] Neglect and abandonment could be just as damaging to production. Both in the Ottoman wars and in the more peaceful eighteenth century observers report unpruned, untended olive groves that produced little fruit (see, for example, Garagnin 1806, 160).

Abandoning the land was one response to the pressures of the sixteenth and seventeenth centuries, but it was not the only possible response. Various other strategies were found in accommodating to the new circumstances. Stony marginal land on the narrow coastal belt was slowly brought into cultivation, for example, as landlords whose hinterland properties had been lost or destroyed began to offer good terms for vineyards on this hitherto unworked land, taking advantage of the labour available with the relatively high level of population in the area farthest away from the Ottoman border (Raukar *et al.* 1987, III, 252).

The Venetian administration attempted to control the way in which abandoned lands were reclaimed, regulating various aspects of land use in the sixteenth and seventeenth centuries. Because of the need to encourage grain production and avoid paying for expensive imports, the Venetian officials who parcelled out land to Vlach immigrants, former Ottoman subjects accustomed to live from livestock raising, required that the land be liable for rent at the same rate as if it had been sown, even if it was used for pasturage, in an attempt to ensure grain cultivation.[15] Venice also tried to promote the replanting of vineyards and olives (to an extent in hopes of ameliorating the problems of supplying oil to Venice), forbidding the destruction of trees, ordering that they be properly pruned and maintained, and laying down regulations for the number of trees or vines to be replanted on each unit of land.[16]

In spite of replanting programmes for vines and trees on the mainland, these continued to suffer from devastation and neglect in the period of Ottoman wars – the more so the farther they lay from the protection of the city, for intensive work in the vineyards and olive groves exposed the labourers to the danger of Ottoman attack. (There are many references to the continuing need for guards to protect field workers.) Even the milling of olives for oil and grain for flour had become more difficult with the Ottoman occupation of the hinterland, not least because most of the mill streams that had traditionally served the area were now on Ottoman territory.[17] Encouragement of agriculture could have little practical effect until the problem of security was solved when the Ottoman border shifted deeper into the hinterland in the eighteenth century.

With the changes in the Ottoman–Venetian frontier in the seventeenth and eighteenth centuries and the allocation of the lands by the state to individuals, the legal ownership of the land changed, but the pattern of cultivation probably continued in much the same way as it had under the Ottomans, the main difference being that the end of warfare and a rise in village populations permitted more intensive cultivation, with fields that had long lain uncultivated once again put to the plough. One indication of the proportions of land used for different purposes comes from cadastral surveys of the early eighteenth century: twenty-three villages in the Zadar district supported 4,713 inhabitants, making up 1,100 families, and worked 2,456 *campi* of ploughed land; 1,746 *campi* of vineyards; 4,204 *campi* of common pasture land; 827 *campi* of meadows (used for hay and limited grazing); and 10,611 *campi* of enclosed, partly wooded pastures (*gajevi*) (Stanojević 1987, 108).[18] Some of these proportions would change over the century. With greater security in the fields (and the continued profit to be made from wine) the area planted with vines in the Zadar territory would double between 1709 and 1781 (Raukar *et al.* 1987, III, 475). Viticulture was largely concentrated in the coastal area and the *vecchio acquisto*, however, because of Venetian regulations protecting these interests by limiting the cultivation of vines on the newly acquired territories (Novak 1961, 508–9). Cereals continued to be the most widely grown crop in the hinterland territory. The state tithes collected in the newly acquired territories, 1778–82, gives some idea of the proportions in which various crops were grown in the late eighteenth century (and of the magnitude of the effects of two crop failures caused by drought in 1779 and 1782) (table 42).

Over the course of the eighteenth century, various attempts were made to expand the scope of agriculture in the Zadar lowlands, both by state and private initiatives. The most wide-ranging effort of this kind was the Lex Grimani of 1775, a comprehensive agrarian law which both regulated landholding conditions and laid down guidelines for agriculture on state-owned lands. The agricultural

Table 42 State tithes from the Zadar hinterland 1778–82[1]

	1778	1779	1780	1781	1782
Wheat	1,588	370	937	630	524
Barley	4,200	630	2,063	1,756	1,355
Spelt and Oats	3,630	740	1,709	1,478	1,235
Rye	376	25	363	327	271
Millet	1,029	455	1,949	376	460
Legumes	—	–	165	34	40
Sorghum	50	30	1,230	31	195
Maize	520	180	3,332	364	475

1 From the data in Berengo 1954, 487–8. All quantities are in Venetian *stara* (approx. 1.83 litres)

specifications for the Zadar district ordered the cultivation of flax, hemp, onions and garlic for even the smallest landholders, and stipulated the planting of a certain number of olives, mulberries, almonds and chestnuts to each unit of land, encouraging the landholders by a reduction in dues on the harvest (all with a view to reducing Dalmatia's dependence on imports of these items). The law also promoted the designation of a proportion of land grants as meadows, the collection of fodder for wintering livestock ('hay, straw, fodder ("*li strami*"), and anything else that could serve to feed the oxen'), the maintenance of saddlehorses for state use, and the rationalization of bee-keeping (Luzzatto 1921b, 236: 1922c. The text of the Zadar version of the Lex Grimani is also available in Stanojević 1987, 138–44). Though its terms were sensible, the law was never effectively enforced, and it appears to have had very little effect on agriculture in the Zadar area – although some years later an observer noted that onions and garlic, which had previously been purchased in large quantities on the coast, were now widely cultivated in the kitchen gardens of the hinterland (Novak 1959; an observation supported by another eighteenth-century commentator, Lovrić 1948, 77).

In the second half of the century, some private landowners, under the influence of physiocratic ideas, discussed agricultural innovations as a means of improving Dalmatia's economy. A number of agrarian academies were set up in the eighteenth century to coordinate this activity (Zadar's *Accademia* was founded in 1787). The work of these academies often went little further than words – though, in the case of Giulio Parma, a member of the Zadar academy, the words took the form of a handbook of practical agricultural instruction for the Dalmatian peasant (published in Italian in 1791 and in Croatian in 1795: Luzzatto 1928). Though the members of the academy did work to encourage the planting of olives, and to introduce flax, hemp and mulberries in the hinterland, the practical results of their work were very limited.

Much greater results were achieved by landowners with extensive land grants who were both willing and able to take a direct interest in the management of their land and to invest in agriculture. Under the direction of the Borelli family, members of the Zadar patriciate, large investments were made in the lands they had been granted around Vrana, improving the land through the construction of a canal to channel off the overflow from the lake, draining the marshes, and returning the land to cultivation and pasture (Peričić 1971). Similarly, the Zadar landowning Manfrin family established a tobacco plantation on their extensive estates around Nin, using contemporary fertilizing techniques and modern equipment, and hiring seasonal labour from the surrounding villages (Mastrović 1968–9, 198–9). Such enterprises could reap enormous profits, but they depended heavily on a large initial investment, often with support from the state.

The villagers seem only rarely to have adopted the innovations suggested by the Venetian state or by the urban agrarian theorists. Perhaps this was in part due to ignorance, the envy of others' success, or the conservatism of a peasantry which preferred the 'customs of our forefathers', as observers often claimed.[19] Perhaps, too, villagers were not convinced of the benefits claimed for the new crops by their propagandists, or saw no reason to underwrite changes in cultivation that would serve merely to increase the incomes of their landlords. In many cases villagers had no incentive to make improvements to their land when their families had no hope of inheriting the results of their labours. The anecdote about a Sinj villager who felled all the trees on his land because he had only daughters (who could not inherit), and felt he might as well profit from their wood himself, must have had parallels in the Zadar district as well (from Rados Ante Michieli-Vitturi, quoted in Berengo 1954, 476). Perhaps even more importantly, villagers whose land grants were often barely enough to support their families and who were hard pressed by state or landlord obligations and by debt, found their ability to make even minimal investments in agricultural innovations severely limited in the eighteenth century.

Stockherding

In the fifteenth century, common rights to village pasturage were included in the contracts to work a landlord's land, with no further payment necessary to the owner. Such pastures were used under the supervision of a village stockherd for grazing the oxen used for field work and flocks of sheep and goats owned by the villagers. The greatest expanses of pasture land in the district (and on the islands) were owned, however, by the Venetian fiscal chamber and by Zadar patricians. Landowners, and those who leased pastures from the state, invested these lands in livestock raising on a large scale. A typical contract between such a landowner and a shepherd would take the form of the establishment of a company, formed on the basis of the owner's pasture and the stockherder's animals, the profit from the livestock, cheese and wool to be divided half-and-half (Raukar 1977, 202–3; this half-and-half arrangement was usual into the eighteenth century). The large amounts of wool and hides that were produced in the Zadar area supplied local textile production, tanning works and dye shops, with the finished products both used locally and exported (*ibid.*, 221, 242).

There are some indications that village stockherding expanded on the Zadar lowland territory in the sixteenth century, not necessarily absolutely, but in relation to agriculture. Some scattered statistics are available for total numbers of livestock in the territory and in individual districts, but even more than with population statistics it is difficult to tell whether these are comparable in interpreting the changes that take place over a long period.[20] Certainly the subjective impression of several observers was that stockherding was gaining in importance at the expense of cultivation. 'They leave the greater part of the lands unworked because they are concentrating on pasturing animals, from which they draw great benefit' (1559) (*Commissiones*, III, 128). One reason given was that this branch of village economy offered the advantages of mobility in the threatened conditions of the territory. The peasants' 'largest holdings consist of animals, for they say that they can always save these and take them wherever they like' (*ibid.*, II, 198–9). This included, as noted above, sheltering the flocks within the city walls. Those in the vicinity of Nin used the island of Vir (Pontadura) as a refuge for their flocks, driving them across the shallow, easily defended straits and pasturing them there in time of danger (*ibid.*, IV, 255–6. This land was owned by the Venetian fiscal chamber, and there was much anxiety lest the conditions under which it was leased should preclude its use in this way).

By the early sixteenth century, landlords had begun trying to maximize income from pasture land by enclosing village pastures, limiting the number of livestock that a peasant could graze there, and charging a fee for each head over this number. This process of restricting access to village pasturage so that the landlord could draw a greater profit from the livestock grazed there was a long one, extending well into the eighteenth century. Although it continued throughout the sixteenth and seventeenth centuries, as landlords tried to bolster their falling incomes by imposing new obligations on the lands that remained to them, villagers do not seem to have been hindered from expanding their flocks in the face of the Ottoman threat. Many were able to graze their flocks on the tracts of abandoned, uncultivated no-man's land that had been created in the wars, often avoiding payment of any fee to a landowner.

A mixed economy of agriculture and stockherding had been common in the Zadar territory before the sixteenth century, so it was presumably natural for the villagers to shift their efforts to the more profitable and easily defended livestock when conditions demanded it. But could an increase in stockherding in this period also have been due to an influx of hinterland Vlach stockherder-settlers? Transhumant Vlachs had long been descending from the Velebit mountains in winter to pasture their flocks of sheep on the coastal pastures in parts of the Zadar district (Ljubać, Novigrad), paying a fee for this privilege, and returning to the mountain pastures in the spring. This pattern of inverse transhumance was quite different from that of the professional shepherds in the district or on the islands who contracted with a landlord to graze flocks year-round on a specific pasture, or from that of the lowland villagers who, according to the customary law of Novigrad, grazed all their livestock in common each day under the supervision of a shepherd chosen by the commune (Barada 1957, 163–4).

From the middle of the sixteenth century, large numbers of Vlachs from deep within the hinterland had been crossing the Ottoman border to settle in the Zadar district. As mentioned above, Venetian officials, obviously fearing that they would persist in stockherding to the exclusion of agriculture, imposed conditions on land grants to some of such Vlachs, intending to prevent them from using cultivable land for pasture (see above). However, though these stockherders seem to have largely abandoned their transhumant pattern of grazing, settling down to an economy of mixed agriculture and stockherding like the earlier inhabitants, they may well have contributed to the increased emphasis on stockherding in the Zadar lowland economy, by bringing both their flocks and their inclination to livestock raising with them when they immigrated.[21]

Herds belonging to transhumant Vlachs based outside the area also seem to graze more frequently on Zadar territory from the seventeenth century on, particularly in times of relative peace. This had been common in the fifteenth century, with the condition that the Vlachs pay a fee for the privilege and restrict their flocks to common pastures (they were not to trespass on ploughed land, meadows, or enclosed pasturage; see Klaić and Petricioli 1976, II, 419–20). Throughout the sixteenth century, there are indications that fear of *uskoks* and other raiders kept these Vlachs away from certain parts of the shore – including the Novigrad Channel. Certainly they ran a greater risk of raiding when close to the shore, illustrated by an incident in 1551 when uskoks seized a Vlach and some of his livestock that had descended to graze near Slivnica for the winter (H.A.Z., Spisi Civran, I, March 1551). The Venetian officials reported that, without such constraints, the Vlachs of Velebit would inundate the shores of the channel with flocks that exceeded 50–60,000 animals. From the early seventeenth century, there is evidence that these Vlachs were making pasturage arrangements with the villagers of the Ljubać and Novigrad districts (Posedarje and Ražanac in particular), presumably paying fees, as they had earlier, but apparently to the villagers rather than to the owners of the land. They are reported to 'have begun to ferry their animals across the straits of Novigrad to the pastures of the said villages, so that because of the numbers, which grow ever more superabundant on the shores of Velebit, the grass is beginning to suffer' (*Commissiones*, VIII, 95).

In this case, neither the Venetian administration nor the landowners approved of such arrangements, and the practice was prohibited. However, in spite of such bans, the pattern continued, usually by agreement between the Vlachs and the local villagers. By the end of the seventeenth century, it was common that grazing should be regulated by reciprocal arrangements whereby flocks from around Novigrad and Nin would be grazed on pastures in Bukovica and Podgorje in the summer, and Vlach flocks from Lika and Krbava allowed to graze on the coast in winter in return (Desnica 1950–1, 410; Raukar *et al.* 1987, III, 380). This sort of grazing on Ottoman territory was banned by the Ottoman authorities following the Treaty of Passarowitz (Požarevac) in 1699, as a result of an Ottoman–Venetian rivalry over the floating population on the borders (Venice similarly prohibited its subjects from working land on Ottoman territory, a long-established practice). Difficulties in finding summer pasturage caused some stockherders to emigrate to Ottoman territory with their flocks, while others allegedly coped with the ban by settling half their family on each side of the border (Stanojević 1987, 9–10). Yet another solution was found by expanding the use of pastures in Austrian Lika, agreeing to an exchange of pasturage, winter and summer, with the Austrian commandants of Lika.[22] Eventually this arrangement was regulated by the Lika Convention of 1776, with Venice opening up the pastures between the Zrmanja and the Adriatic from Privoz to Tribanj to flocks from Lika in the winter, and Austria providing summer pasturage for the Zadar flocks in the uplands of Lika, shepherds from both sides paying a fee to the respective state calculated on the number of animals (Tomić 1909, 51–2; *I libri commemoriali della Republica di Venezia*, registri, vol. VIII (Venice, 1914), 213–14. Raukar *et al.* 1987, III, 477, gives the sizes of the Lika flocks grazing on Zadar pastures based on the tax collected by the fiscal chamber).

As this discussion of eighteenth-century developments indicates, stockherding retained its importance in the economy of the Zadar lowlands even once the new security of the borders made an expansion of agriculture possible once again. The taxes and fees paid on livestock seem to have compared very favourably to those on agricultural production, even after the newly won lands had been opened up to farming and the conditions on grazing tightened. However, not all branches of stockherding had an equal importance in the eighteenth-century village economy. Throughout the century, observers reported that larger stock (oxen, cows, horses) were far outnumbered by small livestock (sheep and goats) in the area (Garagnin 1806, table 1; Novak 1961, 488–9).[23] To an extent this was natural. The nature of the pastures available was one reason – rock-strewn, shrubby pastures that could be used for little more than sheep-raising were far more extensive than the richer grasslands needed to graze cattle profitably, and required less of an investment from the villagers.[24] But contemporary observers are insistent that the proportions of plough animals raised in the district were lower than might have been expected, in spite of measures intended to increase their numbers (including an exemption on the pasture tax for plough oxen) (Berengo 1954, 503).

A number of factors contributed to the low numbers of oxen and horses. Not only was there more maquis in the Zadar lowlands than there was grassland but the Venetian state is reported to have reserved the richest grassland for its own use, pasturing its cavalry horses there and cutting the hay for its own use (Novak 1961, 488; Raukar *et al.* 1987, III, 475). The proportion of grassland in private hands was much lower. The Lex Grimani of 1775 ordered that a portion of each land grant be reserved for growing hay, that enclosed common pastures be reserved during ploughing for the oxen used in fieldwork, and that winter forage be provided for the cattle, so that the start of ploughing would not be delayed by the need for weakened oxen to restore themselves first by spring grazing (Luzzatto 1921a, 233, 236). However, like the other provisions of the law, this was rarely enforced. Even if the villager had wished to, it was not always possible to carry out these regulations. In the not infrequent years of drought, it was difficult to gather winter fodder, when there was scarcely enough grass for summer grazing. Small land grants did not often contain suitable meadowland for growing hay, and common lands intended for grazing plough animals were frequently usurped for private use (Tomić 1909, 81). According to one contemporary observer, the regulations reserving some pastures during ploughing actually harmed the animals by providing an excuse for excluding them at other times of the year, when they were forced to wander at large, finding their own forage by the roadsides (Luzzatto 1921b, 306–7). Even when fodder could be provided, one observer noted that much was wasted, claiming that the villagers 'have never learned to…make their animals eat out of a hay rack, and through the lack of this must give their animals the hay or straw to eat on the ground, so that the fodder is for the most part lost or fouled' (Provedditore Generale Dandolo, writing in 1806, quoted in Luzzatto 1921b, 328). As a result of all these difficulties, and also because of the lack of shelter provided for them, cattle weakened by the winters suffered from a high mortality rate, aggravated by spring frosts and by cattle epidemics.

Cattle were also subject to human depredation. Both large and small livestock had always been the targets of hinterland *hajduks* (bandits), but livestock theft was an expected hazard with long-established rules in this region, a game played by ordinary herdsmen as well as professional brigands. The usurer and the tax collector in many ways posed a more serious threat to the villager's oxen. Many lowland villagers found themselves deep in debt in the eighteenth century, partly as the result of crop failures and cattle epidemics,[25] but also as a result of higher tax and rent obligations, extensive usury and legal abuses. In theory, land granted by the state could not be seized for debt, but the oxen and horses used for ploughing could. After this had happened, the villager could either run further into debt by borrowing the oxen needed for ploughing or the money to pay for them, or else abandon work in the fields, perhaps selling his land illegally to pay his debts. This was a conclusion which a sixteenth-century codification of customary law for Vrana had identified and tried to forestall, forbidding the seizure of oxen if the debt could be paid with any other form of property 'for a peasant cannot work without oxen' (Freidenberg 1971, 337).[26]

Debt was not the only way in which a villager could lose the use of his horse or ox. Increasingly, over the course of the century, public labour obligations were imposed on those who worked state lands in the newly acquired territories, rising to as much as four days a week at some points. This could mean either personal labour or the use of privately owned animals (used for hauling or transport in working state lands or building roads, public buildings, etc.). Because so many large Zadar landowners were exempt from these labour obligations for various reasons, the burden fell most heavily on the villagers. Rather than pay for the upkeep of animals whose labour was then claimed by the state, many villagers preferred to sell their horses or oxen and invest instead in small livestock (Berengo 1954, 505; Peričić 1971, 50).

Summary

The Zadar lowlands experienced a long decline in the period under discussion. The fifteenth century saw the waning of a lively trade (both between the city and the hinterland and between the city and the Mediterranean world) that had marked Zadar's medieval economic expansion, and a retrenchment by the patriciate and the wealthy citizens who invested more heavily in local landholding. However, the Ottoman wars swept over the territory in the sixteenth and seventeenth centuries, decimating the population, cutting incomes from the villages, and disrupting patterns of village life. The threat posed by the Turk was accompanied by some opportunities for the lowland villagers to improve their positions vis-à-vis their landlords – in contrast to peasants in other parts of Eastern Europe, they were able to retain their personal freedom, and even to increase their rights to the land they worked – but the costs paid in human and economic terms were very high. In this period, the lowland villages retained a subsistence economy, producing very little for the market, while the city of Zadar was forced to rely on its islands and on imports to supply its most basic needs, maintaining a precarious economic stability by virtue of its status as the capital city of Venice's Dalmatian possessions. With the final redrawing of the Ottoman frontier in the beginning of the eighteenth century, the opening up of the newly liberated lands and the gradual increase in population through immigration from the hinterland, the district laid the basis for a new economic expansion.

However, this expansion was slow to take effect. Eighteenth-century commentators largely saw the Zadar lowlands – as indeed they viewed Dalmatia in general – as poor, underdeveloped, stagnating, backward and paralysed, in spite of the area's natural resources. Explanations were sought in a variety of spheres. Some blamed village culture, seeing these conditions as the result of laziness and ignorance, as peasant conservatism, or as a heroic disdain for manual labour. This last explanation, with its inevitable emphasis on the martial attitudes and values learnt over three hundred years spent battling the Turk, gun in hand, merged with a historical interpretation of the territory's development, in which all impetus towards change was seen as constrained by the patterns of the past. Towards the second half of the eighteenth century, some Dalmatian observers became more sensitive to the socio-economic circumstances that shaped the economic life of the villages: the unequal division of land, the conditions of land tenure, the burdens of obligations to landlord and state. Little first-hand testimony has survived to tell us the opinions of the villagers themselves, but the evidence of agrarian resistance and revolt throughout the century hints that they too identified these factors as the main causes of their troubles.

In spite of the slow pace of change, it would be a mistake to see village economy and society as completely unmoving, resisting all improvements with a stubborn peasant conservatism in the eighteenth century. Throughout the previous centuries, the villagers had constantly adapted to the changing circumstances of war and peace, dearth and plenty, evolving strategies that would allow them to feed their families without exposing them to unnecessary risks. Innovations did take root: new methods of fertilization crept in; new crops appeared in the village fields as balance between risk and profit slowly altered in the villagers' calculations, or as the landlords gained greater control over production on their lands. This process of change would only accelerate with the nineteenth century, as the Zadar lowlands became integrated into a newly expanding market economy.

Notes

1 City censuses were regularly carried out and reported to the Venetian Senate in the sixteenth century (though less regularly in the seventeenth and eighteenth centuries). They appear to be consistent and fairly accurate, though some problems may have been caused by copiers' errors (see the figures for 1553 in table 41) and by the fact that the precise boundaries of the area surveyed are not always specified. Thus it is not always clear, for example, whether figures for the Zadar territory include those for Nin and its district, officially a separate administrative entity (though I believe that they are usually *not* included).

2 It should be repeated that Venetian sources referring to the territory of Zadar reflect the territory held by Venice at the time – not the whole of the Zadar lowlands. Particularly between 1576 and 1671 the area of this territory was greatly circumscribed.

3 These were not necessarily ethnic Vlachs, but rather stockherder/military irregulars, used by the Ottomans to defend the borders and colonize the deserted frontiers. For a group of these recent settlers causing apprehension among the Venetian population around Vrana, see *Commissiones*, II, 42.

4 In 1553 the Venetian authorities noted that, of 280 settlements on the wider Zadar territory before 1540, only 96 now remained. Of these only 85 were in fact inhabited – some with no more than five to six houses (*Commissiones*, II, 198–9). The estimate of 280 villages is probably too high, judging by other statistics for villages given in the censuses (86 in 1527, *ibid.*, I, 203–23; 45 in 1528, *ibid.*, I, 171), but does indicate the scale of change that the Venetian officials perceived.

5 A description of the Zadar district from the mid-seventeenth century by Simun Ljubavac notes the many villages defended by mortared or dry stone walls, many of which are no longer visible today. Some of these had been torn down in Ljubavac's time by the Ottomans (Ražanac, Slivnica and Posedarje, for example). *Storica disertazione del Contado e Territorio di Zara del Dot.r Simon Gliubavac...*, Naučna biblioteka, Zadar, Inv. 16530, MS 459.

6 In the seventeenth century Filip-Jakov was reported to be surrounded 'by a circuit of dry wall' *Storica disertazione*, Naučna biblioteka, Zadar, Inv. 16530, MS 459.

7 Details of the labourer's obligations to the landlord in the mid-sixteenth-century customary law of Novigrad can be found in Barada 1957, especially 161–2. For a discussion of land tenure obligations on the Zadar territory in general, see Raukar 1977, 80–104.

8 In 1562, for example, the villagers of Podnosje contracted to work lands owned by the parish of St Nicholas for dues of one-fifth plus one-tenth of the harvest 'notwithstanding the municipal laws or the Statute of Zadar to the contrary' (H.A.Z., Spisi Zadarskih Notara: Simun Budineus I/6, fol. 365–365v, 19 May 1562). In the same year, the leprosarium of the Holy Spirit reduced the obligations usually due on unworked land by contracting with Matthias Busanich and his family to work two *sortes* for one-sixth the first year, one-fifth the second, and the customary one-fourth only in the third year, in addition to the usual labour services (*ibid.*, fol. 371–371v, 8 June 1562).

9 The document is printed in Filipi 1972, 495–6. Naučna biblioteka, Zadar. Misc. B. No. 2220/25142, 'Stampa. Per li fedeli germani Signinini contro il Comun di Pacoschiana', 1–4. Similar arrangements can be traced through the contracts recorded in the Zadar notarial documents. In the 1620s the Marchiol/de Marchi family of Zadar, landlords of Turanj, were engaged in a similar effort, trying to raise an income from wooded common land near Turanj. H.A.Z., Spisi Zadarskih Notara: Simon Pasini, Ia/1: 4 January 1621 and 10 August 1621 contain contracts with villagers of Turanj to clear wooded common land near Tukljačan 'in a place called Gilovazze', for which they would pay the de Marchis one-tenth on grain and grape must

as *terratica*. The landlords in turn promised that neither they nor their heirs would demand more.

10 While in the fifteenth century land tenure contracts generally only involve a single *sors* (approximately 7–7.5 hectares) of arable land for one worker, in the sixteenth and seventeenth centuries they often allocate much more land. A single volume of notarial documents from the mid-sixteenth century (H.A.Z., Spisi Zadarskih Notara: Simun Budineus I/6) gives a number of examples besides those quoted here: sixteen *sortes* divided among six villagers (fols. 355–355v, 5 April 1562); two *sortes* to a single peasant (fols. 371–371v, 6 June 1562); twelve *sortes* divided between seven villagers (fols. 392v–393, 2 November 1562).

11 Particularly where the lands under the new system bordered on the older territories and where the contrast in obligations was immediately evident, such as the village of Sukošan, which acquired some new territory in the Candian War. The Venetian officials, urged on by the landlords, found it necessary at first to prevent the original inhabitants abandoning their old lands to move to the new territories (Grgić 1960, 561).

12 'La terra essendo di Dio, i frutti sono delle braccia che la coltivano' (Garagnin 1806, 213).

13 Details are hard to come by, but the income of the Rogovo monastery for 1562–4 included barley, rye, millet, beans, lentils and spelt as well as wheat, wine, oil and livestock (Raukar 1977, 262). Various brief comments on lowland agriculture usually refer only to wheat and barley (see for example, *Commissiones*, VIII, 45; Novak 1960, 504, etc.).

14 To give just two examples from either end of the period, M. Sanuto reports a severe storm in 1524 which destroyed a high proportion of the olives in the territory (Sanuto 1879–1903) vol. 37, 383–4), while in 1782 and 1788 hard freezes in the spring killed so many trees that the drop in the production of olive oil severely worried the Venetian government (Michieli Vitturi 1811, 19). There has been insufficient research to speculate whether the Zadar olive groves may have been affected by a seventeenth-century 'Little Ice Age' (cf. Le Roy Ladurie 1982, 293–319).

15 H.A.Z. Datia et incantus, box 3, vol. VII (1531–61), sv. 19, fols. 263–263v (3 October 1560). These Vlachs had first been settled in Istria, but in mid-sixteenth century they returned to the Zadar district, where they were granted state land with very favourable rents (one-seventh rather than a quarter). In the documents they are usually referred to as 'Istrians'.

16 Twelve to each *gonjaj* – 2,370 square metres – in 1566 (*Commissiones*, III, 167); eight to the area that could be sown by a *star* (1.83 litres) of wheat in 1623 (Raukar *et al.* 1987, III, 378).

17 The notarial records mention mills in Ljubac, Zablata, Kašiči near Novigrad, Posedarje, Blačane. Many of these mills were owned by the Venetian fiscal chamber and leased at auction to wealthy Zadar citizens or patricians. Their revenues rise and fall with the threat of Ottoman attack – and indeed, in 1557 the fiscal chamber was forced to concede that Venice would bear the costs if the mills on the Ljubac mills were burnt by the Turks in order to find a taker (H.A.Z., Datia et incantus, box 3, vol. VII (1531–61), sv. 18, fol. 248). Others were owned and let by private landlords (cf. the contract for the lease of a flour mill in Posedarje for twenty years, for eight '*quarti*' of wheat annually and the right of the owner to mill grain without charge. Again, if the lessee could not use the mill because of a war with the Ottomans, the owner was to bear the expense. H.A.Z., Spisi Zadarskih Notara: Simon Pasini, IIa/5, 14 December 1618).

18 A *campo padovano* is equivalent to 0.9 acre (3,656 sq. m). A similar survey from the end of the eighteenth century allows us to compare the distribution of land in the *vecchio* and *nuovo acquisto*. In the *vecchio acquisto* (129 sq. Italian miles), there were 18,763 *campi* of land in fields and vineyards; 340 *campi* of marshes; 6,145 *campi* of enclosed woods (used only for limited grazing); 79,769 *campi* of wood, shrub and rocky or alpine pasture. On the *nuovo acquisto* (604 sq. Italian miles, there were 93,268 *campi* of arable or vine-growing land, 2,892 *campi* of meadows; 12,050 *campi* of marsh; 683 *campi* of 'woods for cultivation'; and 390,512 *campi* of woods, shrubs and rocky or alpine pastures (Foretić 1963, 291–304).

19 Agrarian writers of eighteenth-century Dalmatia advance all these theories. See Tomić 1909; Lovrić 1948; Pederin 1984 examines the ideological assumptions behind these explanations.

20 A few examples: on the Zadar territory in 1581 there were 1,595 head of large stock, 6,073 small stock (*Commissiones*, IV, 294); in Nin at the same time there were 542 head of large stock and 749 small, and on its district 300 head of large cattle and 900 small (*Commissiones*, IV, 256); Zadar and its district in 1642 had 261 horses, 1,269 donkeys, 4,098 head of cattle, 15,015 small

livestock (sheep and goats); Nin and its district had 52 horses, 323 donkeys, 1,470 head of cattle, 4,904 small livestock; Novigrad had 135 head of cattle, 50 donkeys, 255 small livestock (*Commissiones*, VII, 221, 222, 224); the Zadar territory in 1683 had 5,121 head of cattle, 1,600 horses, and 17,700 sheep (Raukar *et al.* 1987, III, 379); and at the beginning of the eighteenth century the Zadar territory had 7,393 horses, 37,200 head of cattle and 133,135 of small livestock (*ibid.*); Zadar and its territory (including the islands) in 1771 had 524 horses, 34,872 grazing cattle, 7,181 pack-animals, 253,452 small livestock; Nin in the same year had 34 horses, 1,187 grazing cattle, 177 pack-animals 10,600 small livestock; and Novigrad had 77 horses, 5,680 grazing cattle, 1,442 pack-animals, 56,847 small livestock (Bozić-Bužančić 1968–9). The Zadar territory (including the islands and Novigrad) in 1781 had 397 horses, 5,162 pack-animals, 12,225 grazing and ploughing stock, 4,927 pigs, and 206,996 small livestock; while Nin and its territory had 49 horses, 273 pack-animals, 637 oxen, 125 pigs, and 9,725 small livestock (*ibid.*). I have not presented these statistics in the form of a table in order to emphasize that the numbers are not directly comparable because the boundaries of the Zadar territory changed so drastically in the seventeenth and eighteenth centuries. Comparison of the statistics for the territory of Nin (which did not alter so much) may reflect patterns of stockherding more accurately.

21 'Istrian' Vlachs, for example, are found concluding contracts for the cultivation of arable land according to the two-field system in precisely the same way as their other neighbours in the sixteenth century (H.A.Z., Spisi Zadarskih Notara: Simon Budineus I, fasc. 1, sv. 1, fol. 5v (26 October 1556).

22 An observer mentions this as a recent development in the first half of the eighteenth century, but in fact it seems to have been a long-standing practice (Tomić 1909, 81).

23 Certainly the statistics cited in note 20 support this contention.

24 Compare the statistics for pasturage in comparison to ploughed land given above in note 18.

25 There were crop failures requiring public assistance in supplies in 1748 and 1765, but 1779 and 1782 were the years of the worst drought (and 1782 was followed by an outbreak of the plague); 1788 saw a particularly bad spring freeze. There were a number of other less severe drought years. Cattle epidemics hit the Zadar area particularly badly in 1720, 1731, 1765 and 1783–4.

26 See also contemporary complaints about the difficulties caused by the seizure of oxen for debt quoted in Berengo 1954, 484–5; also Tomić 1909, 86. Usury was a serious problem: 'In order to have twenty sequins or a pair of oxen of that value, [the villager] pays sixteen sequins annually as interest...so that after five years he has paid for four pairs of oxen, while still always remaining in debt for the first pair' Provedditore Generale Dandolo again, quoted in Luzzatto 1921b, 328.

9 Summary and conclusions

At the beginning of this book, certain questions were raised and an approach to the study of Dalmatia was discussed. The links between past and present were adumbrated in terms of multiple pasts, in which the different layers of a sequential palimpsest were deposited. No single millennium nor century shared the same past as any other, since the pre-existing sequence of laid-down pasts was, had to be, unique and different. The elements of continuity between different pasts were, however, strongly fixed in the landscape. Its geology and topography provided a context for shorter-term activities but many artefacts helped to embed any given present in the past. The immovable clearance walls of the Roman centuriation system formed the limits for the medieval territory of Zadar as effectively as they delimited the veterans' land and they remain significant field monuments today.

The key issues and questions raised at the onset may now be re-examined, in order to assess the contribution made to Dalmatian prehistory and history by the project's work. We should first turn to the framework of archaeological research dominant in the region before NDP's fieldwork.

Towards a new paradigm

The traditional paradigm for archaeological studies in Dalmatia can be summarized as the invasionist/diffusionist paradigm, in which all key cultural innovations are adjudged to have been stimulated, if not introduced, by external immigrants or invaders, peaceful or warlike, who made Dalmatia their new home. Researchers following this paradigm have laid stress on the stability and continuity exhibited by the indigenous populations, who often assimilated external influences and ideas into a fruitful multi-cultural mix, or 'Mischkultur'.

It would be otiose to deny the impact of historically attested invasions since the Venetian period, any more than to suggest that Dalmatia was not absorbed unwillingly into the Roman Empire. However, the invasion theory for the origins of early medieval Croatia can now be questioned by dint of logistical objections to Chrobatos's warrior bands, and a serious indigenous alternative model proposed, based on local evidence for cultural continuity (see pp. 295–9). The discovery of Iron Age farmsteads in the lowland zone on Arable land undermines the theory that rapacious Roman landlords occupied all the fertile farmland lying empty and unused in the Ravni Kotari. Instead, there are several parts of the Zadar lowlands where settlement continuity can be identified between Late Iron Age farms and Roman farms or villas. North Dalmatia is one of the very few Roman provincial regions where the main defended hilltop settlements continue in use as Roman administrative centres (*municipia*), an indication of political as well as locational continuity (Chapman and Shiel 1991). Nevertheless, the scale of resource extraction and conspicuous consumption in the Roman era exceeded anything 'achieved' by the Iron Age and the landscape was dramatically, perhaps permanently, changed in the Roman period.

The hypothesis that iron-working was initiated by warlords from the North Pontic zone and spread into Dalmatia via Hallstatt invasions may also now be reformulated. The settlement and material culture evidence from North Dalmatia consistently demonstrates the similarities in locational strategies and technologies between the Later Bronze Age and the Early Iron Age. The majority of landscape segments occupied by Bronze Age communities was reoccupied in the Iron Age, in particular the high-status enclosed and defended settlements on ridges and hills. Many cemeteries first used in the Bronze Age boast Iron Age graves as well. The greater part of the repertoire of bronzework found in Later Bronze Age settlements or graves continues to be used in the Iron Age, with the addition of new imports and a small number of iron artefacts. The small number of innovations at the threshold of the Bronze and Iron Ages may readily and satisfactorily be explained by the spread of ideas along the inter-regional exchange networks through which Dalmatia obtained its crucial metal resources.

The long-cherished hypothesis which claims to explain the onset of the Bronze Age through the spread of Indo-European nomadic pastoralists from the same North Pontic zone into Eastern and then Western Europe has recently received many setbacks. The alternative notion of Indo-European language diffusion along with the spread of farming across Europe (Renfrew 1989) has removed the linguistic logic of a Bronze Age diffusion which has always been poorly attested in the archaeological record. The linkage of barrow or cairn burial to nomadic groups whose settlement remains were scanty in the extreme has long been a key element of the archaeological myth of Indo-Europeans. In north Dalmatia, it is possible now to see the cairns which dot the landscape as the remains primarily of field clearance and only then as the recipients of human remains. Thus, quite contrary to the traditional view, cairns are a sign of local cultivation rather than the arrival of nomadic pastoralists and therefore evidence of Bronze Age settlement. The distribution of cairns results from local groups of agriculturalists moving onto the limestone ridges and cultivating their stony soils. Thus, the origin of the Bronze Age in Dalmatia is tied into continuity of settlement in the valleys together with a local expansion onto hillslope Stony land, a local process of demographic change rather than an invasion from the steppe zone.

The origins of farming in Dalmatia were traditionally seen in terms of a diffusion of people from the Near East to Anatolia and Greece, with a subsequent westward spread of population through the Mediterranean. The traditional view of Dalmatian farming was that it began late, in the Middle Neolithic or late fifth millennium Cal. BC. Recent radiocarbon dates produced by NDP and other projects have indicated that mixed farming in Dalmatia, with a full suite of domestic wheat, barley and pulses, sheep, goats, pigs and cattle began almost as early as in Greece, i.e. in the first half of the sixth millennium Cal. BC (Chapman and Müller 1990). However, the absence of dated Mesolithic sites within the survey area means that there is at present no new evidence to support a local development of farming in north Dalmatia. Rather, the development of a marine exchange network linking north-west Greece, Italy and Dalmatia would have provided a mechanism whereby novel plant and animal resources could have spread without the necessity for a population incursion (Chapman 1991b). The flooding of coastal Late Mesolithic sites and the burial of Bottomland by post-Neolithic sedimentation of inland sites mean that the solution to local processes of change will be difficult to trace. The diffusionist model is hardest to refute in the case of the origins of agriculture in north Dalmatia.

Two important components of the diffusionist/invasionist paradigm are the insistent use of the 'site' and the 'culture' as the main units of archaeological analysis and the high priority given to cultural data, leading to a failure to integrate archaeological and palaeoenvironmental data. Given that an alternative paradigm is emerging, it seems clear that these two components require revision. The project has shown that, although sites and monuments have their place at one level of study, a crucial complementary level of study is the regional settlement system, defined by the overall pattern of settlements and the social networks connecting individual sites and monuments. The use of the 'culture' as a unit of analysis to be defined before any other kind of analysis has led to a rigid framework defined more by boundaries than by interactions. The results of the excavations of the Copper Age of Buković illustrated this problem through the discovery of two pottery styles, supposedly of different 'cultures', in the same site. Alternative explanations may be proposed, such as the portrayal of different entities, where material culture is used to reinforce the identities of different cross-cutting status or kinship groups.

Social power in the landscape

The possibilities of integration of palaeoenvironmental and archaeological data have been frequently exploited in the project's research. The most fruitful potential has been in the field of land use studies, where predictive modelling based on climatic, soil and ethnographic data has led to the explanation of several key elements of the changing settlement pattern. The soils mapping and the investigation of buried soils at excavation sites have also broken new ground in Dalmatia. Without an understanding of the constraints and potentials of previous landscapes, any attempt to understand the social dimension of change is an over-simplification. Can this integration of the physical and the social environment lead to further new insights about Dalmatia's past?

The geomorphic structure of the Ravni Kotari, with its catena of valleys and ridges at varying altitudes, forms a mosaic of land use categories with fairly small patch sizes. This landscape forms the enduring backcloth of the *longue durée* of north Dalmatia. In a landscape with such a mosaic, efficient land use strategies would necessitate some combination of mixed farming once food production had been developed. It would be possible but hardly very productive to specialize in wholly crop-farming or purely pastoralism. The highly localized land class distribution, with its small patch sizes, favoured a subsistence strategy based on dispersed settlement patterns, where each settlement unit controlled access to and utilized the full range of available land use classes.

The climatic fluctuations in temperature, precipitation and associated measures had a variable effect on the different land use classes, such that use of a broad spectrum of land resources would have alleviated subsistence risks. Warmer, drier climatic trends would have made Arable and Bottomland more productive than Stony or Karst land both for agriculture and pastoralism. The converse would have been true for cooler, wetter phases, in which Stony and Karst land would have become more attractive. These perhaps cyclical climatic fluctuations provided a rhythm of agro-pastoral change at the time-scale of one to three centuries – still at the level of the *longue durée.* But these changes in land use potential were relative to local land classes; environmental fluctuations resulted less in stringent limits than in broad constraints on farming practice, with the sole possible exceptions of olive and almond cultivation. The positive effect of a eu-Mediterranean 'coastal' effect on higher productivity of vines, olives and almonds in a narrow coastal strip would have been important especially in the Iron Age and Roman periods.

Another characteristic of the study region is the relative under-use of the land use potential for the survey block over most of the last eight millennia. At no period, even during Roman provincial administration, was the terrain of this part of the Ravni Kotari used to the full. While detailed soil studies may contradict this view, the distributional evidence is clear that there was always spare capacity of land capable of growing crops in this area. This relative under-use of the landscape may be accounted for in two ways: an agrarian strategy of risk-alleviation, in which a large buffer zone of generally unused land is available in case of local crop failures, and contrary to appearances, the lowland landscape was much more heavily utilized than is reflected by background discard, with intensive cultivation restricted to areas surrounding settlements and an extensive pastoral component inbetween settled areas. At present, neither of these explanations can be ruled out; the latter strategy could have been especially important in the Iron Age. Even today, the Karst is not used intensively and woodland is spreading by default. This appears to be a trend in most 'developing' societies, where the young leave rural and less capable land is used for pasturage, woodland or recreation.

Linked to this trend in much of past settlement on the plain is the predominance of small-scale, dispersed settlement units. It is this settlement development which most closely approximates to a long-term structure in social terms. On the rare occasions when kinship groups unite to form more nucleated units, site sizes are consonant with population levels of no more than a hundred individuals. The nucleation evident in the Roman *municipium* of Nadin-Gradina represents the largest settlement known from eight millennia of plains occupation. When settlement expansion occurred, it was not based on expansion from one or a few central places, as in Greece, but rather through wider occupation of a still essentially dispersed landscape. In the Roman period in the Ravni Kotari, there was a greater emphasis on centrally-integrated economies combined with similarly dispersed settlement units.

The Land Use Capability model proved good at predicting where cultivation and pastoralism could have been successful under various climatic conditions, but this model was unable to explain how these changes in the use of the landscape actually occurred. Here, the interaction between generational and annual patterning was more helpful, beginning in the Early Neolithic with the establishment of domestic settlements with strong ties to the local ancestors expressed through intra-settlement burial practices. 'Domestication' of the local landscape can be contrasted with regionally-based social networks, through visits to the coast for shell-collecting or fishing or exchange links with coastal groups. The differentiation of time and space occurred relatively slowly in the Ravni Kotari, with few changes in the basic domestic arena of social power throughout the Neolithic and Copper Age.

In the Bronze Age, the major landscape change was the colonization of the Stony and Karst land classes in the Ravni Kotari, land classes mostly distributed on the limestone ridges. The cairns and linear features constructed on these land classes should be viewed not merely as strategies of land management but also as more active territorial events for the creation of places in a newly domesticated landscape. The confirmation of ancestral links by burial in clearance cairns and by the construction of enclosed settlements and fields extended the arenas of social power to a wider proportion of the landscape. In this period, a wide range of exotic prestige goods became available for the first time in Dalmatian prehistory. Thus, the social contradictions that stimulated new arenas of social power were concerned with the tensions between two principles of accumulation – communal acquisition and private accumulation of prestige goods. The ideologically marginal mortuary sphere was often used as a 'safe' domain for the deposition of prestige goods still not entirely suitable for private household hoarding until the end of the Bronze Age.

In the Iron Age, there is what at first seems a puzzling paucity of cairns and linear features, either near or far from the hill-forts. The only exception to this negative pattern is in the Velebit Mountains, where hill-forts and cairns document the spread of transhumant-based seasonal settlement. It could be argued that the Iron Age lowland farmers were occupying segments of the countryside previously settled in the Bronze Age and therefore that local territorial markers were not required to signify ancestral ties. The alternative notion is that, by the Late Iron Age if not earlier, the lowland zone was the focus of a strongly pastoralist subsistence strategy, in which fixed boundaries were important between central places but little crop intensification was practised within the hill-fort territories. If so, the creation of stable political borders marked an enormous symbolic advance in the ideological shaping of the landscape. In any case, the political centralization of kinship groups at the major hill-forts reduced the significance of internal land boundaries, and increased the likelihood of political boundaries at a regional level. This centralization coincided with other ways of defining the relations between ancestors and the living, both in the domestic and the mortuary domains. In the Iron Age, a similar contradiction was felt to that of the Later Bronze Age, not so much over ownership of goods as over land tenure. The struggle for private accumulation of wealth having been won in the Later Bronze Age or Early Iron Age, the main competition for élite power in the Late Iron Age shifted to the possibilities of private land-holding.

The increasingly significant taming of the landscape that occurred in the Roman period reinforced the notion of Roman social power as rooted in the extensive, market-oriented exploitation of the countryside. The differentiation of the concept of the 'linear feature' in the form of roads, aqueducts and centuriated fields is characteristic of the imposition of labour-intensive monuments that have remained rooted in the landscape until the present day. It was only in the early Roman period that private ownership of land became widely accepted in north Dalmatia. At this time, the incorporation of Dalmatia into the Roman Empire led to a wide range of new statuses in the imperial administration. The development of new arenas of social power enabled successful provincials to develop careers, accumulate land, trade in the monetized, market economy, and accumulate great wealth. In this part of the north Dalmatian sequence, the linkage of the study region to an international system of power and dominance created opportunities for local economic and social growth such as had never existed before.

The fluctuating population levels and increasingly militaristic struggles of the medieval and early modern period bring a different set of questions to the fore. One of the characteristic long-term patterns in this period is the migration of people from the Ravni Kotari in time of invasion. The Ottoman raids, for instance, meant loss of kin, land, stock and crops and the desertion of villages was a commonplace. The Ottoman response to the empty lowlands was often to bring in pastoralists (Morlaks = Vlachs) who rented uncultivated land. When uncultivated land fell vacant after Ottoman retreats, the problem for the Zadar authorities was how to entice labour to return to the land. The basic subsistence strategy in the Venetian and Ottoman periods was the pursuit of mixed farming based on sheep, goats, wheat, olive and vines during times of peace and prosperity and a concentration on mobile livestock in times of war. The consumption of surplus production was divided between regional capitals such as Zadar and imperial capitals such as Venice, as much as between civil and ecclesiastical authorities.

The Dalmatians

In this final section, we return to the first questions of our introductory chapter and seek to clarify the identity of the people after whom the study region is named. It is clear that the communities of north Dalmatia would remain anonymous until the combination of sufficiently precise written records and sufficiently homogenous tribal identities. These conditions are not met until the Iron Age, when first Greek and then Roman authors and map-makers peopled the lands of the east Adriatic (Wilkes 1969). The Iron Age tribal grouping that occupied all of north Dalmatia, with periodic expansion into the central parts, is known as the Liburnian group. However, it was the main tribal alliance in central Dalmatia – the so-called 'Delmatae' – whose name was adopted as the title of the Roman province of Dalmatia, as well as successive imperial lands. The location of the Roman provincial capital in the fertile plain of Split, inside the tribal lands of the Delmatae, was sufficient reason for the selection of this indigenous name.

Though anonymous in name, the communities living in Dalmatia before the Delmatae were far from anonymous in their material remains, using specific cultural traits to signify their identities in addition to their own local dialects of the Indo-European language family. Their cultural differences may well add up to more than their similarities. The tendency to live in dispersed settlements connected by extensive kinship and exchange networks and practise a mixed farming subsistence strategy based on the quartet of wheat, oil, vines and sheep is widespread, if not ubiquitous. The significance of upland transhumance and fishing is more culturally specific, despite the claims of every modern Dalmatian to be born in the sea. Whether members of wood-carving families, shepherd stock, ship-building guilds or monastic orders, the Dalmatian is bound to the ancestral lands and seaways, the procession of seasons, the changing face of Dalmatia. It is our hope that, in this book, an impression will be conveyed of those long traditions which have been overlaid to create the only palimpsest which we can now experience – the present with all its diversity of pasts – in this very special region of Europe.

Bibliography

Alföldy, G. 1965. *Bevölkerung und Gesellschaft in der römischen Provinz Dalmatien*, Budapest

Ammerman, A., Shaffer, G. D. and Hartman, N. 1990. 'A Neolithic household at Piana di Curinga, Italy', *J. Field Archaeol.*, 15, 121–40

Antoljak, S. 1978. *Izvori za historiju naroda Jugoslavije: srednji vijek*, Zadar

Barada, M. 1952. 'Hrvatska diaspora i Avari', *Starohrvatska Prosveta*, 3rd ser., 2, 7–14

Barada, M. (ed.) 1957. *Starohrvatska seoska zajedinica*, Zagreb

Barker, G. W. 1981. *Landscape and Society. Prehistoric Central Italy*, London

——, 1985. *Prehistoric Farming in Europe*, Cambridge

Barthes, R. 1972. *Mythologies*, London

Batović, S. 1953. 'Prethistorijksi mačevi u Arheološkom Muzeju u Zadru', *Vjesnik za Arheologiju i historiku dalmatinsku*, 55, 145–61

——, 1965a. 'Prvi paleolitski nalazi u sjevernoj Dalmaciji', *Diadora*, 3, 205–9

——, 1965b. 'Prapovijesna brončana koplja u Arheološkom muzeju u Zadru', *Diadora*, 3

——, 1966. *Stariji Neolit u Dalmaciji*, Zadar

——, 1968a. *Nin u prapovijesno doba*, Zadar

——, 1968b. 'Istraživanje ilirskog naselja u Radovinu', *Diadora*, 4, 53–84

——, 1971. 'Problemi prapovijesti na području Vrane i Biograda', *Radovi Instituta JAZU u Zadru*, 18

——, 1974. 'Ostava iz Jagodnje Gornje u okviru zadnje faze Liburnske kulture', *Diadora*, 7, 159–245

——, 1977. 'Caractéristiques des agglomérations fortifiées dans la région des Liburniens', *Godišnjak (Centar za Balkanološka Ispitivanja)*, 15, 201–25

——, 1979. 'Jadranska zona' in *Praistorija jugoslavenskih zemalja II: Neolit*, (ed. A. Benac), 473–634, Sarajevo

——, 1983. 'Kasno brončano doba na istočnom Jadranskom primorju' in *Praistorija jugoslavenskih zemalja IV: Bronzano Doba*, (ed. A. Benac), 271–373, Sarajevo

——, 1987. 'Liburnska grupa' in *Praistorija jugoslavenskih zemalja V: Bronzano Doba*, (ed. A. Benac), 339–90, Sarajevo

Batović, S. and Chapman, J. 1985. 'The "Neothermal Dalmatia" Project' in *Archaeological Field Survey in Britain and Abroad*, Soc. Antiq. London Occ. Pap., 6, (eds. S. Macready and F. H. Thompson), 158–95, London

——, 1986. 'Buković-Lastvine. Eneolitsko naselje', *Arheološki Pregled*, 24, 52–3

——, 1987. 'Istraživanje Gradine u Nadinu' *Obavijesti*, 19, 28–31

Batović, S. and Kukoš, S. 1986. 'Podvrsje/Matkov brig', *Arheološki Pregled* (1986), 61–3

Behre, K.-E. 1989. 'Some reflections on anthropogenic indicators and prehistoric occupation phases in the Near East', PrePrint from INQUA/BAI Symposium, '*The Impact of Ancient Man on the Landscape of the Eastern Mediterranean Region and the Near East*, 6–9/III/1989, Groningen

Belošević, J. 1980. *Materijalna kultura Hrvata od 7 do 9 stoljeća*, Zagreb

Benac, A. 1977. 'Quelques caractéristiques des agglomérations fortifiées dans la région centrale des Japodes' in *Utvrdjena ilirska naselja*, Posebna Izdanja Knjiga, 24, (ed. A. Benac), 81–92, Sarajevo

——, 1985. *Utvrdjena ilirska naselja (I)*, Sarajevo

Berengo, M. 1954. 'Problemi economico-sociali della Dalmazia Veneta alla fine del '700', *Rivista storica italiana*, 66/4, 469–510

Beug, H.-J. 1961. 'Beiträge zür postglazialen Floren- und Vegetationsgeschichte in Süddalmatien: der See "Malo Jezero" auf Mljet', *Flora*, 150, 600–31

——, 1962. 'Über die ersten anthropogenen Vegetationsveränderungen in Süddalmatien an Hand eines neuen Pollendiagrammes vom "Malo Jezero" auf Mljet', *Veröffentlichen Geobotan, Institut ETH, Stiftung Rubel*, 37, 9–15

——, 1967. 'On the forest history of the Dalmatian coast', *Rev. Paleobotany Palynology*, 2, 271–9

——, 1975. 'Man as a factor in the vegetational history of the Balkan peninsula' in *Proceedings of the 1st International Symposium on Balkan Flora and Vegetation*, 72–7, Varna

——, 1977. 'Vegetationsgeschichtliche Untersuchungen im Küstenbereich von Istrien (Jugoslawien)', *Flora*, 166, 357–81

Bhaskar, R. 1982. 'Emergence, explanation and emancipation' in *Explaining Human Behaviour: Consciousness, Behaviour and Social Structure*, (ed. P. F. Secord), Beverly Hills, CA

Bianchi, C. F. 1887. *Zara Christiana*, (vol. 1), Zadar

Bintliff, J. 1982a. 'Climatic change, archaeology and Quaternary science in the Eastern Mediterranean region' in *Climatic Change and Later Prehistory*, (ed. A. F. Harding), 143–61, Edinburgh

——, 1982b. 'Palaeoclimatic modelling of environmental changes in the East Mediterranean region since the last glaciation' in *Palaeoclimates, Palaeoenvironments and Human Communities in the Eastern Mediterranean Region in Later Prehistory*, Brit. Archaeol. Rep. Int. Ser., 133, (eds. J. L. Bintliff and W. van Zeist), 485–527, Oxford

——, 1982c, 'Settlement patterns, land tenure and social structure: a diachronic model', in *Ranking, Resources and Exchange*, (eds. C. Renfrew and S. Shennan), 106–11, Cambridge

——, (ed.) 1984. *European Social Evolution. Archaeological Perspectives*, Bradford

——, (ed.) 1991. *The Annales School and Archaeology*, Leicester

Bintliff, J. L. and Snodgrass, A. 1988. 'Off-site pottery distributions: a regional and inter-regional perspective', *Current Anthropol.*, 29, 506–12

Bökönyi, S. 1962. 'Zur Naturgeschichte des Ures in Ungarn und das Problem des Domestikation des Hausrindes', *Acta Archaeologica Hungarica*, 11, 39–102

——, 1974. 'The vertebrate fauna', in *Obre I and II*, Wissentschaftliches Mitteilungen des Bosnisch-Herzegovinisch Landesmuseums, Band IV, Heft A, Archäologie (ed. M. Gimbutas), 55-144, Sarajevo

Bottema, S. 1974. *Late Quaternary Vegetation History of North Western Greece*, Groningen

——, 1982. 'Palynological investigations in Greece with special reference to pollen as an indicator of human activity', *Palaeohistoria*, 24, 257–89

——, 1989. 'Anthropogenic indicators in the pollen record of the Eastern Mediterranean', PrePrint from *The Impact of Ancient Man on the Landscape of the Eastern*

Mediterranean Region and the Near East, INQUA/BAI Symposium, 6–9/III/1989, Groningen

Bourdieu, P. 1977. *Outline of a Theory of Practice*, Cambridge

Bourke, A. 1984. 'Impact of climatic fluctuations on European agriculture', in *The Climate of Europe: Past, Present and Future*, (eds. H. Flohn and R. Fantechi), 269–314, Dordrecht

Bozić-Bužančić, D. (ed.) 1968–9. 'Dvije anagrafske tabele za područje Dalmacije iz druge polovice 18. stoljeća,' *Arhivski vjesnik*, 11–12, 43–53

Bradford, J. 1957. *Ancient Landscapes*, London

Brakspear, R. 1986. *Technological Analysis of Prehistoric Pottery from Dalmatia*, unpub. B.A. (Hons) dissertation, Department of Archaeology, University of Newcastle upon Tyne

Brande, A. 1973. 'Untersuchungen zur postglazialen Vegetationsgeschichte im Gebiet der Neretva-Niederungen (Dalmatien, Herzegovina)', *Flora*, 162, 1–44

——, 1989. 'Patterns of Holocene vegetation and landscape changes in South Dalmatia', *Ecologia Mediterranea*, 15.1–2, 45–53

Braudel, F. 1972. *The Mediterranean and the Mediterranean World in the Age of Philip II*, London

——, 1981. *The Structures of Everyday Life*, Vol. I, London

——, 1989. *The Identity of France*, London

British Trust for Conservation Volunteers 1977. *Dry Stone Walling – a Practical Conservation Handbook*, Wellingborough

Čače, S. 1982. 'Liburnske zajednice i njihovi teritoriji', *Dometi*, 15, 41–52

——, 1985. *Liburnija u razdoblju od 4. do 1. stoljeća prije nove ere*, Ph.D. thesis, Universitet Zadar

Callander, R. 1982. *Drystane Dyking in Deeside*, Aberdeen

Carlton, R. 1988a. 'An ethno-archaeological study of pottery production on the Dalmatian island of Iž' in Chapman *et al.* 1988, 101–23

——, 1988b. 'Ethno-archaeological study of pottery production in Dalmatia', *Archaeological Reports for* 1987, Durham and Newcastle upon Tyne, 50–5

Carrier, E. H. 1932. *Water and Grass: A Study in the Pastoral Economy of Southern Europe*, London

Chagnon, N. A. 1990. 'Reproductive and somatic conflicts of interests in the genesis of violence and warfare amongst tribesmen' in *The Anthropology of Warfare*, (ed. J. Haas), 77–104, Cambridge

Chang, J. 1968. *Climate and Agriculture*, Chicago

Chapman, J. C. 1981. 'The value of Dalmatian museum collections to Dalmatian settlement studies' in *The Research Potential of Anthropological Museum Collections*, Annals of New York Academy of Science, 376, (eds. A.-M. Cantwell, J. B. Griffin and N. A. Rothschild), 529–55, New York

——, 1988. 'From "space" to "place": a model of dispersed settlement and Neolithic society' in *Enclosures and Defences in the Neolithic of Western Europe*, Brit. Archaeol. Rep. Int. Ser., 403, (eds. C. Burgess, P. Topping and D. Mordant), 21–46, Oxford

——, 1989. 'The Early Balkan village', *Varia Archaeologica Hungarica*, 2, 33–53

——, 1991a. 'The creation of social arenas in the Neolithic and Copper Age of South East Europe: the case of Varna' in *Sacred and Profane*, (eds. P. Garwood *et al.*), 152–71, Oxford

——, 1991b. 'The origins of farming in South East Europe', *Cota Zero*, 7, 126–35

——, 1992. 'Arenas of social power in Serbian prehistory', D. Garašanin Festschrift, *Zbornik Narodnog Muzeja (Beograd)*, 14, 305–17

——, 1993. 'Social power in the Iron Gates Mesolithic' in *Cultural Transformations and Interactions in Eastern Europe*, (eds. J. C. Chapman and P. M. Dolukhanov), 61–106, London

——, 1994a. 'The living, the dead and the ancestors: time, life cycles and the mortuary domain in later European prehistory' in *Ritual and Remembrance. Responses to Death in Human Societies*, (ed. J. Davies), 40–85, Sheffield

——, 1994b. 'The origins of farming in south east Europe', *Préhistoire Européenne*, 6, 133–56

Chapman, J. C. and Batović, S. 1985. 'The Neothermal Dalmatia Project – Third (1984) Season', *Archaeological Reports (Durham and Newcastle) for 1984*, 8–11

——, and Shiel, R.S, 1987. 'Settlement patterns and land use in Neothermal Dalmatia, Yugoslavia: 1983–1984 seasons', *J. Field Archaeol.*, 14, 123–46

Chapman, J. C. and Müller, J. 1990. 'Early farmers in the Mediterranean Basin: the Dalmatian evidence', *Antiquity*, 64, 127–34

Chapman, J. C. and Shiel, R. 1988. 'The Neothermal Dalmatia Project – archaeological survey results' in J. C. Chapman *et al.* 1988, 1–30

——, 1991. 'Settlement, soils and societies in Dalmatia' in *Roman Landscapes. Archaeological Survey in the Mediterranean Region*, (eds. G. Barker and J. Lloyd) 62–75, London

——, 1993. 'Social change and land use in Dalmatia', *Proc. Prehistoric Soc.*, 59, 61–104

Chapman, J. C., Bintliff, J., Gaffney, V. and Slapšak, B. (eds.) 1988. *Recent Developments in Yugoslav Archaeology*, Brit. Archaeol. Rep. Int. Ser., 431, Oxford

Chapman, Schwartz, C. A., Turner, J. and Shiel, R.S. 1992. 'New absolute dates for prehistoric and Roman Dalmatia', *Vjesnik za Arheologiju i Historiju Dalmatinsku*, 83, 29–46

Cherry, J., Gamble, C. and Shennan, S. (eds.) 1978. *Sampling in Contemporary British Archaeology*, Brit. Ser., 50, Oxford

Childe, V. G. 1925. *The Aryans*, London

——, 1936. *Man makes Himself*, London

Childe, V. G. and Thorneycroft, W. 1938. 'The experimental production of the phenomena distinctive of vitrified forts', *Proc. Soc. Antiq. Scotland*, 72, 44–55

Clarke, D. L. (ed.) 1977. *Spatial Archaeology*, London

——, 1979. 'The economic context of trade and industry in barbarian Europe till Roman times' in *Analytical Archaeologist: Collected Papers of David L. Clarke*, 263–331, London

Clutton-Brock, J. 1987. *A Natural History of Domesticated Mammals*, London

Cohen, M. N. 1977. *The Food Crisis in Prehistory. Overpopulation and the Origins of Agriculture*, New Haven

Coles, J. 1973. *Archaeology by Experiment*, London

——, 1979. *Experimental Archaeology*, London

Coles, J. and Harding, A. F. 1979. *The Bronze Age in Europe*, London

Collis, J. 1984. *The European Iron Age*, London

Commissiones. *Commissiones et relationes Venetae* (Monumenta spectantia historiam Slavorum meridionalium, vols. 6, 8, 11, 47, 48, 49, 50, 51, Zagreb, 1876–1974; edited by Novak 1964–74)

Conroy, S. 1992. *A Comparative Work Study of Irish Stone Forts*, Unpub. B.A. (Hons.) dissertation, Department of Archaeology, University of Newcastle upon Tyne

Coones, P. 1985. 'One landscape or many? A geographical perspective', *Landscape History*, 7, 5–12

Cosgrove, D. E. 1984. *Social Formation and Symbolic Landscape*, London

Courty, M. A., Goldberg, P. and MacPhail, R. I. 1989. *Soils and Micromorphology in Archaeology*, Cambridge

Čović, B. 1980. 'Počeci metalurgije željeza na sjevernozapadnom Balkanu', *Godišnjak XVIII (Centar za Balkanološka Ispitivanja* 16), 63–79

——, 1983a. 'Regionalne grupe ranog bronzanog doba' in *Praistorija Jugoslavenskih Zemalja IV, Bronzano Doba*, (ed. A. Benac), 114–89, Sarajevo

——, 1983b. 'Eneolitski substrat' in *Praistorija Jugoslavenskih Zemalja IV, Bronzano Doba*, (ed. A. Benac), 103–12, Sarajevo

——, 1987. 'Sredno-dalmatinska grupa' in *Praistorija Jugoslavenskih Zemalja V, Željezno Doba*, (ed. A. Benac), 442–80, Sarajevo

Criado, F. 1989. 'We, the post-megalithic people' in *The Meaning of Things*, (ed. I. Hodder), 79–89, London

Cvijić, J. 1922. *Balkansko poluostrvo i južnoslovenske zemlje*, Belgrade

Davey, N. 1961. *A History of Building Materials*, London

Dédijer, J. 1916. 'La transhumance dans les pays balkaniques', *Annales de Géographie*, 25, 347–65

Department of Urban Archaeology. 1984. *Finds Processing Manual*, London

Desnica, B. (ed.) 1950–1. *Istorija kotarskih uskoka*, Zbornik za istoriju, jezik i književnost srpskog naroda, vol. 13, 2 vols., Belgrade

Dietler, M. 1989. 'Greeks, Etruscans and thirsty barbarians: interaction in the Rhone Basin of France' in *Centre and Periphery. Comparative Studies in Archaeology*, (ed. T. Champion), 127–41, London

Dimbleby, G. W. 1985. *The Palynology of Archaeological Sites*, London

Drechsler-Bižić, R. 1987. 'Japodska grupa' in *Praistorija Jugoslavenskih Zemalja V, Željezno Doba*, (ed. A. Benac), 391–440, Sarajevo

Ehrich, R. W. 1956. 'Culture area and culture history in the Mediterranean and the Middle East' in *The Aegean and the Near East. Studies presented to Hetty Goldman*, (ed. S. S. Weinberg), 1–21, Locust Valley, New York

Erasmus, C. J. 1965. 'Monument building: some field experiments', *Southwestern J. Anthropol.*, 21/4, 277–301

Evans, H. M. A. 1989. *The Early Medieval Archaeology of Croatia, AD 600–900*, Brit. Archaeol. Rep. Int. Ser., 539, Oxford

Evens, E. 1966. *Prehistoric and Early Christian Ireland*, London

Faber, A. 1976. 'Prilog kronologiji fortifikacija u primorskom Iliriku', *Jadranska Obala u Protohistoriju*, 227–246, Zagreb

Fairbridge, R. W. 1977. 'Eustatic changes in sea level' in *Physics and Chemistry of the Earth*, 4, 99–185

Feyerabend, P. K. 1975. *Against Method*, London

Filipi, A. Rube 1972. 'Biogradsko-vransko primorje u doba mletačko-turskih ratova', *Radovi Instituta JAZU u Zadru*, 19, 405–98

Filipović, G. and Čirić M. 1969. *Soils of Yugoslavia*, Beograd

Filipović, M. S. (ed.) 1963. *Simpozium o srednjevjekovskom katunu*, Sarajevo

Fleming, A. 1982. 'Social boundaries and land boundaries' in *Ranking, Resources and Exchange*, (eds. C. Renfrew and S. Shennan), 52–5, Cambridge

——, 1984. 'The prehistoric landscape of Dartmoor: wider implications', *Landscape History*, 6, 5–19

——, 1985. 'Land tenure, productivity and field systems' in *Beyond Domestication in Prehistoric Europe*, (eds. G. Barker and C. Gamble), 129–46, London

——, 1987. 'Coaxial field systems: some questions of time and space', *Antiquity*, 61, 188–202

——, 1988. *The Dartmoor Reaves. Investigating Prehistoric Land Divisions*, London

Forenbaher, S. 1987. 'Vlaška pec kod Senja', *Opuscula Archaeologica*, 11–12, 83–97

Forenbaher, S. and Vranjičan, P. 1982. 'Pećina u Pazjaničama – V. Paklenica', *Senjski Zbornik*, 9, 5–14

——, 1985. 'Vaganačka pećina', *Opuscula Archaeologica*, 10, 1–21

Foretić, D. (ed.) 1963. 'Tabella enciclopedica del Regno di Dalmazia', *Radovi Instituta JAZU u Zadru*, 10, 291–304

Foucault, M. 1984. 'Interviews' in *The Foucault Reader*, (ed. P. Rabinow), London

Fox, C. 1923. *The Personality of Britain*, Cardiff

Freidenberg, M. M. (ed.) 1971. 'Vranski zakonik: novi spomenik hrvatskog običajnog prava', *Radovi Instituta JAZU u Zadru*, 18, 323–40

Frenzel, B. 1966. 'Climatic change in the Atlantic/Boreal transition on the Northern Hemisphere botanical evidence' in *World Climate 8000–0* BC, (ed. J. S. Sawyer), 99–125, London

——, (ed.) 1991. *Evaluation of Climate Proxy Data in Relation to the European Holocene*, Strasbourg

Frere, S. S. 1988. 'Roman Britain since Haverfield and Richmond', *History and Archaeology Review* (Spring 1988), 31–6

Gabrovec, S. and Mihovilić, K. 1987. 'Istarska grupa' in *Praistorija Jugoslavenskih Zemalja V, Željezno Doba*, (ed. A. Benac), 293–337, Sarajevo

Gaffney, C., Gaffney, V. and Tingle, M. 1985. 'Settlement, economy or behaviour? Micro-regional land use models and the interpretation of surface artefact patterns' in *Archaeology from the Ploughsoil*, (eds. C. Haselgrove, M. Millett and I. Smith), 95–108, Sheffield

Gaffney, V. and Stančič, Z. 1991. *Geographical Informations Systems and Archaeology. A Case Study from Hvar, Yugoslavia*, Ljubljana

Gallant, T. W. 1982. *The Levkas-Pronnoi Survey*, unpub. Ph.D. dissertation, University of Cambridge

Garagnin, G. L. 1806. *Riflessioni economiche politiche sopra la Dalmazia*, Zadar

Garner, H. V. and Dyke, C. V. 1969. 'The Broadbalk yields', *Annual Report of Rothamsted Experimental Station for* 1968, part 2, 26–49

Geddes, D. 1985. 'Mesolithic domestic sheep in West Mediterranean Europe', *J. Archaeol. Sci.*, 15, 25–48

Gibbon, G. 1989. *Explanation in Archaeology*, Oxford

Gilman, A. 1981. 'The development of social stratification in Bronze Age Europe', *Current Anthropol.*, 22, 1–23

Glavičić, A. 1983. 'Nalazi kamenih gromila na Velebitu', *Senjski Zbornik*, 10, 17–27

Glentworth, R. and Muir, J. W. 1963. *The Soils of the County Around Aberdeen, Inverarie and Fraserburgh*, Memoir of the Soil Survey of Great Britain: Scotland, Edinburgh

Govedarica, B. 1982. 'Prilozi kulturnoj stratigrafiji gradinskih naselja u jugozapadnoj Bosni', *Godišnjak 20 (Centar za Balkanološka Ispitivanja Knjiga, 18)*, 111–88

Grafenauer, B. 1952. 'Prilog Kritici izvjestaja Konstantina Porfirogeneta o doseljenju hrvata', *Hist. Zbornik V*, 1/2, 1–15

Greene, K. 1990. 'Perspectives on Roman technology', *Oxford J. Archaeol.*, 9/2, 209–19

Grgić, I. 1960. 'Buntovni pokret dalmatinskih težaka 1736–1740 godine', *Radovi Instituta JAZU u Zadru*, 6–7, 551–603

Harbison, P. 1971. 'Wooden and stone chevaux-de-frises in Central and Western Europe', *Proc. Prehist. Soc.*, 37/1, 195–225

Harding, A. 1972. 'Illyrians, Italians and Myceneans: trans-Adriatic contacts during the Late Bronze Age', *Studia Albanica*, 9/2, 215–21

——, (ed.) 1982. 'Introduction' in *Climatic Change in Later Prehistory*, (ed. A. F. Harding), 1–10, Edinburgh

Hart, E. 1980. *The Craft of the Dry Stone Waller*, Wellingborough

Harvey, D. 1973. *Social Justice and the City*, London

Haselgrove, C. 1987. 'Culture process on the periphery: Belgic Gaul and Rome during the late Republic and the early Empire' in *Centre and Periphery in the Ancient World*, (eds. M. Rowlands, M. Larsen and K. Kristiansen), 104–24, Cambridge

Higgs, E. S. and Jarman, M. R. 1969. 'The origins of agriculture: a reconsideration', *Antiquity*, 43, 31–43

Hobley, B. 1971. 'An experimental reconstruction of a Roman military turf rampart' in *Roman Frontiers Studies* 1967, (ed. S. Applebaum), 21–33, Tel Aviv

Hodder, I. 1990. *The Domestication of Europe*, Oxford

Hogbin, H. I. 1939. 'Native land tenure in New Guinea', *Oceania*, 10, 120–65

Hopf, M. 1958. 'Neolitische Getreidefunde aus Bosnien und Herzegovina', *Glasnik Zemalskog Muzeja u Sarajevu*, N.S., 13, 97–103

Horvat, I., Glavać, V. and Ellenberg, H. 1974. *Vegetations Südosteuropas*, Stuttgart

Howell, J. 1983. *Settlement and Economy in Neolithic Northern France*, Brit. Archaeol. Rep. Int. Ser., 157, Oxford

Huntley, B. 1988. 'Europe', in *Vegetation History*, (eds. B. Huntley and T. Webb III), 341–84, Dordrecht

Ilakovac, B. 1965. 'Pećina Buta', *Diadora*, 1, 27–36

——, 1982. *Rimski akvedukti na području sjeverne Dalmacije*, Zagreb

Jahns, S. 1990. 'Preliminary note on human influence and the history of vegetation in southern Dalmatia and southern Greece' in *Man's Role in the Shaping of the Eastern Mediterranean Landscape*, (eds. S. Bottema, G. Entjes-Nieborg and W. van Zeist), 333–40, Rotterdam

——, 1991. *Untersuchungen über die holozäne Vegetationsgeschichte von Süddalmatien und Südgriechenland*, unpub. Ph.D. thesis, Göttingen

Jarman, M. R., Bailey, G. and Jarman, H. N. 1981. *Early European Agriculture*, London

Jelgersma, S. 1966. 'Sea level changes during the last 10000 years' in *World Climate 8000–0 BC*, (ed. J. S. Sawyer), 54–71, London

Jewell, P. 1963. *The Experimental Earthwork at Overton Down, Wiltshire, 1960*, London

Jones, M. 1984. 'The plant remains' in *Danebury. An Iron Age Hillfort in Hampshire*, Vol. 2, *The Excavations 1969-1978: The Finds*, (ed. B. Cunliffe), 483–95, London

——, 1985. 'Archaeobotany beyond subsistence reconstruction' in *Beyond Domestication in Prehistoric Europe. Investigations in Subsistence Archaeology and Social Complexity*, (eds. G. Barker and C. Gamble), 107–28, London

Keay, S. 1991. 'The Ager Tarraconensis in the late Empire: a model for the economic relationship of town and country in eastern Spain' in *Roman Landscapes. Archaeological Survey in the Mediterranean Region*, (eds. G. Barker and J. Lloyd), 79–87, London

Klaić, N. 1975. *Povijest Hrvata u ranom sredjnem vijeku*, Zagreb

——, 1986. 'Najnoviji radovi o 29, 30, 31 poglavljuu djelu DAI car Konstanin VII Porfirogeneta', *Starohrvatska Prosveta III*, 15, 31–60

Klaić, N. and Petricioli, I. 1976. *Zadar u srednjem vijeku do 1409, Prošlost Zadra II*, Zadar

Klingebiel, A. A. and Montgomery, P. H. 1961. *Land Capability Classification*, U.S. Department of Agriculture Soil Conservation Service Agricultural Handbook No. 210, Washington D.C.

Kossinna, G. 1896. 'Die vorgeschichtliche Ausbreitung der Germanen in Deutschland', *Zeitschrift des Vereins für Volkskunde*, 6, 1–14

——, 1911. *Die Herkunft der Germanen. Zur Methode der Siedlungsarchäologie*, Mannus-Bibliothek, 6, Würzburg

Kristiansen, K. 1984. 'Ideology and material culture: an archaeological perspective' in *Marxist Perspectives in Archaeology*, (ed. M. Spriggs), 72– 100, Cambridge

Kučan, D. 1984. 'Kulturpflanzenfunde aus Pod bei Bugojno, Zentralbosnien (Hallstatt- u. La-Tène-Zeit)' in *Plants and Ancient Man. Studies in Paleoethnobotany*, (eds. W. van Zeist and W. A. Casparie), 247–56, Rotterdam

Lamb, H. H. 1977. *Climate: Present, Past and Future*, Vol. 2, *Climatic History and the Future*, London

——, 1982. *Climate, History and the Modern World*, London

Lawrence, A. W. 1979. *Greek Aims in Fortification*, Oxford

Le Roy Ladurie, E. 1982. *The Territory of the Historian*, London

Lemerle, P. 1954. 'Invasions et migrations dans les Balkans depuis la fin de l'époque romaine jusqu'au 7ème siècle', *Revue Historique*, 211, 265–308

Lewthwaite, J. G. 1986. 'Nuraghic foundations: an alternative model of development in Sardinian prehistory *c.* 2500–1500 BC' in *Studies in Sardinian Archaeology*, Vol. II, *Sardinia in the Mediterranean*, (ed. M. S. Balmuth), 19–37, Ann Arbor

Liebig, J. 1841. *Chemistry in its Application to Agriculture and Physiology*, London

Lovrić, I. 1948. *Biljeske o putu po Dalmaciji opata Alberta Fortisa*, Zagreb

Lowenthal, D. 1985. *The Past is a Foreign Country*, Cambridge

Luzzatto, F. 1921a. 'I due testi della Legge Agraria Grimani', *Archivio storico per la Dalmazia*, 7

——, 1921b. 'La Legge Agraria Grimani nel giudizio de Vicenzo Dandolo e di Melchiore Gioia', *Archivio storico per la Dalmazia*, 7

——, 1921c. 'La Legge Agraria Grimani nella critica degli scrittori Dalmati', *Archivio storico per la Dalmazia*, 7

——, 1928. 'Scrittori Dalmati della politica agraria nel sec. XVIII', *Archivio storico per la Dalmazia*, 5–6

MacPhail, R. I. and Courty, M. A. 1984. 'Interpretation and significance of urban deposits' in *Proceedings of the 3rd Nordic Conference on the Application of Scientific Methods to Archaeology*, (eds. T. Edgren and H. Jünger), 71–84, Helsinki

MAFF. 1964. *The Farmer's Weather*, Ministry of Agriculture Bulletin, 165, London

Malez, M. 1965. *Čerovačka pećina*, Zagreb

——, 1979. 'Paleolitsko i mezolitsko doba u Hrvatskoj' in *Praistorija jugoslavenskih zemalja I: Paleolit i Mezolit*, (ed. A. Benac), 195–295, Sarajevo

Mann, M. 1986. *The Sources of Social Power*, Vol. I, *A History of Power from the Beginning to A.D. 1760, Cambridge*

——, 1993. *The Sources of Social Power*, Vol. II, *The Rise of Classes and Nation-States, 1760–1914, Cambridge*

Maran, J. 1987. 'Kulturbeziehungen zwischen Nordwestlichen Balkan und Südgriechenland am Übergang vom Spät Äneolithikum zür Frühen Bronzezeit (Reinecke A1)', *Archäologisches Korrespondenzblatt*, 17, 77–85

Marchesetti, C. 1903 (1981). *I castellieri preistorici di Trieste i della regione Giulia*, Trieste

Margetic, L. 1977. 'Konstantin Porfirogenet i vrijeme dolaska hrvata', *Zbornik Histor. Zavoda JAZU*, 8. 5–100

Marić, L. 1964. *Terra rossa u karstu Jugoslavije*, Zagreb

Marijanović, B. 1980–1. 'Ravlica pećina', *Glasnik Zemajskog Muzeja u Sarajevu*, N.S., 35/36, 1–97

Marović, I. 1976. 'Rezultati dosadašnjih istraživanja kamenih gomila oko vrela rijeke Cetine u god. 1953, 1954, 1958, 1966 i 1968', *Materijali*, 12, 55–75

——, 1984. 'Reflexions about the year of the destruction of Salona', *Vjesnik za arheologiju i historiku dalmatinski*, 77, 293–314

Marović, I. and Čović, B. 1983. 'Cetinska kultura' in *Praistorija jugoslavenskih zemalja IV: Bronzano Doba*, (ed. A. Benac), 191–231, Sarajevo

Mastrović, V. 1968–9. 'Nin od pada Mletačke Republike do 1941. god', *Radovi Instituta JAZU u Zadru*, 16-17,

Michieli Vitturi, R. A. 1811. *Opuscoli*, Ragusa

Miličić, M. 1955. *Nepoznata Dalmacija*, Zagreb

Millett, M. 1986. 'Field survey calibration: a contribution' in *Archaeology from the Ploughsoil*, (eds. C. Haselgrove, M. Millett and I. Smith), 31–7, Sheffield

——, 1991. 'Pottery: population or supply patterns? The Ager Tarraconensis approach' in *Roman Landscapes. Archaeological Survey in the Mediterranean Region*, (eds. G. Barker and J. Lloyd), 18–26, London

Money, D. C. 1978. *Climate, Soils and Vegetation*, Slough

Müller, J. 1988a. 'Skarin Samograd – eine frühneolitische Station mit monochromer Ware und Impresso-Keramik an der Ostadria', *Archäologisches Korrespondenzblatt*, 18, 219–39

——, 1988b. 'Cultural differentiation of the Early Neolithic and its interaction in the Eastern Adriatic', *Berytus*, 36, 101–25

——, 1991. 'Die ostadriatische Impresso-Kultur: Zeitliche Gliederung und kulturelle Einbindung', *Germania*, 69/2, 311–58

Müller-Karper, H. 1959. *Beiträge zur Chronologie der Urnenfelderzeit nördlich und südlich der Alpen*, Berlin

Myers, A. 1989. 'Reliable and maintainable technological strategies in the Mesolithic of mainland Britain' in *Time, Energy and Stone Tools*, (ed. R. Torrence), 78–91, Cambridge

Nandris, J. 1988. 'Ethnoarchaeology and Latinity in the mountains of the southern Velebit' in Chapman *et al.*, 125-43

Nash, D. 1987. 'Imperial expansion under the Roman Republic' in *Centre and Periphery in the Ancient World*, (eds. M. Rowlands, M. Larsen and K. Kristiansen), 87–103, Cambridge

Neustupný, E. 1977. 'The time of the hill-forts' in *Ancient Europe and the Mediterranean*, (ed. V. Markotić), 135–9, Warminster

Norusis, M. J. 1983. *SPPS-X: Introductory Statistics Guide*, New York

Novak, G. (ed.) 1959. 'Dalmacija godine 1775/6. gledana ocima jednog suvremenika', *Starine*, 49

——, 1961. 'Poljoprivreda Dalmacije u drugoj polovini XVIII stoljeca', *Starine*, 51

——, 1964–74. *Commissiones et relationes Venetae*, vols. IV–VIIII, Monumenta spectantia historiam Slavorum meridionalium, vols. 47, 48, 49, 50, 51, Zagreb

——, (ed.) 1971. *Époques préhistoriques et protohistoriques en Yougoslavie*, VIIIème Congrès UISPP, Belgrade

O'Riordain, S. P. 1942. *Antiquities of the Irish Countryside*, London

Orec, P. 1978. 'Prapovjesna naselja i grobne gomile u zapadnoj Hercegovini', *Glasnik Zemaljskog Muzeja u Sarajevu*, N.S., 32, 184–96

Orme, B. 1981. *Anthropology for Archaeologists: An Introduction*, London

Parry, M. L. 1978. *Climatic Change, Agriculture and Settlement*, Folkestone

Pederin, I. 1984. 'Fiziokratski pokret u Dalmaciji', *Prilozi za istraživanje hrvatske filozofske baštine*, 10 (1–2), 167–203

Peričić, S. 1971. 'Vranski feud i obitelj Borelli', *Radovi Instituta JAZU u Zadru*, 18, 396–408

——, 1980. *Dalmacija uoči pada Mletačke Republike*, Zagreb

Peroni, R. 1979. 'From Bronze Age to Iron Age: economic, historical and social considerations' in *Italy before the Romans*, (eds. D. Ridgway and F. R. Ridgway), 17–30, London

Peterson, G. W., Webb, T., Kutzbach, J. E., Hammen Van Der, T., Wijmstra, T. and Street, F. A. 1979. 'The continental record of environmental conditions at 18000 yr BP: an initial evaluation', *Quaternary Res.*, 12, 47–82

Petrić, N. 1975. 'Spila kod Nakovane, Pelješac – prethistorijsko naselje', *Arheološki Pregled*, 17, 65–6

Predelli, R. (ed.) 1914. *I libri commemoriali della Republica di Venezia*, registri, vol. VIII, Venice

Raikes, R. L. 1978. 'Climate in the Mediterranean and Middle East semi arid zones from the Mesolithic to the Chalcolithic (VIII to III millennia BC)' in *Papers in Italian Archaeology, 1*, Brit. Archaeol. Rep. Int. Ser., 21, (eds. H. McK. Blake, T. W. Potter and D. B. Whitehouse), 1–24, Oxford

Rainsford-Hanney, F. 1972. *Drystone Walling*, 2nd edition, Stewartry of Kirkcudbright

Ralston, I. 1986. 'The Yorkshire Television vitrified wall experiment at East Tullos, City of Aberdeen District', *Proc. Soc. Antiq. Scotland*, 116, 17–40

Raukar, T. 1970–1. 'Ekonomski odnosi na posjedima rogovskog samostana u XV i XVI stoljeću', *Historijski zbornik*, 23–4, 215–64

——, 1977. *Zadar u XV stoljecu: Ekonomski razvoj i društveni odnosi*, Zagreb
Raukar, T. *et al.* 1987. *Prošlost Zadra*, vol. III, Zadar
Reed, C. A. (ed.), 1977. *The Origins of Agriculture*, The Hague
Renfrew, C. 1972. *The Emergence of Civilisation*, London
——, 1973. 'Monuments, mobilisation and social organisation in neolithic Wessex' in *The Explanation of Culture Change*, (ed. C. Renfrew), 539–58, London
——, 1989. *Archaeology and Language. The Puzzle of Indo-European Origins*, London
Roberts, N. 1989. *The Holocene: An Environmental History*, London
RCHME, 1978. Royal Commission on the Historic Monuments of England, *A Survey of Surveys*, London
Rozoy, J. 1989. 'The revolution of the bowmen in Europe' in *The Mesolithic in Europe*, (ed. C. Bonsall), 13–28, Edinburgh
Runnels, C. N. and Hansen, J. 1986. 'The olive in the prehistoric Aegean: the evidence for domestication', *Oxford J. Archaeol.*, 5/3, 299–308
Sanuto, M. 1879–1903. *I diarii*, Venice
SAS Inc. 1990. *SAS Language: Reference, Version* 6, first ed., Cary, North Carolina
Sawyer, J. S. (ed.) 1966. *World Climate 8000–0 BC*, Proceedings of the international symposium on world climate, London
Schiffer, M. B. 1976. *Behavioral Archeology*, London
——, 1987. *Formation Processes of the Archaeological Record*, Albuquerque
Schwartz, C. A. 1988. 'The Neolithic animal husbandry of Smilčić and Nin', in Chapman *et al.* 1988, 45–75
Šercelj, A. 1979. 'Pregled pleistocenske flore na teritoriju Jugoslavije' in *Praistorija jugoslavenskih zemalja I: Paleolit i Mezolit*, (ed. A. Benac), 35–53, Sarajevo
Shennan, S. J. 1985. *Experiments in the Collection and Analysis of Archaeological Survey Data: The East Hampshire Survey*, Sheffield
Sherratt, A. 1979. 'Plough and pastoralism: aspects of the secondary products revolution' in *Patterns in the Past*, (eds. I. Hodder, N. Hammond and G. Isaac), 261–305, Cambridge
Shiel, R. S. 1991. 'Improving soil fertility in the pre-fertiliser era' in *Land, Labour and Livestock*, (eds. B. M. S. Campbell and M. Overton), 51–77, Manchester
Shiel, R. and Chapman, J. C. 1988. 'The extent of change in the agricultural landscape of Dalmatia, Yugoslavia, as a result of 7,000 years of land management' in Chapman *et al.* 1988, 31–44
Simek, E. 1948. 'When fortified settlements came into being', *Z dávnych věku (Brno)*, 1, 127–31
Srdoč, D., Obelić, B., Sliepčević, A., Krajčar Bronić, I. and Horvatinčić, N. 1987. 'Rudjer Bošković Institute Radiocarbon measurements X', *Radiocarbon*, 29/1, 135–47
Stampfli, H. 1963. 'Wisent, *Bison bonasus* (L., 1778), Ur, *Bos primigenius* (Boj., 1827), und Hausrind, *Bos taurus* (L., 1758)' in *Seeberg Burgäschisee-Sud: die Tierreste*, (eds. J. Boessneck, P. Jequier and H. Stampfli), Acta Bernensia, 23, 117–95
Stančić, Z. and Slapšak, B. 1988. 'A modular analysis of the field system at Pharos' in Chapman *et al.* 1988, 191–9
Stanojević, G. 1970. *Jugoslovenske zemlje u mletacko-turskim ratovima XVI–XVII vijeka*, Belgrade
——, 1987. *Dalmatinske krajine u XVIII vijeku*, Belgrade

Startin, W. n.d. *The Labour Involved in the Construction of the Beaker Monuments at Stonehenge*

Startin, W. and Bradley, R. 1981. 'Some notes on work organisation and society in prehistoric Wessex' in *Astronomy and Society in Britain during the Period 4000–1500 B.C.*, Brit. Archaeol. Rep. Brit. Ser., 88 (eds. C. L. N. Ruggles and A. W. R. Whittle), 289–96, Oxford

Stephens, H. 1908. *Stephens' Book of the Farm*, Vol. 3. 5th edition, Edinburgh

Sterud, E. 1975. 'Prehistoric populations of the Dinaric Alps: an investigation of interregional interaction' in *Social Archaeology: Beyond Subsistence and Dating*, (eds. C. L. Redman *et al.*), 381–408, London

Stuiver, M. and Reimer, P. J. 1993. 'Extended 14C data base and revised Calib. 3.0 14C age calibration program', *Radiocarbon*, 35, 215–30

Suić, M. 1955. 'Limitacija agera rimskih kolonija na istočnoj jadranskoj obali', *Zbornik Instituta historijskog u Zadru*, 1, 1–36

——, 1974. *Antički grad na istočnom jadranu*, Zagreb

——, 1981. *Zadar u starom vijeku*, Posebna izdanja, Zadar

Tapper, R. L. 1988. 'Animality, humanity, morality, society', in *What is an Animal?*, (ed. T. Ingold), 47–62, London

Taylor, C. C. 1971. 'The study of settlement patterns in pre-Saxon Britain', in *Man, Settlement and Urbanism*, (eds. P. J. Ucko, R. Tringham and G. W. Dimbleby), 109–13, London

Thomas, D. H. 1975. 'Non site sampling in archaeology: up the creek without a site' in *Sampling in Archaeology*, (ed. J. W. Mueller), 61–81, Tucson

Tomić, J. (ed.) 1909. 'Memorijal Franceska Boreli o Dalmaciji u prvoj polovini XVIII stoljeća', *Spomenik SKA*, 47, 49–94

Torrence, R. 1989. 'Tools as optimal solutions' in *Time, Energy and Stone Tools*, (ed. R. Torrence), 1–6, Cambridge

Tosi, M. 1981. '"Comments" on Gilman 1981', *Current Anthropol.*, 22, 15–17

Tringham, R. 1971. *Hunters, Fishers and Farmers in Eastern Europe 6000–3000* BC, *London*

Van Andel, T. J. and Sutton, S. B. 1987. *Landscape and People of the Franchthi Region*, Fasc. 2, *Excavations at Franchthi Cave, Greece*, Bloomington

Van Der Leeuw, S. and Torrence, R. (eds.) 1989. *What's New? A Closer Look at the Process of Innovation*, London

Van Der Veen, M. 1985. 'The plant remains' in *The Excavation of an Iron Age Settlement at Thorpe Thewles, Cleveland, 1980–1982*, (ed. D. Heslop), 93–9, London

——, 1992. *Crop Husbandry Regimes. An Archaeobotanical Study of Farming in Northern England 1000 BC–AD 500*, Sheffield Archaeological Monographs, 3, Sheffield

Van Straaten, L. M. J. U. 1965. 'Sedimentation in the northwestern part of the Adriatic Sea', *Colston Papers*, 17, 143–60

——, 1970. 'Holocene and late-Pleistocene sedimentation in the Adriatic Sea', *Geologische Rundschau*, 60, 106–31

Van Zeist, W. and Bottema, S. 1982. 'Vegetational history of the Eastern Mediterranean and the Near East during the last 20,000 years' in *Palaeoclimates, Palaeoenvironments and Human Communities in the Eastern Mediterranean Region in Later Prehistory*, Brit. Archaeol. Rep. Int. Ser., 133, (eds. J. L. Bintliff and W. van Zeist), 277–323, Oxford

Vinski, Z. 1959. 'O prethistorijskim zlatnim nalazima u Jugoslaviji', *Arheološki Radovi i Rasprave*, 1, 207–36

Westropp, T. J. 1901. 'The ancient forts of Ireland: being a contribution towards our knowledge of their types, affinities and structural features', *Trans. Roy. Irish Acad*, 31, 579–730

——, 1910. 'A study of the fort of Dun Aengusa in Inishmore, Aran Isles, Galway Bay: its plan, growth and records, *Proc. Roy. Irish Acad.*, 28C, 1–4

Whittle, A. 1985. *Neolithic Europe. A Survey*, Cambridge

Whyte, R. O. 1963. 'The significance of climate change for natural vegetation and agriculture', *Arid Zone Res.*, 20, 381–6

Wilkes, J. J. 1969. *Dalmatia*, London

Wobst, H. M. 1974. 'Boundary conditions for Paleolithic social systems: a simulation approach', *American Antiquity*, 39, 147–78

——, 1975. 'The demography of finite populations and the origins of the incest taboo' in *Population Studies in Archaeology and Biological Anthropology*, Mem. Soc. American Archaeol., 30, (ed. A. C. Swedlund), 75–81, Washington D.C.

——, 1976. 'Locational relationships in Paleolithic society, *J. Human Evolution*, 5, 49–58

Zadarski Otoci Zbornik, 1974. *Zadarski otoci Zbornik*, Zadar

Zaninović, M. 1977. 'The economy of Roman Dalmatia' in *Aufstieg und Niedergang der Römischen Welt. II.6, Principat*, (ed. H. Temporini), 767–809, Berlin

Zvelebil, M. (ed.) 1986. *Hunters in Transition. Mesolithic societies of Temperate Eurasia and their Transition to Farming*, London

Index